William R. Hull

6 ⚡ FOR A HEALTHIER YOU

Sam, an active teenager, was shocked when the dentist found several cavities in his teeth. Frequently hungry between meals, Sam often snacks. Pastries, cookies, and candy bars are high in sugar. Sam never stopped to think about their impact on his health. How does the frequent intake of foods high in sugar contribute to tooth decay?

Carlos works part-time while attending school, and he's always eating on the run. Because high blood pressure is a problem for several of his family members, he worries about the sodium content of his diet. What foods would it be wise for Carlos to limit?

Constipation and related colon disorders are often considered embarrassing subjects. But for Samantha, a musician, the problem is very real. Her long hours of practice and performance result in erratic meals and rest breaks. Did you know that a change in diet may help bowel disorders?

Alecia's mother is recovering from a heart attack. The doctor recommended diet consultation as part of her therapy. The dietitian helped Alecia's mother design a diet lower in fat and cholesterol. Alecia wonders whether modifying the amount of fat and cholesterol in her own diet might be of value.

Adequate intake of essential nutrients is the foundation for health. However, nutrient deficiency diseases are no longer the major concern in the United States. Instead, the relationship between diet and the development of chronic disease has become the focal point. In the presence of an abundant food supply, the opportunity for overeating increases. Consuming excess Calories or an imbalance of certain nutrients may increase the likelihood of disease. Eating a variety of minimally processed foods will help to provide nutrient balance.

Your objectives in this chapter will be to:

■ *Describe how life-style relates to "wellness"*

■ *Identify risk factors, including dietary practices, linked to the development of major chronic diseases*

■ *Describe dietary practices that may reduce the risk of major chronic diseases*

UNDERSTANDING THE CHRONIC DISEASE PROCESS

In the United States today nutrient deficiency disease and starvation are rare. As a result of improved sanitation and the discovery of *antibiotics,* substances that destroy or stop the growth of bacteria and other microorganisms, infectious diseases are readily controlled. The achievements of modern medicine have extended the human life span. A person born in the United States in 1900 could have expected to live only 47 years. Today, a person can expect to live more than 75 years. Since 1900 the death rate in the United States has dropped from 17 per 1000 persons to less than nine per 1000 persons. The major causes of illness and death today are chronic diseases. A *chronic disease* is one that develops over time or recurs often. Table 6.1 lists the leading causes of death.

Heart disease, cancer, stroke, diabetes, and cirrhosis are chronic diseases. Scientists continue to perform laboratory and human studies to determine causes of these diseases. However, the task is complex. Frequently many factors, such as heredity, environment, and life-style, are involved in the disease process. Abnormal blood and urine test results are often the first clues of the presence of chronic

Table 6.1 Leading Causes of Death (1982)	
Cause	**Percentage of Total Deaths**
1. Heart Diseases	38.2%
2. Cancers	21.9%
3. Stroke	8.0%
4. Accidents	4.8%
5. Chronic Lung Diseases	3.0%

Source: National Center for Health Statistics, Morbidity and Mortality Weekly Report—Annual Summary 1982 (Atlanta: Centers for Disease Control, United States Department of Health and Human Services, 1982), p. 109.

Figure 6.1. Scientists conduct research to find causes of chronic disease.

disease. Symptoms may not be noticed, so the disease may be quite advanced before a person seeks treatment.

Development of a chronic disease often results in physical and emotional changes that decrease a person's quality of life. Disease prevention, not just treatment, is the goal.

Chronic diseases also result in staggering economic and social costs. From 1960 to 1978 spending for health care in the United States rose from $27 billion to $192 billion. Almost 11 cents of every federal dollar goes to pay for health care costs. More than 43.5 million Americans suffer from heart disease, stroke, and related disorders. The annual cost of cardiovascular disease alone is estimated at $78 billion. See Table 6.2. Disease prevention is essential to controlling health care costs.

Scientists are still studying the causes of many chronic diseases, but evidence does exist to suggest possible relationships. Public health officials have compared rates of disease in the United States with those in other population groups. For example, Table 6.3 compares cancer rates in different countries. Based on this comparison, officials identify features of the people, their life-style, and their environment that might explain the differing rates of disease.

Figure 6.2. Regular exercise and a nutritious diet are essential ingredients for fitness and health.

Table 6.2   Projected Cost of Heart Disease[a]

Expenditure	Estimated Cost (in billions)
Physician and Nursing Services	$11.8
Hospital and Nursing Home Services	$48.2
Costs of Medication	$ 5.0
Lost Output Due to Disability	$13.6
Total Cost	$78.6

Source: Reproduced with permission. © 1986 Heart Facts. American Heart Association (Dallas, 1985).

[a]Estimated economic costs in billions of dollars of cardiovascular diseases by type of expenditure, United States 1986 estimate.

Table 6.3   Annual Average Cancer Incidence

Country	Incidence per 100,000	
	Men	Women
Germany (Hamburg)	360	347
U.S.A. (Connecticut)	344	311
England and Wales	319	288
Canada (5 provinces)	263	229
Sweden	261	282
Denmark	255	286
Finland	238	217
Norway	222	235
Israel	200	220
Iceland	200	213
Poland (Warsaw)	197	279
Yugoslavia	182	191
Japan (Miyagi)	147	133
Chile	92	117
Uganda	38	48

Source: R.R. Brown, "The Role of Diet in Cancer Causation." Reprinted from *Food Technology,* 1983, 37 (3). Copyright © by Institute of Food Technologists.

This approach is known as *epidemiology.* However, many health professionals are uneasy about making dietary advice on this evidence alone. Researchers are continuing to conduct laboratory and clinical studies to verify cause and effect. In the meantime, there are changes individuals can make to reduce the risk of chronic disease.

Optimal health, or *wellness,* means being physically fit and emotionally sound. An individual cannot alter his or her heredity to prevent disease. However, the choice of *life-style,* or the way you live, is within your control. Many people maintain unhealthful life-styles, which contribute to chronic disease. Smoking, overeating, and drug and alcohol abuse are some unhealthy practices. On the other hand, reducing stress, exercising regularly, and following a nutritious diet can contribute to fitness and health. Thus the major responsibility for achieving wellness and preventing disease rests with *you.*

DIET AND DISEASE

Your diet is part of your life-style. Chronic diseases that are related to diet include heart and circulatory disease, cancer, dental caries, diabetes, and some diseases of the liver and colon. Dietary changes alone cannot guarantee protection against these diseases. However, the chance of developing one of these diseases may be reduced by diet modification.

In 1977 the Senate Select Committee on Nutrition and Human Needs published a report entitled, "Dietary Goals for the United States." This report identified seven dietary goals for Americans. Table 6.4 compares the current American diet and the report's recommendations. There was much debate about the type of evidence available to support drastic changes in the American diet. Some people felt the goals were too specific. Out of this debate evolved a set of guidelines published jointly by the Department of Health and Human Services and the United States Department of Agriculture. This publication is known as "Nutrition and Your Health: Dietary Guidelines for Americans." These revised guidelines were identified in Table 5.2. To understand the role of diet in the disease process, let's examine some of the factors that contribute to disease.

Cardiovascular Disease

Cardiovascular diseases (CVD), heart and blood vessel diseases, are the leading cause of death and involve changes in the heart

Table 6.4   Current American Diet and Recommended Goals

	Current Diet	Goals
Fat	42%	30%
Protein	12%	12%
Complex Carbohydrate	22%	48%
Sugar	24%	10%

Source: Adapted from Senate Select Committee on Nutrition and Human Needs: Dietary Goals for the United States, ed. 2 (Washington, D.C., 1977), Report No. 052-070-04376-8.

or blood vessels. Changes in the blood vessels result in a decreased blood flow, which limits the supply of oxygen delivered to the cells. Without adequate oxygen the affected area of tissue dies. When this occurs in arteries of the brain, the result is a *stroke*. A *heart attack* occurs when affected arteries are in the heart.

A disease process that often precedes these events is atherosclerosis. *Atherosclerosis* is the build-up of plaque, primarily composed of cholesterol, on the inner walls of vessels. See Illustration 6.1. The process may begin as early as childhood. For many people the disease does not progress beyond the presence of a fatty streak. For others the plaque spreads into the vessel and thus interferes with blood flow. The heart must work harder to circulate the blood. Over time the vessel wall may harden, limiting its ability to expand and contract, which also reduces blood flow and hence oxygen supply.

Illustration 6.1. Artery Changes with Atherosclerosis.

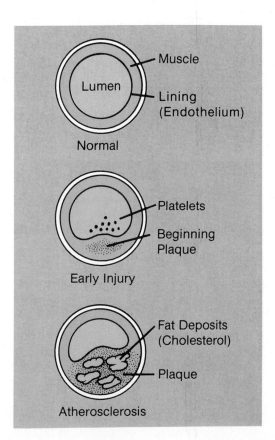

Risk Factors. CVD affects more than 40 million Americans. There is no known cause, but several risk factors have been linked with CVD. Risk factors are traits or habits that increase the likelihood of developing the disease. Major risk factors related to CVD are smoking, high blood pressure, and high blood cholesterol levels. In addition, heredity, obesity, lack of exercise, diabetes, stress, and personality type have been linked to the disease. The rate of CVD is much greater for men than for women. This is believed to be a result of the "protective value" of the hormone estrogen. A *hormone* is a chemical substance produced in the body that stimulates an activity or secretion. *Estrogen* is the female sex hormone.

High Blood Cholesterol Level. How does diet relate to CVD? Scientific studies show that a high blood cholesterol level increases the chance of CVD. Generally, the blood cholesterol level rises with age. The risk of a heart attack increases as the blood

Figure 6.3. The risk of cardiovascular disease is greater for men than for women.

cholesterol level rises. A blood test can determine if you have an elevated cholesterol level. The cholesterol deposited in the vessel comes from the bloodstream. There are two sources of this cholesterol. Cholesterol is present in the diet when animal foods are consumed. Foods high in cholesterol include meats, organ meat, egg yolk, shrimp, butter, and cream. In addition, the body has the ability to make its own cholesterol.

The type and amount of food you eat can affect blood levels of fat *(triglycerides)* and cholesterol. Consuming more Calories in comparison to energy used results in weight gain. In some people this weight gain produces a rise in blood triglyceride levels. Thus maintaining an ideal body weight is important. Drinking alcohol may produce a similar rise.

Generally, people who eat many foods high in cholesterol tend to have higher blood cholesterol levels. The type of fat also makes a difference. See Table 6.5 for food sources of fat. Saturated fats tend to

Table 6.5   Saturated and Polyunsaturated Fat Content

Type of Oil or Fat	Polyunsaturated Fat	Saturated Fat
Safflower Oil	74%	9%
Sunflower Oil	64%	10%
Corn Oil	58%	13%
Average Vegetable Oil (soybean plus cottonseed)	40%	13%
Peanut Oil	30%	19%
Chicken Fat	26%	29%
Olive Oil	9%	14%
Average Vegetable Shortening	20%	32%
Lard	12%	40%
Beef Fat	4%	48%
Butter	4%	61%
Palm Oil	2%	81%
Coconut Oil	2%	86%

Source: National Institutes of Health, Public Health Service, United States Department of Health and Human Services, "Facts about . . . Blood Cholesterol" (Washington, D.C.: United States Government Printing Office).

raise blood cholesterol levels. In contrast, foods high in monounsaturated and polyunsaturated fat can lower blood cholesterol levels. Consuming certain types of fiber and exercising tend to lower blood cholesterol levels. Some people can consume high-fat, high-cholesterol diets and maintain a normal blood cholesterol level. Why others cannot is not completely understood.

Normally the liver will produce more or less cholesterol depending on dietary intake. For some people this regulation fails and the liver produces too much cholesterol. For these individuals, dietary control of cholesterol doesn't appear to help. Instead, a physician may prescribe one or more drugs to lower the blood cholesterol level.

A moderate fat intake is sensible for Americans in general. For those who smoke or have high blood pressure, limiting fat is especially important. The American Heart Association recommends consuming only one third of the daily Calories as fat and one half as carbohydrate. Protein would provide the remaining Calories. In addition, the Association recommends minimizing saturated fats and increasing polyunsaturated fats so that the amounts eaten are about equal. The general daily meal plan would include:

- Lean meat, fish, poultry, or vegetable protein, 6 ounces
- Vegetables and fruits, 4 servings (1 serving = ½ cup)
- Egg whites as desired (limit egg yolks to three per week)
- Bread and cereals (whole grain, enriched), 4 servings or more
- Fortified skim or low-fat milk products
- Polyunsaturated vegetable fats and oils, 2 to 4 tablespoons

Table 6.6 shows a sample low-fat menu. Table 6.7 offers tips to achieving a lower fat and cholesterol intake. You may find it helpful to review the section on fats in Chapter 3 to identify the differences in types of fat.

High Blood Pressure. Another risk factor for CVD is *hypertension,* or high blood pressure. Blood pressure is a measure of the force with which the heart pumps blood through the arteries. There is a range of "normal" values that compares two different numbers, for example, 120/70 mm Hg (millimeters of mercury). The first number measures the pressure as blood is being pumped out of the heart. The second value is when the heart is at rest. A value often used as a cutoff between normal and hypertensive is 140/90 mm Hg. See Illustration 6.2. As these two numbers rise, blood vessel damage may occur and the risk of stroke or heart attack increases. A rise in blood

Table 6.6   Sample Low-Fat Menu

Breakfast	Orange Juice Bran Flakes with Skim Milk
Lunch	Water-packed Tuna Sandwich with Lettuce and Tomato on Whole Wheat Bread Green Grapes Low-Fat or Skim Milk
Dinner.....................	Broiled Chicken Baked Potato and 1 Tbsp. Margarine Steamed Broccoli Fresh Fruit Salad Low-Fat or Skim Milk
Snack......................	Low-Fat Cheese Whole Wheat Crackers Diet Soda

pressure may begin early in life without any visible signs. In many cases the cause of high blood pressure is unknown.

Heredity is the major factor in determining blood pressure. An individual's chance of developing hypertension increases if there is a family history of the problem. *Race* is also a factor. For example, hypertension is twice as common in blacks as it is in the general population.

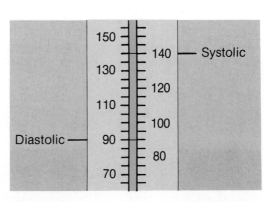

Illustration 6.2.   Blood Pressure Values.

Table 6.7   Tips to Achieve Lower Fat and Cholesterol Intakes

Total Fat	Saturated Fat	Cholesterol	
			Vegetables and Fruits
●			Moderate use of dressings on salads
●	●	●	Season cooked vegetables with herbs, spices, or lemon juice rather than with sauces, butter, or margarine
			Cereals and Baked Products
●	●	●	Be selective in use of high-fat desserts such as pies and some cookies and cakes
			Milk and Milk Products
●	●	●	Select lowfat or skim milk and milk products often
●	●	●	Moderate use of cheese and turn to lower fat varieties when possible
●	●	●	Use sour cream and cream cheese only occasionally
			Meat, Poultry, and Fish
●	●		Select lean meat, poultry, and fish
●	●		Trim visible fat from meat, including the fat between muscles
●	●		Roast, bake, broil, or simmer meats, poultry, and fish. Drain fat from meat and poultry after cooking
		●	Use organ meats, such as liver, only occasionally
●	●	●	Eat moderate servings of meat and poultry. Combine with vegetables or grain products to increase portion size
			Dry Beans and Peas
●	●	●	Use dry beans or peas as an occasional main dish, as an ingredient in combination with meat, or as a vegetable side dish
			Eggs
		●	Be moderate in the use of egg yolks, including those contained in prepared foods
		●	Try substituting egg whites in recipes calling for whole eggs; for example, in muffins, cookies, and puddings

Source: Reprinted from "Food3" by the American Dietetic Association (Chicago, Ill., 1982).
Circles indicate change in intake resulting from use of tip—for example, moderate use of dressings on salad will reduce total fat intake.

Table 6.7 (cont'd)

Total Fat Saturated Fat Cholesterol

Fats and Oils
- ● Cook without added fat
- ● Moderate use of fried foods, especially those which are breaded or have a batter coating
- ● ● Make sauces, gravies, and soups with little or no fat. Skim fat from broth
- ● ● ● Be moderate in the amount of butter used at the table
- ● Be moderate in the amount of margarine used at the table
- ● ● Use soft margarine rather than butter most of the time
- ● ● Use oil or margarine rather than hydrogenated vegetable shortening, lard, or butter to prepare baked products

Snack Foods
- ● ● ● Choose foods for snacks that are low in total fat, saturated fat, and cholesterol

Obesity also contributes to an increase in blood pressure, which is another reason for maintaining ideal body weight. The inability to cope with a stressful life-style tends to raise blood pressure as well. Research suggests that excess sodium and perhaps inadequate calcium intake are related to hypertension.

Sodium, primarily consumed as table salt (sodium chloride), also plays a role in hypertension. Generally, as the amount of sodium eaten increases in a population group, the frequency of hypertension also increases. Scientists have not been able to show that a high salt intake causes high blood pressure in most people. However, for the 10% to 15% of the population who are genetically "salt-sensitive," limiting dietary sodium may be a key in preventing hypertension. For people with hypertension, a low-sodium diet usually lowers blood pressure. In addition, a *diuretic,* a drug that increases sodium and

Figure 6.4. Inability to cope with stress can raise a person's blood pressure.

fluid loss, is often prescribed. For the American population in general, the average sodium intake of 2½ teaspoons a day far exceeds our needs. Because it is difficult to predict who will develop hypertension, cutting back on foods high in sodium is sensible for all of us.

Table 6.8 Herbs and Spices to Use Instead of Salt	
Spices	**Herbs**
Allspice	Basil
Cayenne	Chives
Chili Powder	Majoram
Cloves	Oregano
Curry	Parsley
Ginger	Rosemary
Mace	Sage
Mustard, Dry	Tarragon
Nutmeg	Thyme
Paprika	
Pepper	

Spices are seeds and roots. Herbs are leaves.

Table 6.9   Seasonings Containing Sodium

Celery Salt	Meat and Vegetable Extracts
Garlic Salt	Barbeque Sauce
Onion Salt	Meat Sauce
Catsup	Meat Tenderizer
Chili Sauce	Soy Sauce
Commercial Bouillon	Worcestershire Sauce

For many people, learning to appreciate the flavor of food with little added salt is a challenge. How many different seasonings listed in Table 6.8 have you tried? Salt is used as a seasoning and preservative in many processed foods. Some foods are obviously high in sodium, such as ham, sausage, bacon, luncheon meats, pickles, and salty snacks. Condiments and sauces are less obvious sources of sodium. Table 6.9 lists seasonings that contain sodium. Try these tips for limiting sodium:

- Read food labels carefully to determine the amounts of sodium in processed foods and snacks
- Learn to enjoy the unsalted flavors of food
- Use only small amounts of salt when cooking
- Add little or no salt to food at the table
- Experiment with other seasonings that are not sources of salt
- Limit your intake of salty foods

Cancer

Cancer is not just one disease. It is a collective term for disorders with abnormal cell growth. Cancer is the second most common cause of death in adults and children in the United States today. Table 6.10 lists the types of cancer and shows the percentages of men and women who have the different types of cancer. Heredity is a factor in cancer. For some cancers you are more likely to be at risk if a family member has had the disease. However, individual resistance or susceptibility to cancer is a complex process.

Table 6.10   Cancer Incidence by Site and Sex

Site or Type	Men	Women
Skin	2%	2%
Mouth	5%	2%
Lung	22%	8%
Breast	—	27%
Colon and Rectum	14%	15%
Pancreas	3%	3%
Prostate	17%	—
Ovary	—	4%
Uterus	—	13%
Urinary tract	9%	4%
Leukemia and Lymphomas	8%	7%
All other types	20%	15%

Source: Adapted from the American Cancer Society (1981).

Causes of Cancer. A wide variety of agents are thought to influence the onset and development of cancer. Most of the agents are believed to be environmental, including radiation, viruses, and chemicals. Thus many cancers may be preventable.

A substance that causes cancer is called a *carcinogen.* A *cocarcinogen,* or promoter, is a substance that favors the development of the cancer after its onset. These substances may occur naturally or result from processing.

One naturally occurring carcinogen, found in moldy grains and peanuts, is *aflatoxin.* Aflatoxins have been related to tumors of the stomach and kidney. *Nitrates* occur naturally and are also used as additives in cured meats and sausage. In the acid medium of the stomach, nitrates can be converted to the chemical compounds called *nitrosamines.* Nitrosamines have been linked to stomach cancer. Another additive, the noncaloric sweetener *saccharin,* has been shown to cause bladder cancer in rats. The verdict is still uncertain for humans. Food dyes, such as red dye no. 2, have also been implicated as possible carcinogens. Even cooking over a flame, such as a charcoal grill, has been shown to produce a carcinogen called *benzopyrene.*

Although these substances are carcinogens, scientists are not able to predict the amount considered to be harmful. For example, when they are combined with nondietary causes of cancer, such as smoking, their effects may be more profound. Because many other carcinogens are present in our environment, it is difficult to judge the impact of diet alone in cancer.

The Role of Diet. What is the relationship of diet to cancer? Certain nutrients in the diet may advance or inhibit the effect of carcinogens. A diet high in fat has been linked to cancer of the colon and breast. The exact relationship, however, remains unclear. A diet high in fat, for example, may increase the intestinal release of bile acid, a chemical compound used to emulsify fat. Some bile acids are known to be carcinogenic. The risk of colon cancer may also be increased by a diet low in fiber and high in fat. The value of fiber in the diet is still being studied. One theory is that it may bind harmful substances and permit faster excretion. For women, a high-fat diet may affect the levels of certain hormones. An imbalance in these hormones may promote cancer of the breast.

On the positive side, vitamins C and A (as carotene) are believed to protect against some cancers. For example, vitamin C inhibits the conversion of nitrates to nitrosamines.

If you are at risk for colon or breast cancer, then modifying your diet is advisable. In general, limiting food sources of known carcinogens is worth consideration. Eating a variety of foods lessens your chance of being exposed to excess amounts of a harmful substance. The American Institute of Cancer Research has promoted dietary changes to lower cancer risk. See Illustration 6.3.

Diseases of the Colon

Dietary fiber is a term for nondigestible carbohydrate. *Cellulose,* a type of fiber, takes up water in the colon and increases stool bulk. A diet high in fiber is related to a shorter transit time for waste products. See Illustration 6.4. The average American diet is generally low in fiber. As a result, the passage of food and waste products through the intestine may take up to 72 hours. Usually, the longer the waste products remain in the colon, the more water is removed. Thus it becomes more difficult to pass the stool. The low-fiber diet

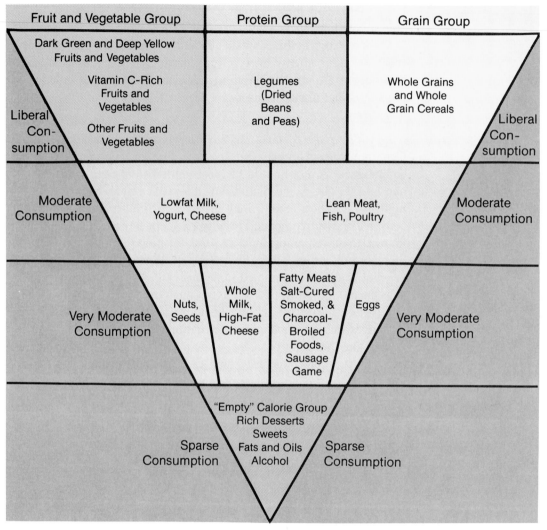

Illustration 6.3.   Dietary Guidelines to Lower the Risk of Cancer. Adapted from "Planning Meals that Lower Cancer Risk: A Reference Guide" (Washington, D.C.: American Institute for Cancer Research).

combined with lack of exercise, limited water intake, and irregular meals and restroom breaks often results in *chronic constipation*.

Diverticulosis, or the bulging of the colon, is also a disease linked to lack of fiber. This disease is practically unknown in areas where diets are less refined.

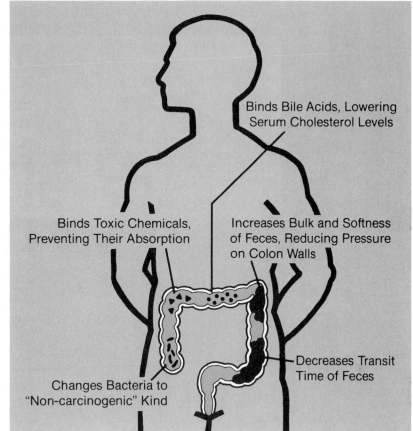

Illustration 6.4. Role of Fiber in the Colon. Adapted from R.D. Smith, "Checking Out the Fiber Fad," *The Sciences,* March/April, 1976, p. 27.

Given these diet-disease relationships, it is wise for Americans to eat foods with adequate starch and fiber. Good sources of fiber include fruits and vegetables, whole grain breads and cereals, dried beans and peas, and nuts. Refer to Table 6.11 for ways to increase fiber in your diet.

Dental Caries

The development of strong, healthy teeth begins before birth. A mother's diet during pregnancy provides the minerals needed to

Table 6.11   Food Trade-Offs to Increase Fiber

Try	Instead of
Unpeeled Apple	Applesauce
Whole Grain Cereals	Processed Cereals
Whole Wheat Bread	White Bread
Brown Rice	White Rice
Whole Wheat Crackers	Soda Crackers
Popcorn	Potato Chips
Bean Dip	Sour Cream Dip
Orange	Orange Juice

build primary teeth. These teeth, fully formed at birth, begin to appear in the baby's mouth during the first year of life. At the same time the permanent teeth are being formed below the primary teeth. A combination of diet and genetic factors determines tooth strength and resistance to damage. After erupting into the mouth, teeth are exposed to substances that may produce dental cavities, or *dental caries*. What causes this decay? Several factors are involved.

Bacteria and Sugars: A Harmful Combination. Your mouth contains bacteria. These bacteria feast on carbohydrates, particularly sugars, that are present in the mouth. An acid is formed as a result of bacterial action on sugar. The acid breaks down the protective enamel covering the tooth. As the enamel is removed, the acid begins to destroy the minerals that form the inner tooth structure. Dental caries are the result. The more often sugars are consumed, the more often teeth are attacked by acid during the day. Also, the longer a sugar is present in the mouth, the more acid is formed at any one time. Thus eating a few sticky carmels every hour may do more damage than drinking a sweetened soda with lunch.

Bacteria and sugar also combine in the mouth to coat the tooth enamel with a substance called *dental plaque*. The plaque provides an ideal surface for bacteria to live and multiply.

Prevention. An important factor is the ability of the tooth to resist erosion by the acid. The mineral *fluoride* makes the tooth less susceptible to decay. In some areas, fluoride occurs naturally in drinking water. In other areas, however, it must be added to the water

Figure 6.5. Strong, healthy teeth begin to develop even before a person is born.

supply. Fluoride may also be taken as a dietary supplement or may be obtained from toothpaste, mouth rinse, or treatments by a dentist.

What can *you* do to prevent dental decay? Brush and floss your teeth after eating and before sleeping to help to keep plaque from forming. In addition, limit the amount and frequency of sugar-containing foods in your diet. Remember, sugar is often a hidden ingredient in processed foods. Follow these dietary tips to reduce sugar:

- Use less of *all* sugars—natural and processed
- Eat less of foods containing these sugars
- Select fresh fruits, fruits canned without sugar, or fruits canned with light syrup rather than heavy syrup
- Read food labels for clues on sugar content (if the words sucrose, maltose, dextrose, lactose, fructose, or syrups appear first, the food contains a large amount of sugar)

Diabetes Mellitus

Diabetes mellitus is a disorder in which the body fails to regulate energy nutrients properly. The primary problem is that cells are not able to effectively use *glucose,* a form of sugar. In persons with uncontrolled diabetes the amount of glucose in the blood rises above the normal level. See Illustration 6.5. There are two types of diabetes. One type, which usually affects children and young adults, is *insulin-dependent diabetes.* This means the person will require an injection of the hormone *insulin* each day. The more common form of the disease is *non-insulin-dependent diabetes,* which affects adults. This type of diabetes is regulated by following a Calorie-controlled diet without the need for extra insulin.

Causes. Scientists have proposed several theories about the causes of diabetes. Genetic factors and a virus are thought to be involved in the onset of insulin-dependent diabetes. Genetics and obesity are believed to be major factors in the development of non-insulin-dependent diabetes. At this time scientists are not able to show an effect between diets high in sugar or fat and the development of diabetes.

Control. Dietary control is essential to the treatment of both types of diabetes. The diet is controlled for the total number of Calories as well as the percent of Calories from each energy nutrient. Exercise and insulin are also part of the treatment for insulin-dependent diabetics. Weight reduction and an oral medication are often recommended for non-insulin-dependent diabetics.

Illustration 6.5.
Glucose Response Curve in Diabetes Mellitus.

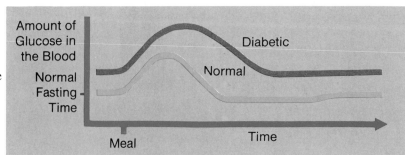

A number of short-term and long-term complications are associated with diabetes. The severity of some of these problems can be lessened by maintaining as normal a level of blood sugar as possible. Because people with diabetes are more likely to have CVD, maintaining desirable body weight and limiting dietary fat are important. To decrease your risk of non-insulin-dependent diabetes, avoid becoming overweight.

Effects of Alcohol

Drinking alcoholic beverages, such as wine, beer, and distilled spirits, affects the whole body. The effect of *ethanol* (chemical name for the type of alcohol consumed) on the nervous system is well known. Judgment and motor coordination are impaired by drinking even small amounts of alcohol. Because of these impairments, the dangers of drinking and driving are real. Each year thousands of injuries and deaths are caused by alcohol-impaired or drunk drivers. Laws setting a minimum age for drinking and severe penalties for drunk driving are society's responses to this problem. In addition,

Figure 6.6. Alcohol impairs a person's judgment and reaction time.

abuse of alcohol is often associated with family conflict and personal problems in school or at work.

Excess drinking can severely affect a person's health over a period of time. A number of diseases, including ulcers, *cirrhosis* (injury to liver tissue), and *malnutrition* (inadequate nutrition) can result from frequent and extended alcohol consumption. Cirrhosis is the seventh leading cause of death. One of its primary causes is frequent and excessive consumption of alcohol. The chemical break- down of alcohol occurs in the liver. The by-products of this breakdown are toxic to liver cells. The cells die and the liver is unable to perform its many functions.

Although ethanol is not a nutrient, it does provide energy. In fact, ethanol yields almost twice as many Calories as an equal weight of carbohydrate or protein. Translated into practical terms, this means 150 Calories to 12 ounces of beer, 85 Calories to 3½ ounces of wine, and 100 Calories to 1½ ounces of whiskey. Because of such high caloric values, another major problem associated with drinking is obesity. And since these excess Calories also lack essential nutrients, malnutrition may be a problem for a heavy drinker.

Finally, consuming ethanol poses another concern for women during the child-bearing years. Consumption of alcoholic beverages during pregnancy can have tragic effects on the unborn baby, including mental retardation and physical defects. Together these abnormalities are referred to as the *fetal alcohol syndrome*. Scientists do not know how much ethanol it takes to harm the unborn baby. Thus medical authorities strongly suggest that women do not drink alcoholic beverages during pregnancy.

HEALTH: A PRICELESS TREASURE

Sometimes it is difficult to imagine the impact that an illness or injury might have on our lives. It is easy to take health for granted until our health is threatened. The challenge is yours. Examine your life-style by studying "A Test for Better Health" beginning on page 169. After completing the risk assessment inventory, you can set your own nutrition and health goals. These changes need not be unpleasant or radical. Start with small goals that are realistic. Each positive change contributes to maintaining your health—a commodity you can not buy at any price.

A TEST FOR BETTER HEALTH

This is not a pass-fail test. Its purpose is simply to tell you how well you are doing to stay healthy. The behaviors covered in the test are recommended for most Americans. Some of them may not apply to persons with certain chronic diseases or handicaps. Such persons may require special instructions from their physician or other health professional.

You will find that the test has six sections: smoking, alcohol and drugs, nutrition, exercise and fitness, stress control, and safety. Complete one section at a time by circling the number corresponding to the answer that best describes your behavior (2 for "Almost Always," 1 for "Sometimes," and 0 for "Almost Never"). Then add the numbers you have circled to determine your score for that section. Write the score on the line provided at the end of each section. The highest score you can get for each section is 10.

Cigarette Smoking

	Almost Always	Sometimes	Almost Never
If you never smoke, enter a score of 10 for this section and go to the next section on Alcohol and Drugs.			
1. I avoid smoking cigarettes	2	1	0
2. I smoke only low tar and nicotine cigarettes or I smoke a pipe or cigars........	2	1	0

Smoking Score: _____

(Continued)

Source: United States Department of Health and Human Services (Washington, D.C.: United States Government Printing Office, 1981), Publication No. (PHS) 81-50155.

A TEST FOR BETTER HEALTH (cont'd)	Almost Always	Sometimes	Almost Never
Alcohol and Drugs			
1. I avoid drinking alcoholic beverages or I drink no more than 1 or 2 drinks a day	4	1	0
2. I avoid using alcohol or other drugs (especially illegal drugs) as a way of handling stressful situations or the problems in my life	2	1	0
3. I am careful not to drink alcohol when taking certain medicines (for example, medicine for sleeping, pain, colds, and allergies) or when pregnant	2	1	0
4. I read and follow the label directions when using prescribed and over-the-counter drugs	2	1	0

Alcohol and Drugs Score: _____

Eating Habits			
1. I eat a variety of foods each day, such as fruits and vegetables, whole grain breads and cereals, lean meats, dairy products, dry peas and beans, and nuts and seeds	4	1	0
2. I limit the amount of fat, saturated fat, and cholesterol I eat (including fat on meats, eggs, butter, cream, shortenings, and organ meats such as liver)	2	1	0
3. I limit the amount of salt I eat by cooking with only small amounts, not adding salt at the table, and avoiding salty snacks	2	1	0
4. I avoid eating too much sugar (especially frequent snacks of sticky candy or soft drinks)	2	1	0

Eating Habits Score: _____

	Almost Always	Sometimes	Almost Never
Exercise/Fitness			
1. I maintain a desired weight, avoiding overweight and underweight..................	3	1	0
2. I do vigorous exercises for 15 to 30 minutes at least 3 times a week (examples include running, swimming, brisk walking)	3	1	0
3. I do exercises that enhance my muscle tone for 15 to 30 minutes at least 3 times a week (examples include yoga and calisthenics).....................................	2	1	0
4. I use part of my leisure time participating in individual, family, or team activities that increase my level of fitness (such as gardening, bowling, golf, and baseball)	2	1	0

Exercise/Fitness Score: _____

	Almost Always	Sometimes	Almost Never
Stress Control			
1. I have a job or do other work that I enjoy	2	1	0
2. I find it easy to relax and express my feelings freely....................................	2	1	0
3. I recognize early, and prepare for, events or situations likely to be stressful for me	2	1	0
4. I have close friends, relatives, or others whom I can talk to about personal matters and call on for help when needed	2	1	0
5. I participate in group activities (such as church and community organizations) or hobbies that I enjoy	2	1	0

Stress Control Score: _____

(Continued)

A TEST FOR BETTER HEALTH (cont'd)

Safety

	Almost Always	Sometimes	Almost Never
1. I wear a seat belt while riding in a car...	2	1	0
2. I avoid driving while under the influence of alcohol and other drugs.........	2	1	0
3. I obey traffic rules and the speed limit when driving....................................	2	1	0
4. I am careful when using potentially harmful products or substances (such as household cleaners, poisons, and electrical devices)...	2	1	0
5. I avoid smoking in bed	2	1	0

Safety Score: _____

Healthstyle Scores

After you have figured your scores for each of the six sections, circle the number in each column that matches your score for that section of the test.

Cigarette Smoking	Alcohol & Drugs	Eating Habits	Exercise & Fitness	Stress Control	Safety
10	10	10	10	10	10
9	9	9	9	9	9
8	8	8	8	8	8
7	7	7	7	7	7
6	6	6	6	6	6
5	5	5	5	5	5
4	4	4	4	4	4
3	3	3	3	3	3
2	2	2	2	2	2
1	1	1	1	1	1
0	0	0	0	0	0

Healthstyle Scores (cont'd)

Remember, there is no total score for this test. Consider each section separately. You are trying to identify aspecs of your lifestyle that you can improve in order to be healthier and to reduce the risk of illness. So let's see what your scores reveal.

Scores of 9 and 10

Excellent! Your answers show that you are aware of the importance of this area to your health. More importantly, you are putting your knowledge to work for you by practicing good health habits. As long as you continue to do so, this area should not pose a serious health risk. It's likely that you are setting an example for your family and friends to follow. Since you got a very high score on this part of the test, you may want to consider other areas where your scores indicate room for improvement.

Scores of 6 to 8

Your health practices in this area are good, but there is room for improvement. Look again at the items you answered with a "Sometimes" or "Almost Never." What changes can you make to improve your score? Even a small change can often help you achieve better health.

Scores of 3 to 5

Your health risks are showing! Would you like more information about the risks you are facing and about why it is important for you to change these behaviors? Perhaps you need help in deciding how to successfully make the changes you desire.

(Continued)

A TEST FOR BETTER HEALTH (cont'd)

Scores of 0 to 2

Obviously, you were concerned enough about your health to take the test, but your answers show that you may be taking serious and unnecessary risks with your health. Perhaps you are not aware of the risks and what to do about them. You can easily get the information and help you need to improve, if you wish. The next step is up to you.

CHECK YOUR PROGRESS

1. List three major factors believed to be involved in the development of many chronic diseases.
2. Define epidemiology.
3. Identify several life-style practices that negatively affect health. What personal practices have a positive effect on health?
4. Name several chronic diseases in which diet is believed to be a factor.
5. Identify the leading cause of death in America.
6. Describe the process of atherosclerosis.
7. Define risk factors. What risk factors are associated with CVD?
8. Which dietary practices may reduce the risk of CVD?
9. Define hypertension. Identify the risk factors associated with this medical problem.
10. Who might benefit the most from limiting salt (sodium) intake? Identify the type of drug often prescribed for someone who has hypertension.
11. List five foods high in sodium content.
12. Define cancer, carcinogen, and cocarcinogen.
13. Identify several carcinogens found in food.

14. Which energy nutrient, when consumed to excess, may present an increased risk for the development of breast and colon cancer?
15. Name two nutrients believed to offer some protective value against some cancers.
16. List the factors that contribute to chronic constipation. What other disease of the colon may be linked to low fiber intake?
17. Describe the role of sugar in the development of dental caries. What measures can you take to prevent dental decay?
18. Name the disorder in which body cells are unable to use glucose effectively. Identify the two types of this disorder. What factors are believed to be related to development of each type?
19. What is insulin? Who would require daily injections of insulin?
20. Define cirrhosis. How is this disorder related to alcohol consumption?
21. How many calories does 1 gram of alcohol provide? Explain why obesity may be a problem for a person who frequently drinks alcoholic beverages?
22. Describe fetal alcohol syndrome. What medical advice should a pregnant woman follow?

7 DIETING: WHAT HAVE YOU HEARD?

Wendy and Lonnie are anxiously awaiting summer. Trying on their new swimsuits prompts them to look carefully at their bodies. Lonnie decided her legs are too flabby. Wendy is going to concentrate on trimming her midriff bulge. "I think I'll try Dr. Stillman's Diet. You can eat all of the hamburgers you want, but no bun or french fries," says Lonnie. Wendy replies "Eating only hamburgers can be boring! It might be more fun to follow a diet that allows us to eat ice cream, too!"

Wendy and Lonnie are concerned about their *body image,* or the mental picture they have of their own physical appearance. Teenagers begin to perceive themselves as having adult rather than children's bodies. Feelings of confusion about one's body image are common, and body weight is often a focus of concern. How would you decide if your weight is right for you? If your weight is currently not within a desirable range, what steps are important in achieving and maintaining your best weight?

Your objectives in this chapter will be to:

- *Determine if your weight is right for you*
- *Compare various activities requiring different energy expenditures*
- *Calculate and compare Calories of different meals*
- *Evaluate the safety of popular diets*
- *Recognize signs of eating disorders*
- *Explain your attitudes about food, exercise, and body image according to the principles of energy balance*

TO WEIGH OR NOT TO WEIGH

What is the right weight for you? Desirable body weight is as individual as your own personality. Determining a desirable weight is difficult when so many advertisements proclaim that slim is beautiful. But there are some guidelines that can help you decide.

Weight Guidelines

There are several sources available to help you determine your ideal weight.

National Center for Health Statistics Growth Charts.
The growth charts presented here as Illustrations 7.1 and 7.2 are most useful when used over time. The National Center for Health Statistics growth charts were developed after thousands of American children were weighed and measured. They are designed to follow the normal curve of growth beginning at birth and continuing through 18 years of age. If you compare boys' and girls' charts, you will see that boys are taller and weigh more than girls at most ages. An interesting thing about human growth is that most people have the same pattern.

Figure 7.1. A person's desirable body weight is as individual as his or her personality.

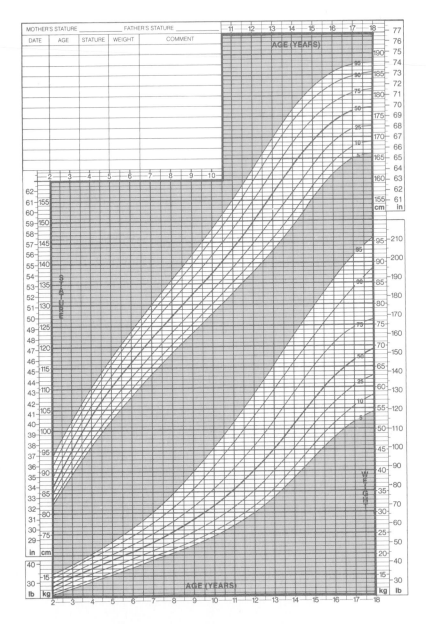

Illustration 7.1. National Center for Health Statistics Growth Chart for Girls 2 to 18 years old. *Adapted from P. V. V. Hammil, T. A. Drizd, C. L. Johnson, R. B. Reed, A. F. Roche, W. M. Moore, "Physical Growth: National Center for Health Statistics Percentiles," *American Journal of Clinical Nutrition* 32 (1979):607-629. Data from the National Center for Health Statistics, Hyattsville, Md. © 1982 Ross Laboratories.

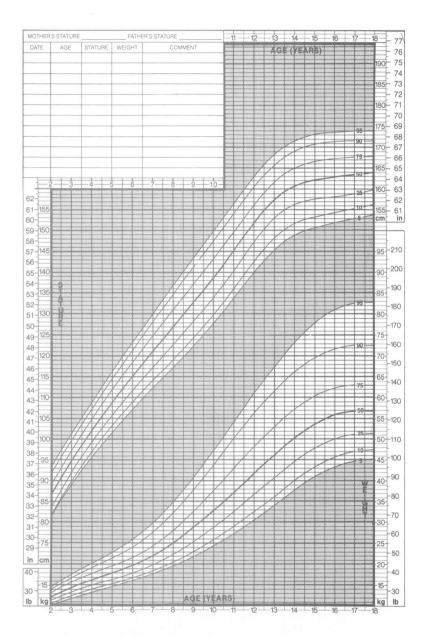

Illustration 7.2. National Center for Health Statistics Growth Chart for Boys 2 to 18 Years Old. *Adapted from P. V. V. Hammil, T. A. Drizd, C. L. Johnson, R. B. Reed, A. F. Roche, W. M. Moore, "Physical Growth: National Center for Health Statistics Percentiles," *American Journal of Clinical Nutrition* 32 (1979):607-629. Data from the National Center for Health Statistics, Hyattsville, Md. © 1982 Ross Laboratories.

Table 7.1 Metropolitan Height and Weight Tables, 1983

Men

Height Feet	Inches	Small Frame	Medium Frame	Large Frame
5	2	128-134	131-141	138-150
5	3	130-136	133-143	140-153
5	4	132-138	135-145	142-156
5	5	134-140	137-148	144-160
5	6	136-142	139-151	146-164
5	7	138-145	142-154	149-168
5	8	140-148	145-157	152-172
5	9	142-151	148-160	155-176
5	10	144-154	151-163	158-180
5	11	146-157	154-166	161-184
6	0	149-160	157-170	164-188
6	1	152-164	160-174	168-192
6	2	155-168	164-178	172-197
6	3	158-172	167-182	176-202
6	4	162-176	171-187	181-207

Women

Height Feet	Inches	Small Frame	Medium Frame	Large Frame
4	10	102-111	109-121	118-131
4	11	103-113	111-123	120-134
5	0	104-115	113-126	122-137
5	1	106-118	115-129	125-140
5	2	108-121	118-132	128-143
5	3	111-124	121-135	131-147
5	4	114-127	124-138	134-151
5	5	117-130	127-141	137-155
5	6	120-133	130-144	140-159
5	7	123-136	133-147	143-163
5	8	126-139	136-150	146-167
5	9	129-142	139-153	149-170
5	10	132-145	142-156	152-173
5	11	135-148	145-159	155-176
6	0	138-151	148-162	158-179

Source: Courtesy of the Metropolitan Life Insurance Company, "Height and Weight Tables" (1983).

After you have charted your height and weight for your age, you will have a better scientific idea about your weight. Most adolescents will be between the 10th and 90th percentile for both height and weight. This is considered the "normal" range. People above or below these ranges may also be normal, because heredity plays a role in body size.

Metropolitan Life Insurance Height/Weight Tables. Table 7.1 presents the most commonly used height/weight standard for adults. The Metropolitan tables were revised in 1983, which resulted in about a 10% increase in recommended weights. The Metropolitan tables are based on clients insured with the company. These tables represent heights and weights of people over 25 years of age who were the most likely not to have health problems.

An important feature of these tables are the guidelines for determining *frame size*. Generally 25% of all people will have a small frame, 50% will have a medium frame, and 25% will have a large frame. The measurement used to determine frame size is the *elbow breadth*. Table 7.2 gives the elbow breadth measurements for a medium frame. A lower measurement indicates a small frame and a higher measurement a large frame.

Table 7.2   Elbow Breadth Measurements for a Medium Frame[a]

Men		Women	
Height in 1" Heels	**Elbow Breadth**	**Height in 1" Heels**	**Elbow Breadth**
5'2"-5'3"	2½"-2⅞"	4'10"-4'11"	2¼"-2½"
5'4"-5'7"	2⅝"-2⅞"	5'0"-5'3"	2¼"-2½"
5'8"-5'11"	2¾"-3"	5'4"-5'7"	2⅜"-2⅝"
6'0"-6'3"	2¾"-3⅛"	5'8"-5'11"	2⅜"-2⅝"
6'4"	2⅞"-3¼"	6'0"	2½"-2¾"

Source: Courtesy of the Metropolitan Life Insurance Company, 1983 data.

[a]A smaller measurement indicates a small frame, whereas a larger measurement indicates a large frame.

The Mirror Image. A less scientific but helpful test is to judge your weight by appearance. Using a full-length mirror, determine whether there is too little or too much of you reflecting back. It is a good idea to ask someone else what they think, too, as your own perception may be overcritical.

The Pinch Test. Another way to help you evaluate your weight is to pinch yourself. Use your thumb and forefinger to pinch your upper back arm, waist, or midriff area. Were you able to pinch an inch? If not, congratulations! You are probably at a good weight. If you could pinch an inch or more, you probably need more exercise or fewer calories.

Ruler Test. Lie on your back on a firm, flat surface. Place a 12-inch ruler on your stomach, pointing from your toes to your nose. See Illustration 7.3. If the entire ruler touches your body, you are probably not overweight. If the ends are not touching your body, you need to find out why.

For Men Only. Place a belt firmly around your waist. Mark the spot where you fasten the belt. Now move it to your chest. See Illustration 7.4. If the belt is too small, great! If it fits too loosely, then you may be overweight.

Overweight or Fat: What is the Difference?

Before you decide on weight reduction, it is important to determine whether the weight is fat or lean tissue. Body weight includes lean muscle, bone structure, fat tissue, and water. A scale

Illustration 7.3. The Ruler Test.

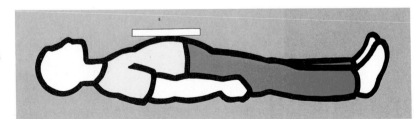

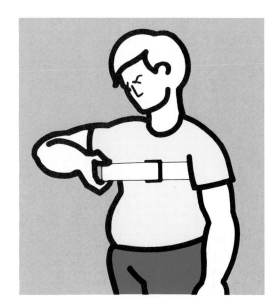

Illustration 7.4. The Belt Test (for men only).

measuring your total weight does not tell you how much of the total weight is fat tissue. The normal range of body fat is 14% to 16% of total weight for men and 20% to 23% for women. Being overweight is a judgment that is made against an acceptable standard, such as a height/weight table. Generally, people are considered overweight if their weight is 10% above the desirable weight range for the person's height. *Obesity,* when measured only by weight, is defined as greater than 20% above desirable weight for height. However, weight alone is not accurate in determining fatness. A body builder, for example, may increase muscle mass and weigh more than the standard indicates as desirable weight. However, the increased weight is lean tissue, not fat.

Several methods exist for determining the percent of body fat. An accurate but impractical way is to measure body density by weighing a person under water. A more convenient method is to measure *subcutaneous fat,* which is the layer of fat just beneath the skin. An instrument called a *skin caliper* is used to pinch a fold of skin with a given amount of pressure. The skin fold measurement is compared with standards for people of a similar age and sex. Common sites for measuring subcutaneous fat are the back of the arm, the abdomen, and beneath the shoulder blade. Training and practice in use of the calipers are required to obtain accurate readings.

THE BALANCING ACT

Americans are in pursuit of slimness. It is estimated that over 50% of Americans weigh more than the recommended weight for their height. Many individuals seem to have trouble balancing exercise (an output of energy) with food intake (an input of energy). The key to weight control is developing a sense of Calorie balance. Illustration 7.5 shows how changes in food intake and exercise affect body weight.

Changing weight like a seesaw, especially during growth periods, is not advisable. If a young person is too heavy, the best advice is to let him or her grow in height to match his or her weight. Weight reduction, except in extreme cases, is usually not necessary.

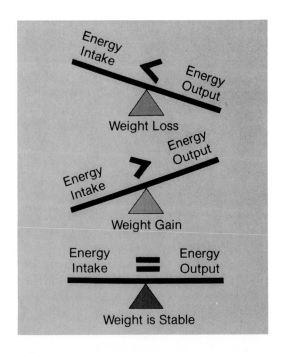

Illustration 7.5.   The Energy Balance.

Figure 7.2. Weight control for a child includes increasing activity, improving food choices, and allowing growth in height to match his or her weight.

Weight *maintenance* should be the method of choice. A growing child or teenager can maintain a desirable body weight by choosing foods and activities that balance energy needs. Review Chapter 2 for details on energy requirements.

Evaluating Your Energy Life-Style

Your life-style includes many daily food and activity choices. A quick review of your preferred foods and activities allows you to judge your energy balance. Is energy balance a concern for you?

Plan your activity level to balance with your Calorie intake. See Table 7.3. *Sedentary activities* include reading, writing, watching television, and typing. Your body requires only 80 to 100 Calories per hour to fuel these activities. *Light activities,* such as walking slowly, ironing, or doing dishes, require 110 to 160 Calories per hour. Walking moderately fast and playing table tennis are considered *moderate activities* and require 170 to 240 Calories per hour. *Vigorous*

Table 7.3   Plan Your Level of Activity

		Minutes of Activity Needed to "Burn Up" Food Calories				
Food	Calories	Sedentary Activity	Light Activity	Moderate Activity	Vigorous Activity	Strenuous Activity
2 8-inch Celery stalks	15					
2 medium Graham Crackers	55					
2 tblsp Fruit-Nut Snack	70					
2 tblsp Peanuts	105					
1 cup Plain Low-Fat Yogurt	145					
1 cup Split-Pea Soup	195					
1 cup Fruit-Flavored Yogurt	225					
½ cup Crunchy Cereal with Coconut	280					
Hamburger (3 oz patty on bun)	365					
12 oz Chocolate Milkshake	430					

Source: United States Department of Agriculture, "Calories and Activity Level," Food and Fitness Chart (Washington, D.C.: United States Government Printing Office).

Legend: Symbols represent the approximate minutes of activity required to burn up food Calories at different activity levels, sedentary through vigorous. The Calorie value of strenuous activity was calculated using a rate of 350 Calories per hour based on average activity values. Numbers are based on average activity values. Some strenuous activities may require more than 350 Calories per hour and would take less time to burn up energy or Calories.

Key: Minutes

7   30   60

15   45

activities, such as walking fast, bowling, gardening, or golfing, require 250 to 350 Calories per hour. The most *strenuous activities,* such as swimming, tennis, dancing, and running, require at least 350 Calories per hour.

As you can see, the higher the activity level, the more food Calories can be consumed without gaining weight. What activities do you enjoy? Which would help you improve your energy balance?

Food Choice for Energy Balance

Beside varying your activity level, another route to achieving energy balance is to consume fewer Calories. Table 7.4 compares the

Table 7.4   Food Energy Values

Food Item	Portion Size	Calories
Celery, raw	1 stalk	5
Tomato Juice	1 cup	45
Crackers, Saltine	4 crackers	50
Apple	1 medium	70
White Bread, enriched	1 slice	70
Banana	1 medium	85
Milk, Skim	1 cup	85
Mixed Nuts, shelled	10 nuts	94
Peanut Butter	1 tblsp	95
Donut, cake-type	1 donut	100
Cheddar Cheese	1 oz	115
Potato Chips	10 chips	115
Cookie, plain	1 cookie	120
Chocolate Cupcake	1 cupcake	130
Cheese Pizza	4¾" piece	145
Cola soft drink	12 oz	145
Chocolate Candy Bar	1 bar	145
Milk, Whole	1 cup	150
Ice Cream	1 cup	270
Danish Pastry	4¼" diameter	275
Apple Pie	4" piece	350

energy value of different foods. Which foods are your favorites? Do you prefer eating high-Calorie or low-Calorie foods?

Compare the meals in the "Main Meal Menu" on page 189. What was added to the 400-Calorie meal to increase its Calorie content? The foods are essentially the same, but portion sizes and fat content account for the difference in Calories.

Variety: The Spice of Life. In previous chapters different foods were identified as primary sources of major nutrients. In general, the same food was not listed as a good source of each vitamin or mineral. Balancing Calories does not necessarily provide a quality diet. The key to nutritional quality is eating a wide variety of foods. A lunch that consists of a hamburger on a whole wheat bun with lettuce, tomato, mayonnaise, cheese, a glass of milk, and a banana provides a wide variety of food items, but eating the same lunch every day limits the variety of foods you eat. Vary your selections by trying different items. Also, varying your lunch allows you to regulate your daily caloric intake.

Choose different restaurants to vary your food and Calorie intake when you eat out. You might select one specializing in hamburgers on one occasion, another for fish, and a third featuring an array of fresh vegetables, salads, and fruit. "Fast foods" are often high in Calories. Table 7.5, on pages 190 and 191, compares the amount of Calories and sodium found in various "fast food" items.

Comparing Nutrient Density. To obtain the most nutritional value for Calories spent, compare the nutrient density of possible food choices. *Nutrient density* means a food has a high amount of nutrients compared to the number of Calories. Therefore, your task is to determine which foods provide maximum amounts of essential nutrients without providing excessive Calories. The number of Calories in a food depends on the percent of fats, carbohydrates, and proteins present in the food. Fats provide twice as many Calories per gram as carbohydrate and protein. Identifying the fat content of a food will help you judge its relative Calorie content.

Pizza can be a relatively low-fat restaurant favorite (18% of the total Calories as fat), while fried chicken or fish dinners will provide more than 30% of the total Calories as fat. A broiled hamburger with a glass of skim milk will provide approximately 60% of the Calories from carbohydrates, 30% from fats, and 10% from

MAIN MEAL MENU

This menu shows food selections for a 400-calorie and an 800-calorie main meal—whether eaten at noon or in the evening. The 400-calorie meal might be used by a woman on a 1,200-calorie diet; the 800-calorie meal might suit a man on 2,400 calories a day. Each meal provides at least one-third of the Recommended Dietary Allowances for 13 nutrients. Several alterations were made to the 400-calorie meal to boost the calorie count to 800. These include the addition of an extra half serving of meat, a slice of bread, a teaspoon of margarine, and a fruit dessert. Regular salad dressing was used in place of low-calorie dressing, and lowfat milk was used in place of skim milk. Also, the amount of milk was increased to 1 cup.

400-Calorie Meal

Baked steak in creole sauce 1 serving
Corn-on-cob 1 medium ear **or whole kernel** ½ cup
Mixed green salad 1¼ cups
Salad dressing, Italian, low-calorie 1 tablespoon
Whole-wheat bread 1 slice
Skim milk ½ cup

800-Calorie Meal

Baked steak in creole sauce 1½ servings
Corn-on-cob 1 medium ear **or whole kernel** ½ cup
Mixed green salad 1¼ cups
Salad dressing, Italian, regular 1 tablespoon
Whole-wheat bread 2 slices
Margarine 1 teaspoon
Watermelon 2 pieces, each about 5 inches in diameter and
    1 inch thick
Lowfat (2% fat) milk 1 cup

Source: Reprinted from "Food2" by the American Dietetic Association (Chicago, Ill., 1982).

Table 7.5   How the Fast Foods Compare

Item	Price ($)	Serving size[a] (oz)	Calories	Sodium (mg)
Cheeseburgers[b]				
Arby's	1.45	5½	492	576
Burger King Whopper	1.83	9	663	1081
Hardee's Big Deluxe	1.49	8¼	557	900
Jack in the Box Jumbo Jack[c]	1.49	7¾	544	839
McDonald's Big Mac	1.67	7	587	888
Roy Rogers ¼ lb.	1.48	6	416	597
Wendy's Single	1.55	7¼	547	886
Fries (small)				
Arby's	0.55	2¼	195	31
Burger King	0.59	1¾	158	56
Hardee's	0.50	2¼	202	48
Jack in the Box	0.59	2¼	217	117
Kentucky Fried Chicken	0.65	3½	221	92
Long John Silver's	0.58	3½	282	59
McDonald's	0.62	3	268	45
Roy Rogers	0.56	3	230	161
Wendy's	0.72	3½	317	110
Chocolate Shakes				
Arby's	0.79	11	365	295
Burger King	0.79	9¾	367	251
Hardee's	0.70	8½	273	262
Jack in the Box	0.80	11¼	324	118
McDonald's	0.79	10¼	377	287
Roy Rogers	0.78	13¼	518	219
Wendy's	0.77	8½	367	281
Fish[b]				
Burger King Whaler	1.34	6½	502	466
Hardee's Big Fish	1.19	6¼	515	702
Long John Silver's Fish Sandwich	2.29[d]	7¼	560	1118
McDonald's Filet-O-Fish	1.20	5	373	519

Table 7.5 (cont'd)

Item	Price ($)	Serving size[a] (oz)	Calories	Sodium (mg)
Chicken[b]				
Jack in the Box Chicken Supreme	1.99	7¾	572	1272
Kentucky Fried Chicken Fillet Sandwich	1.89	5½	399	1012
Kentucky Fried Chicken Original Recipe 2-piece Dinner	1.72	7¼	720	1445
McDonald's McNuggets	1.63	3¾	284	444
Roy Rogers Fillet Sandwich	1.65	6	526	1054
Wendy's Fillet Sandwich	1.87	6	441	699
Roast Beef Sandwiches[b]				
Arby's	1.79	5½	416	887
Hardee's	1.29	4¾	294	776
Roy Rogers	1.87	5¼	298	665
Miscellaneous Entrees[b]				
Hardee's Chili Dog	0.75	4¾	329	879
Hardee's Ham & Cheese	1.49	4½	326	897
Jack in the Box Taco	0.85	2½	174	376
Jack in the Box Super Taco	0.99	4¼	311	662
Roy Rogers Ham/Swiss	1.82	6	416	1392
Taco Bell Taco	0.73	2¾	194	213
Taco Bell Taco Light	1.29	4¾	375	417
Wendy's Chili (small)	1.17	10½	310	1086

Source: Copyright 1984 by Consumers Union of United States, Inc., Mt. Vernon, New York 10553. Reprinted by permission from CONSUMER REPORTS, July, 1984.

[a]Rounded to nearest ¼ oz.

[b]Burgers and sandwiches include sauce and extras, where available.

[c]Does not include cheese.

[d]Price includes fries and cole slaw.

Illustration 7.6.
Find the Fat. The
food item with the
longest blue bar con-
tains the greatest per-
centage of Calories
from fat. Reprinted
from "Food 2" by the
American Dietetic
Association (Chicago,
Ill., 1982).

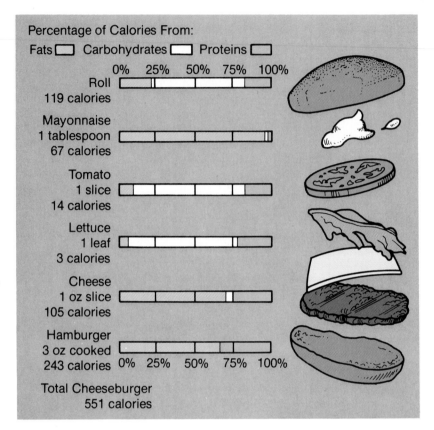

Percentage of Calories From:
Fats ☐ Carbohydrates ☐ Proteins ☐

Roll
119 calories

Mayonnaise
1 tablespoon
67 calories

Tomato
1 slice
14 calories

Lettuce
1 leaf
3 calories

Cheese
1 oz slice
105 calories

Hamburger
3 oz cooked
243 calories

Total Cheeseburger
551 calories

proteins. Of course, this can vary depending on the portion size. Analyze the composition of the cheeseburger in Illustration 7.6.

In addition to fat, refined sugar can also add extra Calories without providing nutrients. Whole wheat bread and a raised donut provide the same number of Calories, but which is the most nutrient dense? See Illustration 7.7.

Remember from Chapter 5 that processing, preparation, and storage can alter a food's nutrient density and Calorie profile. For example, in the process of making a potato chip, certain minerals will be lost when the potato skin is peeled off. Ascorbic acid, present in the raw potato, will be lost during heating. The Calorie content will increase sixfold because the potato absorbs fat during deep-fat frying. The sodium level will increase because salt is added for flavor and sodium is added to preserve the chip.

Illustration 7.7. Which is the Most Nutrient Dense? Reprinted from "Food 2" by the American Dietetic Association (Chicago, Ill., 1982).

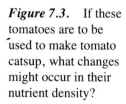

Figure 7.3. If these tomatoes are to be used to make tomato catsup, what changes might occur in their nutrient density?

WEIGHT CONTROL: CHANCE OR CHOICE

Weight control is life-long endeavor. A person who exercises vigorously can consume more Calories than someone who is inactive. Taller people can consume more Calories than shorter people. Males can maintain appropriate weight consuming more Calories than can females. In order to achieve a stable weight, a person must balance Calorie intake and energy output. For most people this seems to be a normal part of living. For others it is often very difficult and requires changes in the person's life-style.

The Behavior Change Process

If maintaining energy balance is difficult, a process of behavior change is often successful in achieving weight control. First, a person must be aware of current food choices, activity patterns, and feelings. Frequently a food diary is kept for a period of time. Foods eaten and the time, location, and person's feelings are recorded. Current eating and activity behavior patterns are analyzed and eating cues are identified.

Activities and behaviors that contribute to energy imbalance are targeted for change. A plan for changing behavior is designed. This plan includes setting specific goals related to eating, exercise, and expression of feelings. The process of change includes developing and practicing decision-making skills. Although behavior change is an

Figure 7.4. Support groups can provide rein-forcement for behavior change.

individual process, success is more likely with the guidance of health professionals (doctor, dietitian, or nurse) and the support of a peer group.

What about Popular Diets?

In America everyone seems to diet! Many diets, diet books, diet powders or pills, and special foods are available. Some diets are for gaining muscle mass, others deplete fat mass, some even claim to offer you the ability to eat everything and not gain one pound of unwanted weight. Most diet promoters say that their method is best. How do you know who to believe?

First, identify the claim being made for the diet plan, pill, or powder. Based on your nutrition knowledge, does the claim make scientific sense? As you know, energy output must increase or input decrease for weight loss to occur. Answer the following questions to judge the merits of any diet plan:

1. Is it safe? Does the plan promote a loss of no more than two pounds per week? Are Calories and nutrients adequate to permit a young person to continue to grow in height?

2. Is the diet nutritionally balanced? Does the plan include a wide variety of foods from four food groups?

3. Are the recommended foods ones that can be enjoyed for a lifetime? Does the plan allow occasional consumption of your favorite foods?

4. Can you obtain the foods at your grocery store at an affordable price?

5. Does the diet plan fit your life-style? Does the plan accommodate eating away from home, permit use of convenience foods, or require limited special food preparation?

6. Does the plan encourage an increase in activity?

7. Is the diet promoted by someone who is selling something (a book, vitamins, food, etc.)? If so, the diet probably is not in your best interests, because it is likely designed only to make the promoter a lot of money.

8. Does the diet promise unbelievable weight loss (usually due to a new secret)? Remember, a pound of body fat is equal to 3500 Calories. To lose 1 pound you need to eat

3500 fewer Calories or through additional exercise burn up 3500 Calories. To gain a pound you must increase your Calorie intake by 3500 Calories. Few people eat enough food daily to equal 3500 Calories. A plan that states you will lose 10 pounds in 2 weeks is counting on most of the "weight" loss to be water. A quart of water weighs 2 pounds.

9. Does the diet literature use testimonials from "satisfied" customers? Be wary! These people may have been well paid to say that the diet worked. Diets should be tested by thousands of people with careful evaluation of the results.

10. Does the promoter have a background in nutrition? A promoter may say he or she is a nutritionist without having any recognized nutrition training. Look for the promoter's credentials. Is the person a registered dietitian? These professionals have completed a 4-year college nutrition program and internship, and have passed a registration examination. Other persons are most likely less informed.

Types of Popular Diets

Most popular diet plans can be classified by the nutrient content or balance recommended. You may desire more information about a particular diet. The Consumer's Guide book, *Rating The Diets,* provides an excellent review of the latest diets and diet centers.

Low-Carbohydrate, Unlimited Protein Diets. These diets usually recommend eating only lean meat, fish, eggs, poultry, and low-fat cheese. Beverages include coffee, tea, diet soda, alcohol, and *water*—at least eight 10-ounce glasses a day. Weight loss is often rapid but is not completely sustained. A major drawback to these diets is the lack of a variety of foods. As a result, vitamins, minerals, and fiber may be lacking. Blood cholesterol levels may increase and the body may become abnormally acidic. Food choice is limited and monotonous. Eating behavior is not changed.

Low-Carbohydrate, Unlimited Protein and Fat Diets. The dieter is told to eat only high-protein, high-fat foods in order to burn "body fat," which is a fallacy. As the diet progresses, up to 40 grams of carbohydrates is allowed per day. Only limited varieties of

Figure 7.5.   Beware: Liquid diets may be dangerous to your health.

foods are permitted so minerals, vitamins, and fiber are lacking. Blood cholesterol levels may increase. The foods recommended are relatively high in Calories, so weight gain may occur. The body becomes abnormally acidic because of the limited carbohydrates. The ability to enjoy food may decrease. Eating behavior is not changed.

Liquid Diets. These include liquid protein diets and supplemented fasting. This type of diet contains only 300 to 500 Calories per day. Food is not chewed and eaten, and many nutrients are missing. The diet is monotonous. Muscle breakdown, nausea, vomiting, diarrhea, faintness, constipation, muscle cramps, and fatigue may occur. Food and Drug Administration research has associated life-threatening health problems with this type of diet. Eating behavior is not changed because eating is avoided.

Low-Calorie, High-Fiber Diets. Highly refined and processed foods are eliminated. Raw fruits, vegetables, whole grain products, nuts, and seeds are promoted. Small to moderate amounts of poultry, fish, and lean meat are allowed. Fat is minimal. Nutritional adequacy depends on the Calorie level. The increase in fiber could cause some discomfort until the digestive system adjusts to it. People who enjoy meat, poultry, and fish may find it difficult to follow this diet for long periods.

EATING DISORDERS

Because of the increasing social and medical concerns about weight, it is not surprising that people have problems with eating. The most common adolescent eating problems are eating too much or too little. The reasons for both situations may be somewhat similar. In coping with life situations, people often use food inappropriately. In recent years theories regarding the development of eating disorders have focused on family living patterns. Three eating disorders are currently recognized: *obesity, anorexia nervosa,* and *bulimia.*

Obesity

As described earlier in this chapter, obesity is an excess accumulation of body fat. Adult men with a body fat content in excess of 20% are considered obese. A body fat content greater than 28% is used to identify obesity in women. The people who carry excess weight are not a uniform group. There are a variety of factors that independently or together may cause obesity. Factors leading to obesity have been divided into two groups: (1) physical and (2) social/psychological.

Physical factors include inherited body structure and altered biochemical reactions that affect energy use or storage. A number of theories have been proposed to explain possible physical causes of obesity. One recent theory is that a person's body may have a *set-point,* or a predetermined normal fat level.

Social/psychological factors related to obesity have been identified through observation of eating and exercise behaviors of obese and nonobese people. Eating patterns are learned at an early age. Family attitudes and practices related to food may encourage overeating. Eating styles that favor weight gain include eating quickly, eating only once or twice a day, and eating large meals.

For some people, eating may become a way of coping with emotional problems. Low self-esteem and depression may trigger an episode of overeating. Because a social stigma is often attached to obesity, an obese teen may feel isolated, shy away from group activities, and develop a distorted body image—increasing the emotional dependence on food. External signals such as the sight or smell of food may cause people to eat even when they are not hungry. In families in which exercise is not valued, inactivity may lead to weight gain.

Methods promoted for the treatment of obesity range from diets and drugs to surgery. As described earlier, fad diets are everywhere. The safety and long-term success of each diet must be judged independently. A weight loss program featuring a balanced diet, exercise, and behavior modification is considered the safest and most effective for long-term success.

Several types of drugs have been promoted for weight loss. *Diuretics,* drugs or natural substances that cause the body to excrete fluid, have no effect on appetite or loss of fat tissue. Nonprescription drugs that suppress the appetite contain *phenylpropanolamine,* the same active ingredient found in many decongestant cold tablets. These drugs may cause an increase in blood pressure and metabolism. Appetite suppressants available only by prescription generally contain a substance similar to *amphetamine.* Side effects from these drugs may include increased blood pressure and heart rate, depression, and diarrhea.

For someone who is grossly obese, surgery may be considered. An operation can be performed to staple or tie off part of the stomach or small intestine. Shortening the small intestine poses risks such as diarrhea, malnutrition, and kidney stones. Stapling off part of the stomach requires eating smaller, more frequent meals.

Anorexia Nervosa

Anorexia nervosa, or nervous loss of appetite, is actually misnamed. Most persons suffering from anorexia nervosa have appetites, but for some reasons engage in a process of self-induced starvation. This disease now affects about one in every 200 American girls between the ages of 12 to 18 years and can also occur in older groups. More than 90% of *anorectics,* people suffering from anorexia, are female.

Researchers believe this refusal to eat in order to lose weight is due to an unrealistic or inappropriate perception of body image. The following features are used to identify this disorder in females:

- Fear of fatness

- Obsessive thinking about food and beverage intake, leading to self-induced starvation
- *Amenorrhea,* or the stopping of menstruation

Persons who develop anorexia nervosa are often described as the perfect child—obedient, academically successful, and well liked. Generally the anorectic's family emphasizes perfection and high achievement. There are several theories regarding the cause of the disorder. Factors that may be involved include a fear of growing up, poor self-concept, desire to exert self-control, family interaction problems, and society's emphasis on thinness.

People with anorexia nervosa have been further classified according to the behaviors used to achieve weight loss. Some anorectics severely restrict their food intake and engage in routine exercise to lose weight. Other anorectics binge eat and vomit to avoid gaining weight. This group is described as *bulimic anorectics.* Eating, especially overeating, clashes with the anorectic's denial of hunger. Each episode of overeating decreases the anorectic's ability to resist food. Because eating represents a loss of control, starving becomes harder and panic sets in. This situation is very dangerous.

Physical and biochemical changes that accompany anorexia nervosa depend on the degree of starvation and weight loss. A skeleton-like appearance develops as muscle and fat tissue are lost.

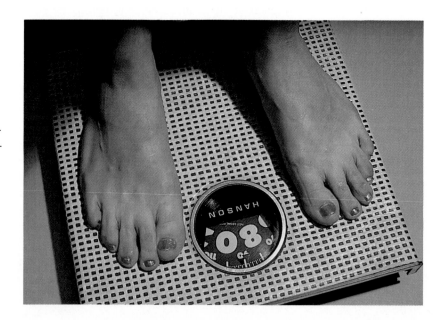

Figure 7.6. Obsession with dieting, exercise, and weight loss can be a sign of *anorexia nervosa.*

Figure 7.7. *Bulimia* is an eating disorder characterized by binge eating and vomiting or the abuse of laxatives and diuretics.

Bone mass may be decreased. Amenorrhea occurs in females. Heart rate and blood pressure decrease. Blood levels of sodium, potassium, calcium, glucose, and cholesterol may be abnormal. Hospitalization may be required to restore nutritional well-being if weight loss is severe. Other treatment procedures include behavior modification, psychological counseling, and family therapy.

Bulimia

Bulimia has recently been identified as a separate eating disorder. *Bulimia* means "ox hunger," or insatiable appetite. An individual with this disorder repeatedly has times of uncontrolled eating of large amounts of food. Shortly after eating, the food is purged either by forced vomiting or by the use of laxatives or diuretics. Once started, this behavior becomes addictive. The disorder is also known as the *binge/purge syndrome*.

Symptoms of bulimia can occur at any body weight. Bulimia occurs more often than anorexia, affecting about 5% of young adult females. *Bulimics,* or people who have bulimia, tend to have problems with impulse control, depression, and anxiety. Emotional stress often brings on an event of binge eating.

Health problems that result from excessive vomiting include:
- Dental problems, because the teeth and gums are frequently bathed in stomach acid
- Soreness of the *esophagus,* or food tube, as a result of the acid, and possible bleeding or rupturing of the esophagus
- Abnormal blood levels of sodium, potassium, and calcium and possible heart beat abnormalities

Laxative overuse may damage the colon. Overuse of diuretics may produce dehydration and abnormal blood levels of potassium.

WHAT HAVE YOU LEARNED?

Food is all around us. It represents enjoyment, special events, and feelings. But variety and moderation are the keys to good health and nutrition. Eating many different foods assures you of getting the necessary nutrients in the right amounts. Moderation is essential in eating appropriate amounts of foods. And exercise will help you balance your caloric intake and your energy output.

CHECK YOUR PROGRESS

1. Name the tool you would use to determine if a growing child's or teenager's weight and height are normal. Using this tool, when might the results signal a problem?
2. Name a standard table used to assess adult weight for a given height. How is frame size determined?
3. Identify several quick, less scientific ways to judge if you are at a good weight.
4. What is the difference between being overweight and being obese?
5. Identify a method for judging the amount of body fat.
6. What happens to body weight if energy input is greater than output? If energy output is greater than input? What is meant by energy balance?
7. What is the safest way for an overweight growing person to achieve his or her desirable weight? Why?

8. List several activities that are described as sedentary, light, moderate, vigorous, and strenuous.
9. How does food choice and portion size effect energy balance?
10. How does choosing a variety of foods assist in maintaining energy balance?
11. Given the percentage of Calories from carbohydrate, protein, and fat, which food item has more Calories? *Item A:* 30% carbohydrate, 25% protein, and 45% fat; or *Item B:* 40% carbohydrate, 30% protein, and 30% fat.
12. How does behavior modification assist someone to control his or her weight?
13. Describe how you would judge the safety and validity of any diet plan.
14. What are some of the factors involved in obesity?
15. What are some of the features of anorexia nervosa? Name both physical and psychological issues in this disorder.
16. Name some of the health hazards associated with bulimia.

8 NUTRITION POWER FOR YOUR BEST PERFORMANCE

Marianne is determined to be a body builder. To develop her muscles, she works out and lifts weights every day at the gym. Because muscles are made of protein, Marianne has decided to supplement her diet with a high-protein drink. Will this extra protein help her?

Sam is a 16-year-old high school wrestler. Last season he was state champion at the 125-pound weight class. The coach needs someone for the same division this year. However, over the summer Sam grew 2 inches and gained 15 pounds. What facts should Sam consider before deciding which weight class he should wrestle at this year?

Angelena's goal is to win a triathalon, an endurance event that includes swimming, bicycling, and running. She has been training rigorously for months. On the day of the event the temperature is over 80° F. What dietary safety measures should she follow before, during, and after the competition?

Jonathan loves to cross-country, or Nordic, ski. This winter he plans on entering beginner races, including some that are 24 kilometers (14.8 miles) long. What foods are best for extra energy during endurance sports?

To achieve a competitive edge, many athletes, dancers, and models search for the winning dietary combination. Whether a person is training for the Olympics or bicycling to keep in shape, exercise places nutritional demands on the body. A well-planned diet is as much a part of the training plan as the exercise routine. Knowing what physically active people require and how to meet these needs is the focus of this chapter.

Your objectives in this chapter will be to:

■ *Compare the energy needs of individuals engaged in a variety of sports and physical activities*

■ *Identify the nutrients most critical to the body during physical exercise*

■ *Give examples of appropriate food intake during athletic training and competition*

■ *Distinguish between food facts and myths related to physical performance*

RECIPE FOR THE BEST PERFORMANCE

Achieving the nutrition "edge" doesn't require a magic formula or expensive supplements. The recipe for nutrition power begins with a well-balanced diet. Following the guidelines described in Chapter 5 provides the basic plan for the athlete. Everyone has a need for the same nutrients, but physically active people expend more energy. Athletes and others who are engaged in prolonged physical activity have a greater need for Calories.

Calorie Needs are Individual

How much food do you need when you participate in sports or other physically demanding activities? The answer depends on you and the sport or activity of your choice. Calorie needs depend on your body size and age. In addition, the type and length of competition and level of physical fitness will influence your needs.

Ideal Weight Ranges. For most sports, maintaining your ideal body weight is desirable. Being overweight can slow you down. Likewise, if you are too thin you may lack stamina and endurance. What is the desirable weight range for your height? Table 8.1 is a list of suggested body weights.

Body Composition. Being within your ideal weight range in pounds is not the only factor to consider. Knowing the percentage of your fat versus muscle weight is also important. A greater muscle mass adds strength and endurance. Men and women differ in their normal range of body fat. Men usually have 14% to 16% of their weight as fat. The range for women is 20% to 23% fat. A conditioned athlete or physical fitness enthusiast may have as little as 5% body fat.

Table 8.1   Suggested Body Weights

Height[a]	Range of Acceptable Weight (lb)	
	Men	**Women**
4'10"..............................		92-119
4'11"..............................		94-122
5'0"...............................		96-125
5'1"...............................		99-128
5'2"...............................	112-141	102-131
5'3"...............................	115-144	105-134
5'4"...............................	118-148	108-138
5'5"...............................	121-152	111-142
5'6"...............................	124-156	114-146
5'7"...............................	128-161	118-150
5'8"...............................	132-166	122-154
5'9"...............................	136-170	126-158
5'10"..............................	140-174	130-163
5'11"..............................	144-179	134-168
6'0"...............................	148-184	138-173
6'1"...............................	152-189	
6'2"...............................	156-194	
6'3"...............................	160-199	
6'4"...............................	164-204	

Source: G. Bray, ed., "Obesity in America" (Washington, D.C.: United States Government Printing Office, 1979), National Institutes of Health Publication No. 79-359, p. 7.
[a]Height is measured without shoes; weight is measured without clothes.

There are several methods to determine body composition. Perhaps the easiest is to determine the amount of fat located under the skin. Several different skin fold measurements (in millimeters) can be taken. The instrument used to measure the skin fold is called a *caliper.* The most commonly measured areas are the *triceps* (backside of the arm) and *subscapular* (shoulder blades) areas. See Illustration 8.1. Results can be compared with standard tables of skin fold measurements.

After comparing your weight and skin fold results, will you need to gain, lose, or maintain your weight? Next you must determine how many Calories you will need to achieve your goal.

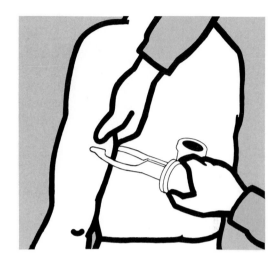

Illustration 8.1.
Measuring Skin Fold
Thickness.

Basal Calorie Need. Your body size, sex, and age determine your basal Calorie need. A growing teenager must eat enough Calories to support his or her growth. See Table 8.2. In addition, you will need to determine the energy cost of your daily activities, including training and competition. For men involved in heavy-energy

Table 8.2	Recommended Dietary Allowances for Energy	

	Total Calorie Intake	
Age (yr)	Average	Range
Children		
7-10..........................	2400	1650-3300
Males		
11-14	2700	2000-3700
15-18	2800	2100-3900
19-22	2900	2500-3300
Females		
11-14	2200	1500-3000
15-18	2100	1200-3000
19-22	2100	1700-2500

Source: Food and Nutrition Board, National Academy of Science, National Research Council, *Recommended Dietary Allowances*, ed. 9 (Washington, D.C.: National Academy Press, 1980).

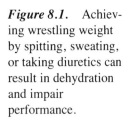

Figure 8.1. Achieving wrestling weight by spitting, sweating, or taking diuretics can result in dehydration and impair performance.

exercise, extra Calorie needs can be determined using the values of 7.5 to 12.0 Calories per minute. For women use the range of 6.0 to 10 Calories per minute of heavy exercise. Finally, your intake must be adjusted if you need to gain or lose weight.

Remember that 3500 Calories equals a pound of fat. Thus cutting 500 Calories per day out of the diet will produce a 1-pound weight loss in 1 week (500 Calories $\times$ 7 days = 3500 Calories). Trying to lose more than 1 to 2 pounds per week can be dangerous to your health. Quick weight loss schemes result in loss of body water, not fat. Wrestlers, for example, have been known to achieve their weight goal by spitting, sweating, or taking diuretics. These practices change body fluid balance and actually hinder performance. Drinking water after weigh-in is not adequate to replace the loss.

FUELING YOUR PERFORMANCE

Sports and other physical activities differ in their demand for energy. Some sports have a relatively low energy cost. These include activities that are short in duration or have a low demand for muscle

Table 8.3   Sports and Activities Classified by Energy Cost

Endurance Sports with Higher Energy Cost (require about 8 to 16 Cal/min)

Climbing	Long-Distance Swimming
Football	Marathon
Gymnastics (especially apparatus)	Middle-Distance Running
Handball	Mountaineering
Hockey (Ice and Field)	Pentathlon
Long-Distance Canoeing	Skin Diving
Long-Distance Rowing	Soccer
Long-Distance Running	Tumbling
Long-Distance Skating	Water Polo
Long-Distance Skiing	Wrestling

Sports of Short Duration and/or Lower Energy Cost (require about 3 to 7 Cal/min)

Archery	Javelin Throw
Baseball	Judo
Basketball	Pole Vault
Boating (Sailing and Ice Boating)	Rowing, slow or moderate speed
Bowling	Shooting
Boxing	Short-Distance Running
Canoeing, slow or moderate speed	Short-Distance Skiing, Slalom
Cycling, slow or moderate speed	Short-Distance Swimming
Dancing	Shot Put
Diving	Skating
Equestrian sports	Ski Jumping
Fencing	Softball
Golf	Sprints
Gymnastics	Tennis
High Jump	Volleyball
Hurdle Races	Weight Lifting

Source: Nutrition for Athletes—A Handbook for Coaches. Reprinted by permission of the American Alliance for Health, Physical Education, Recreation and Dance, 1900 Association Drive, Reston, Virginia 22091.

exertion. Other sports may require the use of leg or arm muscles for an extended period of time, or at a more intense rate. These activities have a much higher energy cost. See Table 8.3, Sports and Activities Classified by Energy Cost.

Table 8.4 High-Carbohydrate Foods

Breads	Fruits
Cereals	Fruit Juices
Pasta	Vegetables
Pancakes	Vegetable Juices
Muffins	Milk
Cakes	Milk Shakes
Cookies	Yogurt
Soft Drinks	Cocoa
Candy	Ice Cream

Foods containing fat should contribute 30% to 35% of the total energy. Carbohydrate foods should provide 50% to 60% of the Calories. On days when the energy need for competition or exercise is high (between 2000 and 4000 Calories), carbohydrates may provide as much as 70% of the total energy. Foods high in carbohydrates are listed in Table 8.4. Cakes, cookies, soft drinks, and candy are high in carbohydrates but low in most other nutrients. Choose these foods only after you meet your basic nutrient needs.

Although protein foods may be used for energy, they are not the primary fuel. The breakdown of muscle tissue is also not the normal source of energy. As a rule, protein should be spared for tissue growth and repair. The teenage years are a period of rapid growth.

Table 8.5 Determine Your Protein Requirement

Calories/Day		Protein Calories/Day		Calories/Gram of Protein		Grams of Protein/Day
2000 × 10%	=	200	÷	4	=	50
2000 × 15%	=	300	÷	4	=	75
3000 × 10%	=	300	÷	4	=	75
3000 × 15%	=	450	÷	4	=	112.5
5000 × 10%	=	500	÷	4	=	125
5000 × 15%	=	750	÷	4	=	187.5

Adequate energy intake from fats and carbohydrates is important to preserve protein for building tissue. A protein intake of 10% to 15% of Calories will meet the needs of an active teenager. Table 8.5 can help you determine your protein requirement.

Muscle Cells Select Their Fuel

Muscle cells will break down glucose, glycogen, and free fatty acids to obtain energy. Fatty acids provide the major fuel source while the body is at rest. This energy is readily available from body fat tissue. During exercise the amount of fatty acids used as fuel decreases as the intensity of work increases. Why does this occur?

Breaking down fatty acids is an *aerobic* process, which means that oxygen is required. Exercises low in energy demand or short in duration permit a steady supply of oxygen to flow to the muscles. As long as cells have an adequate supply of oxygen, fatty acids remain the primary energy source. Training can improve an athlete's oxygen uptake during heavier exercise, thus increasing the use of fatty acids as an energy source.

As the intensity and duration of exercise increases, there is a greater use of glycogen for energy. Breaking down glycogen is an *anaerobic* process, because energy can be produced without oxygen. Thus carbohydrates are the most efficient fuel for endurance sports, such as running a marathon and bicycle racing.

Carbohydrates and Endurance

One factor that limits an athlete's endurance is the amount of carbohydrate available. Only a small amount of carbohydrate, about 1440 Calories, is stored in the body. A tiny portion of this carbohydrate circulates as glucose in the blood. The remainder is stored as glycogen in the muscles and liver. This reserve might fuel a cross-country skier for 2 hours.

Carbohydrate Loading. Carbohydrate loading is a process that attempts to increase the amount of glycogen stored in muscles. Because glycogen is the most efficient fuel for endurance sports, having an extra glycogen reserve may be helpful. Loading is of no added benefit to players in short-duration sports, such as gymnastics or weight lifting.

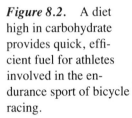

Figure 8.2. A diet high in carbohydrate provides quick, efficient fuel for athletes involved in the endurance sport of bicycle racing.

The carbohydrate loading plan requires following a strict diet-exercise pattern for several days before an event. See Table 8.6. The goal is to deplete and then restore muscle glycogen. There are some harmful side effects, including abnormal water retention. The process is not recommended for young athletes. If used, the practice of carbohydrate loading should be limited to two or three key events per year.

Extra Protein: An Expensive Myth

A common belief among athletes and their coaches is that athletes need extra protein for optimal performance. This belief has led some athletes to eat large servings of high-protein foods, such as meat, fish, and poultry. In addition, protein supplements have gained popularity. Is there any advantage to these practices? Researchers have not proven that a diet high in protein will improve the work efficiency of the muscles. An intake of 1.0 to 1.5 grams of protein per kilogram (2.2 pounds = 1 kilogram) of body weight is believed to meet the needs of the most physically active people.

What about extra protein for building more muscle tissue and added strength? There is some evidence that during intense strength

Table 8.6   Carbohydrate Loading Plan

Day	Training	Diet
7	Long, hard	Basic diet
6	Moderate	Basic diet
5	Moderate	Basic diet
4	Moderate	Basic diet
3	Rest	Carbohydrate-loading diet
2	Rest	Carbohydrate-loading diet
1	Rest	Carbohydrate-loading diet
0	Competition	Precompetition meal

Source: *Food Power: A Coach's Guide to Improving Performance.* Courtesy National Dairy Council (Rosemont, Ill., 1983).

training, such as weight lifting, protein intake of 2.0 grams per kilogram of body weight may be desirable. Protein is needed to support the development of muscle mass and the increase in red blood cells. However, the use of protein pills or liquids is unnecessary.

Water: An Increased Need

The human body is composed of 50% to 60% water. A lean person usually has more body water than does an obese person. Men generally have more body water than do women. Any activity that changes the amount of body water can have dramatic effects on well-being. A loss of body water without fluid replacement results in *dehydration.* Even minor dehydration impairs body functioning. A loss of 5% of body water, for example, can cause heat exhaustion. Greater water loss can result in heat stroke and death.

A normal adult usually requires 2½ to 3 quarts of water per day. Most of this water is obtained from prepared foods. Foods vary in their water content. See Table 8.7, Water Content of Foods. Strenuous exercise, such as mowing the lawn or jogging during hot weather, increases water loss through sweat. Excess sweating can greatly increase the body's need for water. Weighing before and after an event

Table 8.7   Water Content of Foods

High

Lettuce	96%
Watermelon	93%
Orange	88%
Milk	87%
Apple	85%

Medium

Fish (baked)	68%
Ground Beef (lean)	60%
Chicken (fried)	58%
Cheese	40%
Bread	36%

Low

Nuts	5%
Soda Crackers	4%
Peanut Butter	2%
Potato Chips	2%
Chow Mein Noodles	1%

Source: United States Department of Agriculture, "Nutritive Value of Foods" (Washington, D.C.: United States Government Printing Office), Home and Garden Bulletin No. 72.

or activity is an easy way to judge the amount of water lost. See Illustration 8.2. Drinking fluids before, during, and after exercise is important to avoid dehydration. However, thirst is not an adequate signal of the amount of fluid to drink to replace losses. In fact, it may take several days to replace water losses.

Fluids to Drink. What fluids are best to drink when a person is participating in strenuous exercise? Plain water may be the wisest choice, especially during and immediately after athletic competition or other intense physical labor. Fruit juice or skim milk are good choices for the preevent meal. Diluted fruit juices (mixed with three parts water) and vegetable juices (mixed with one part water) are also safe replacement fluids.

Drinks with large amounts of sugar and minerals may cause stomach upset, diarrhea, and added water loss. Commercial sport

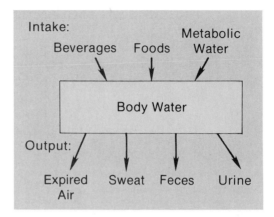

Illustration 8.2. Body Water Balance. *Metabolic water* is a by-product of energy production.

drinks are designed to supply water, sodium, potassium, and carbohydrates. Sport drinks containing salt and sugar are more slowly absorbed by the body. Research shows these drinks are no better than water in replacing fluid. Alcoholic beverages should be avoided, because urinary fluid loss will be increased.

Figure 8.3. Drinking plain water is the best way to replace the body's water losses during exercise.

Focus on Minerals

The minerals most affected by exercise and physical activity are sodium, potassium, and iron. The distribution of water within the body is regulated by the presence of sodium and potassium.

Sodium and Potassium. The balance of sodium and potassium is critical to health. Although sweat is primarily water, some sodium and potassium are also lost. Generally, these losses are small and you can easily replace them in 24 hours by consuming a normal diet. Salt your food liberally after exercising or working in hot, humid weather. Salt tablets should be avoided, because excess salt intake draws water into the stomach and away from the blood vessels. This redirection increases the risk of dehydration. To ensure adequate potassium replacement, eat an extra orange or banana.

Iron. Iron plays an important role in allowing muscle cells to produce energy without fatigue. Iron, found as hemoglobin in red blood cells, is responsible for carrying oxygen to muscle tissue. In addition, hemoglobin returns the waste product, carbon dioxide, back to the lungs to be exhaled. The presence of low hemoglobin values in physically active people has been labeled *sports anemia*. An increase in blood plasma volume without a similar increase in red blood cell mass is believed to occur as a normal response to exercise. Sports anemia is not a true anemia, as iron stores are not reduced. Iron supplementation is not of benefit.

Figure 8.4. Eating an extra banana or orange is a good way to ensure adequate potassium replacement after strenuous exercise and sweating.

Low iron stores have been identified as a problem for some athletes in endurance sports. The serum ferritin level is measured to assess iron storage. A lower than normal level indicates true anemia. Females participating in endurance sports are at risk for anemia. Iron supplements are effective in treating athletes with low iron stores. However, taking iron tablets does not enhance the performance of athletes with normal iron stores. All physically active people should include iron-rich foods in their diet to prevent iron deficiency. Red meats are the best iron source. Less readily absorbed iron is available in vegetables and grains.

Vitamin Pills: No Extra Benefit

Vitamins regulate or control many cell activities. Some of these activities are related to building muscle and the storage and release of energy. To date, controlled studies have shown no measurable improvement in athletic performance after extra vitamin intake. Thus no scientific proof exists to support the need for physically active people to take extra vitamins.

In fact, self selection of vitamin supplements can be dangerous. Read the vitamin pill labels. Does the product meet or exceed the Recommended Daily Allowance? Ask yourself, what happens when your body gets more than it needs of this vitamin? Remember that fat-soluble vitamins A, D, E, and K are stored in the body. Excess intakes of these vitamins may be toxic. Taking more than needed of the water-soluble vitamins makes the kidneys work harder to excrete the excess. Some toxic effects of the water-soluble vitamins have also been identified.

Consuming a well-balanced diet of natural, less-refined foods provides needed vitamins in proper amounts. Fulfill your increased vitamin need by snacking on fruits, vegetables, whole grain foods, and dairy products. This is the smart, safe, and economical way to add vitamins in just the right quantity for *you*.

Ergogenic Foods

An *ergogenic aid* is any factor that enhances work performance. Ergogenic aids can be classified as: (1) mechanical (massage, ultraviolet light), (2) psychological (hypnosis, music), (3) drugs (steroids, hormones), and (4) nutritional (diet patterns, special foods

Figure 8.5. A wise way to meet an increased vitamin need is by snacking on healthful fruits, vegetables, whole grain products, and dairy products.

and nutrients). Are there special athletic super foods? Over the years certain foods have gained popularity among athletes. Foods such as wheat germ oil, lecithin, protein tablets, and bee pollen have been promoted as having an ergogenic effect. Under controlled studies, none of these foods have been shown to improve performance, but the pregame rituals continue. The belief that previous success can be attributed to taking a certain food has a powerful psychological value. A psychological "edge" is important to any athlete, but consider safety before you use any product.

Eating Prior to Physical Activity

Eating two to three hours before an event is recommended. The preevent meal for athletes should provide some fluid, supply a source of glucose to prevent hunger pangs, and be easily digested prior to the event. Food remaining in the stomach during competition may result in cramps and nausea. The same principle holds true for those engaging in physical work, such as shoveling snow, stacking wood, or baling hay. The content and timing of the pregame meal is especially important to the athlete in endurance sports. During lengthy events the meal provides extra energy for immediate use. (In short-duration sports the energy comes from body stores, as discussed earlier.)

Figure 8.6. Most athletes find that a small, easily digested meal of fruit, skim milk, bread, and lean meat is best before athletic competition.

The type and amount of food eaten prior to an event will vary with the person's size and needs. Most athletes find that a small meal of fruit, skim milk, bread, and lean meat is best. Foods high in fat should be avoided, as fats remain in the stomach longer. Recommended pregame intake ranges from 500 to 1000 Calories. Some athletes find that a low-fat liquid meal, homemade or a commercial product, is better tolerated. Because of faster stomach emptying, liquids can also be consumed nearer to the beginning of the event. Whole milk is not recommended, because the fat delays stomach emptying time. Caffeine drinks, such as coffee, tea, and soda pop, should be avoided because of the diuretic and stimulant effects.

HEALTHFUL EATING GIVES YOU THE EDGE

There are no magical nutrition secrets to increasing your athletic performance. The secret is to develop your body through physical training and a life-long healthful diet. A human machine in top-notch nutritional shape can perform to the limits of its capabilities.

Learn to assess your own Calorie needs based on your physical activity routine. Learn to critically judge the safety and validity of food products and diet patterns promoted as beneficial to athletes.

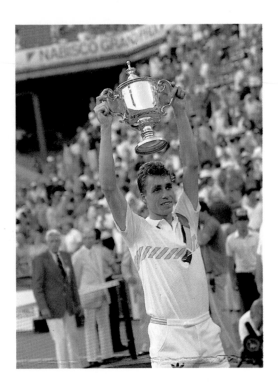

Figure 8.7.   A person in excellent nutritional shape can perform to the limits of his or her capabilities.

CHECK YOUR PROGRESS

1. Identify the factors that determine the calorie needs of someone who is engaging in physical exercise.
2. Describe how desirable body weight is determined.
3. What is the normal percent body fat range for a man? A woman? Describe a method for checking body fat composition.
4. How many Calories equal a pound of fat?
5. List several high-energy sports and several low-energy sports.
6. Define aerobic and anaerobic. How does the cell's use of energy nutrients change as the oxygen available decreases?
7. Describe carbohydrate loading. Why is it practiced? Is it safe to do frequently?
8. Explain the cause and effects of dehydration. What precautions should be followed during competition or training in hot, humid weather?

9. Is thirst an adequate indicator of how much fluid to drink in order to replace water losses? Describe the best fluids to consume before, during, and after competition.
10. Identify the minerals most affected by exercise.
11. Describe the general recommendations for replacing sodium and potassium lost by sweating.
12. Explain why adequate iron intake is important for an athlete. When would iron supplementation be needed?
13. Is vitamin supplementation beneficial for the athlete? Explain your answer.
14. Define ergogenic. List some foods that have been promoted as ergogenic. Have any of these been proven beneficial for the athlete?
15. Describe the composition of a typical pregame meal. What type of foods should be avoided prior to competition?

NUTRITION INFORMATION: FACT OR FICTION

Julie is looking at the selection of vitamins at the drug store. Since school started Julie has been so busy with school work, rehearsals for the fall play, working parttime at Burger Land, and going out with friends that she has hardly had time to eat or sleep. Her friend Mary has suggested that she take some vitamins. Now Julie is confused by the variety of vitamin and mineral products on the drugstore shelf. Does Julie really need to take a supplement? If so, which one is right for her?

Greg has decided he wants to eat only food that is "natural." As he looks at the cereals on the supermarket shelf, he finds several brands that say "all natural" on the box front. The boxes for these products are smaller than those for some other brands and they cost more. Greg compares the labels and tries to decide which kind to buy. What facts would help Greg make an informed decision?

Bobby is a member of his school's cross-country team. He really wants to be selected for the traveling squad this year. Last week he read an article about a special diet for runners. The article promised that a person could improve his or her time by 30% in just 2 weeks by following the diet. What advice would you give Bobby before he starts this diet?

Today it's hard to pick up a magazine, watch television, or read the newspaper without seeing something about food, nutrition, health, or wellness. Sometimes the information you see or hear differs from the information you are learning in this book. How do you know what is correct? How can you find out?

Your objectives in this chapter will be to:

■ *Identify your biases and opinions about nutrition and food*

■ *Develop skill in evaluating the accuracy of nutrition information*

■ *List several risks associated with nutrition misinformation*

222

LEARNING TO SEPARATE FACT FROM FICTION

A great deal is known about nutritional needs and optimal health, yet scientific knowledge in some areas is incomplete. Gaps in knowledge are often exploited or misinterpreted. Consumers spend money on products that are, at best, unnecessary and, at worst, dangerous to health.

No single, easy way can determine the accuracy and truthfulness of the nutrition information you read or hear. To judge the merit of any information presented, you need to consider three parts of the process (See Illustration 9.1):

1. You—the *information receiver*—the listener or reader
2. The *information giver*—the author of the book or article, or the speaker or advertiser
3. The *information purpose and content*

The Information Receiver

Let's talk about you, the information receiver. Almost everyone has biases and opinions about nutrition and food. Nutrition professionals think in terms of nutrients when planning adequate diets. However, people eat food, not nutrients. Sometimes the reasons people choose a food have little or nothing to do with nutrients, but a lot to do with their biases, opinions, life-styles, culture, and region of the country in which they live.

Objective Decision-Making. The first step in judging nutrition information is to be objective in evaluating your own biases. Your

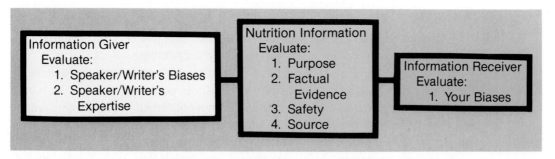

Illustration 9.1.   Nutrition Decisions: Learn to be Objective.

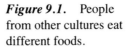

Figure 9.1. People from other cultures eat different foods.

challenge is to decide if a piece of information is of use because it is accurate or because it tells you what you want to hear. The question to ask yourself is, "Does the information appeal to a bias?"

Cultural Biases. Insects are good sources of protein, vitamins, and minerals. Insects are a common food in some parts of the world. Many people in the United States, however, would find it very hard to eat ants for breakfast—even chocolate-covered ants. This is a cultural bias.

Social Biases. Ordering a T-bone steak or lobster tail for dinner in a restaurant conveys to others an image of wealth. Eating a high-priced food implies success and importance. Some people think such foods are "better" than other protein sources, such as chicken or bean and rice mixtures. Their attitude reflects their social bias rather than their objective knowledge about these foods and the nutrients they contain.

Beliefs and attitudes about corporations may bias an individual against food products produced by corporations. Some people feel large companies are unfair to consumers or farmers through their "high" prices, "deceptive" advertising, or use of foreign workers. These people claim companies are not concerned about the consumers who buy their products. Statements that foods are "overly processed," "have lost much of their food value," or "have too many additives" may represent bias, not fact. Some people buy only foods labeled "natural," "organic," or "no additives or preservatives added." Such practices reflect social biases about economic systems as well as beliefs concerning food quality.

Medical Biases. Some people are biased against traditional types of health care. This bias may be reflected in the belief that special foods, herbal remedies, and vitamin supplements are a more "natural" way to attain and maintain health. These individuals often feel that doctors charge too much and prescribe too many drugs. Such attitudes reflect people's ideas about medical care and medical care providers rather than their scientific knowledge about health and disease.

Emotional Biases. Everyone has emotional biases. Special foods are eaten to celebrate happy events. People often select a favorite food that makes them "feel better" when they are upset or depressed. Birthdays are often celebrated with cake and ice cream. For many people Thanksgiving Day would be incomplete without roast turkey, stuffing, and pumpkin pie. Foods for special occasions are often eaten more for our own emotional well-being than to meet a nutritional requirement. Candy, chips, and ice cream may be "celebration" foods for some people; other people may crave these foods most when they are upset.

Figure 9.2. The traditional birthday celebration offers foods to meet an emotional need.

Other Biases. A variety of other factors also bias people's ideas about food. People develop biases against foods that they dislike, have never tried, or do not know how to prepare. For example, you may read that broccoli, carrots, and cauliflower contain special compounds that may help prevent cancer. Because you do not like these foods, you may choose to ignore the information rather than evaluate the nutrition information objectively.

Biases may develop out of a life-style preference for foods that are quick and convenient. Personal goals, such as weight loss or muscle building, may bias food choice without consideration of safety or proven value of specific food products. These biases are based more on fears, hopes, and desires than on nutrition knowledge.

The Information Giver

Being objective about yourself as the information receiver permits consideration of another factor in this information exchange— the information giver. Two questions need to be asked:
1. Who is the information giver?
2. Why is the information presented?

Nutrition has become a popular topic in magazines, in books, and on television. The number of people giving nutrition advice has increased. However, not everyone giving nutrition advice is well informed about the subject. Some of these spokespeople are using their personal biases to influence others. Others may be using inaccurate nutrition information to sell a product. Be critical of what you see and hear. Is the information up-to-date, accurate, and practical? It may be difficult to distinguish a nutrition expert from someone who is pretending to be an expert. Look for the information giver's bias.

Anyone can use the title "nutritionist." A nutritionist may or may not be a qualified nutrition professional, because the title is not legally defined. Look for evidence of the information giver's formal training and experience in nutritional science.

One trademark that assures you that the spokesperson has had this training is the title "Registered Dietitian," or R.D. To use this title, a person must meet several qualifications. Registered dietitians have completed a college degree in nutrition at an accredited college or university. They have completed an internship with qualified professionals to gain practical experience, and have passed a national

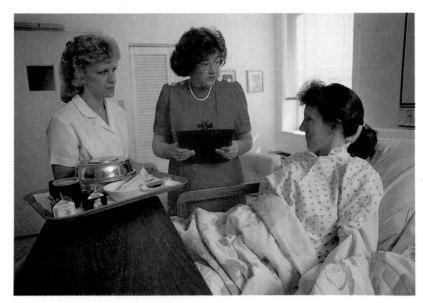

Figure 9.3. Dietitians working in community programs, school districts, and hospitals are reliable sources for nutrition information.

certification examination. Registered dietitians must continue to attend seminars and classes to update their knowledge and maintain their certification.

Dietitians working in hospitals or community programs are a reliable nutrition resource for consumers. Home economists have college training in the broad field of home economics, including applied foods and nutrition. Home economists employed by Cooperative Extension Programs, school districts, or grocery stores are good resources for practical food and nutrition information. School and community health educators may also serve as a nutrition resource.

Purpose and Content of the Information

In addition to the information giver's qualifications, you need to evaluate the information being provided. Is the information factual? Is the information helpful and safe? Or is the information promotional and appealing to a bias? Nutrition professionals know that a nutritious diet is only one component of a healthy life-style. Qualified nutrition professionals will not claim that nutrition can work miracles or prevent or cure any illness. Beware of information that appeals to your hopes, your fears, and your desires, rather than to your common sense.

Identify the Purpose. Nutrition information may be published to educate the public or to communicate new research results. Information may also be presented to entertain the reader or to sell a product to consumers. If the purpose of the message is to sell something—a book, magazine, food product, nutrition supplement, or health service—evaluate the information carefully. Your health and your wallet are at stake! The motivation to sell a product often results in factual information being overstated or only one side of the picture being presented.

Food and nutrition articles are often published in magazines and books to attract readers and sell products. Some books and magazines present reliable information, while others do not. Check the author's credentials and the tone of the article. If it sounds too good to be true, it probably is! Table 9.1 shows an evaluation of accuracy of nutrition articles in popular magazines.

The purpose of advertising is to entice you to buy a product. Always judge the information in an advertisement for accuracy. Some

Figure 9.4. When reading advertisements, you must make your own judgments about the accuracy of the information presented.

Table 9.1 Nutrition Information in Nineteen Popular Magazines

Magazine	Circulation	Nutrition Articles Reviewed			Percent Accurate
		Accurate	Inaccurate	Total	
Generally Reliable					
50 Plus..................	180,000	14	0	14	100
Parents..................	1,500,000	30	1	31	97
Redbook.................	4,200,000	28	1	29	97
Reader's Digest........	18,000,000	20	1	21	95
Good Housekeeping ...	5,400,000	37	3	40	93
Inconsistent					
Glamour.................	1,800,000	41	10	51	80
Vogue	1,100,000	19	5	24	79
Woman's Day...........	7,500,000	35	12	47	74
Ms.	490,000	8	3	11	73
Seventeen	1,500,000	15	6	21	71
Family Circle	7,400,000	24	17	41	59
McCall's................	6,300,000	17	13	30	57
Ladies' Home Journal .	5,400,000	14	14	28	50
Unreliable					
Mademoiselle...........	920,000	17	20	37	46
Essence	600,000	10	17	27	37
Cosmopolitan...........	2,800,000	14	24	38	37
Harper's Bazaar	630,000	12	29	41	29
Organic Gardening.....	1,300,000	2	6	8	25
Prevention..............	2,000,000+	3	28	31	10

Source: M. Hudnall, "ACSH News and Views," *American Council on Science and Health,* 3 (1982):1.

advertisements are designed to appear as written news articles or as scientific reports. The format is intended to impress you with the "scientific" value of the information and product. But when you analyze the ad carefully, you may find the information to be favorable to that company's product, with some important facts omitted.

Identify the aim of the food or nutrition product advertisement. Are any hidden messages conveyed? Frequently, secondary messages appealing to a bias are mixed with nutrition fact. For example, symbols of power or success may be used to present the message. Is the famous baseball player or television star qualified to tell you about the product? How many film stars or sports personalities actually use the products they endorse? Would you buy the product on its own merit or because of the celebrity's endorsement?

Weigh the Evidence. Personal *testimonial,* the relating of a personal experience or observation, is a convincing method often used to sell health and nutrition products. Consumers are led to believe that a product worked for the people testifying, so it will also work for them. Personal testimonials are persuasive, but not necessarily factual. Look for more evidence.

Sometimes products work because of the placebo effect. A *placebo* is something that makes a person feel better because they expect to, not because it had a physical effect on the body. Sugar pills are often used as placebos when the effects of drugs are tested. Half of the people are given the drug and the other half are given a sugar pill. No one knows which people receive the real medicine until the end of the experiment. If only the people who received the real drug get better, then the conclusion is that the drug is effective. If some of the people taking the drug and some of the people taking the placebo get better, the drug is rated not effective. The people in the second example felt better because they expected to feel better after taking medication. Look for proof of cause and effect.

Scientific Research. Evidence based on the results of con-trolled research studies is your best assurance of factual information. Reliable nutrition research measures the differences between a matched *control group* (who receives no treatment) and an *experimen-tal group* (who receives the treatment being tested). Statistical analysis must be done to prove that differences are real and not a matter of chance.

In many research studies, groups of subjects are selected and matched to be as similar as possible in age, sex, life-style, or other characteristics that might influence the experimental results. A change is made in the experimental group and observations or tests are conducted. After a period of time the results are compared with the control group in whom no changes were made.

Reporting Nutrition Information. Nutrition scientists publish results of their experiments in "peer-reviewed" scientific journals, such as the *Journal of the American Dietetic Association* or the *American Journal of Clinical Nutrition.* The articles published in these journals have been reviewed for accuracy by several other scientists. This *peer review* helps prevent misleading information from being published.

The accuracy of the nutrition information reported in the public media depends on the ability of the presenter to translate the scientific language in journals into interesting and meaningful material for the consumer. Sometimes results from animal studies are reported to the public as if the same results could be expected in human subjects. However, what is true for a rat may not be true for humans. It is wise to let researchers complete studies in humans before research findings are applied to our daily life. Occasionally journalists and broadcasters may exaggerate research results to attract readers or viewers. Seek the advice of reliable nutrition experts before making radical changes in your diet.

COMMON NUTRITION CONTROVERSIES

The steps in separating nutrition information from misinformation can be applied to judge popular nutrition controversies critically. Let's take a closer look at several of these issues.

Organic, Natural, and Health Foods

Are "natural," "organic," or "health" foods better for you? These terms are often used interchangeably, and there is little agreement on their precise meanings. *Natural* often means foods with minimal processing and without preservatives, additives, or artificial ingredients. *Organic* foods (sometimes called organically grown) are usually grown without the use of agricultural chemicals. Processing is minimal and chemical additives are not used. The term *health food* is used more generally, often including natural and organic foods, to describe foods believed to have health-promoting properties. See Illustration 9.2.

The Label says . . .

All
Natural
Cereal

Organic
Fruit
Juice

Illustration 9.2. Are
"Natural" Foods Better?

"No Preservatives Added"
Old-Fashioned
Bread

What do these terms mean to you?

Consumers: Be Alert! There is no evidence that natural or organic foods are safer or of higher nutritional quality than conventional foods. Many foods advertised as natural or organic are really no different than other brands on supermarket shelves. Some foods are advertised "all natural" or as containing "no preservatives" because they do not need preservatives.

Impressed by these claims, consumers buy the products and the manufacturers continue to advertise the product. Neither government nor industry has approved standard definitions for the terms "natural," "organic," and "health" foods. The terms are used more often to impress consumers rather than to describe a food product accurately.

Some people say the food grown in the United States is nutritionally inferior because the soil has been depleted by modern farming methods. Claims are also made about chemical fertilizers having "poisoned" foods. However, there is no difference in plants grown with chemical or organic fertilizers. Plants need certain nutrients for growth to occur. Plants will use those specific chemicals regardless of the compound's origin, whether produced in a fertilizer manufacturing plant or obtained from animal manure. Plants are not fussy—they will use the nutrients they need.

Health-Promoting Foods

Some foods are thought to have special health-promoting properties. Almost all foods contribute to health as a part of a balanced diet. No one food, by itself, contains all or even most of the nutrients in the amounts needed for good health. As you have already learned, variety is the first characteristic of a healthful diet.

Vitamin and Mineral Supplements

Selling vitamin and mineral supplements is a billion-dollar business in the United States. In 1980, about one third of the adults in the United States regularly used vitamin supplements. A Food and Drug Administration (FDA) survey reported that many people consume over 20 supplements each day. Consumers can select from dozens of different food supplements available from drug, discount, grocery, and sporting goods stores, as well as mail-order outlets. People believe that "if a little is good, a lot is better" when it comes to vitamins and minerals. These individuals advocate using *megadoses* of vitamins and minerals. *Mega-* means large, so a "megadose" is a large amount. Nutrition professionals define doses of vitamins and minerals that are 10 times the Recommended Daily Allowance (RDA) level or more as megadoses.

Fact and Fiction. One argument presented for consuming megadoses is that some people eat a poor diet or are under stress and need more nutrients. The RDA nutrient levels established by scientists already take into consideration the needs of everyday life. As described in Chapter 1, the RDAs are designed to meet the needs of healthy people.

Too Much of a Good Thing . . . No evidence or research supports the theory that taking these nutrients in amounts greater than needed by the body is helpful. In fact, megadoses of some nutrients may be harmful. Excessive intakes of many vitamins and minerals may be toxic. Refer to Chapter 4 to review some of the symptoms of

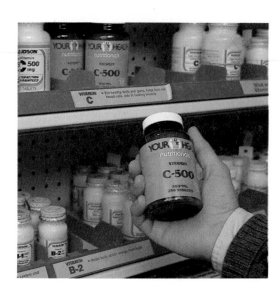

Figure 9.5. Since an excess can be toxic, the use of vitamin and mineral supplements in amounts greater than the RDA should be based on medically identified needs.

vitamin toxicity. High levels of one vitamin or mineral may interfere with the absorption and use of other nutrients. Normal amounts of some nutrients cannot compete with the large amounts of the supplemented nutrients. The nutrient imbalance can result in deficiencies of other nutrients. An FDA panel has published guidelines on vitamin and mineral dosages to prevent or treat deficiencies. See Table 9.2.

Special Groups. Children, pregnant women, women who are breast-feeding, and elderly persons have increased nutrient needs, and may be targets for promoters of large doses of vitamins and minerals. However, nutrients are needed in proper amounts during periods of growth. For example, calcium and phosphorus balance are important for normal bone formation. Infants of women who have taken megadoses of vitamin C while pregnant may develop rebound scurvy because their intakes will be less after birth. Nutrient absorption and use becomes less efficient with age. In the elderly, megadoses may more readily produce nutrient imbalances or deficiencies.

Some supplement products contain contaminants that can be dangerous. For example, some people use bone meal or dolomite as natural calcium supplements. Both of these may contain lead as well as calcium. These supplements can cause lead poisoning when used for a long period.

Table 9.2   Recommendations on Vitamin and Mineral Dosages for Prevention or Treatment of Deficiencies

Vitamins	Minerals
Vitamin C (Ascorbic Acid)	**Calcium**
50 to 100 mg/day prevention	For prevention only
300 to 500 mg/day treatment	Adults, children 1 to 10 and 12 years
Niacin (Niacinamide or Niacinamide	and over—400 to 800 mg/day
Ascorbate)	Children 10 to 12 years and pregnant
10 to 20 mg/day prevention	and lactating women—600 to 1200
25 to 50 mg/day treatment	mg/day
Vitamin B$_6$ (Pyridoxine)	Adults over 51 years—500 to 1000
1.5 to 2.5 mg/day prevention	mg/day
7.5 to 25 mg/day treatment	Infants 6 months to under 1 year—300
Vitamin B$_2$ (Riboflavin)	to 600 mg/day
1 to 2 mg/day prevention	Infants under 6 months—200 to 400
5 to 25 mg/day treatment	mg/day
Vitamin B$_1$ (Thiamin)	**Iron**
1 to 2 mg/day prevention	For prevention only
5 to 25 mg/day treatment	Menstruating and lactating women—
Vitamin A	10 to 30 mg/day
1250 to 2500 IU/day prevention	Pregnant women—30 to 60 mg/day
5000 to 10,000 IU/day treatment	Children 6 months to under 5 years—
Vitamin B$_{12}$	10 to 15 mg/day
3 to 10 μg/day prevention	In combination products other than for
Not to be used to treat deficiency	use in pregnancy: adults and chil-
Folic Acid	dren over 5 years—10 to 20 mg/day
0.1 to 1.4 mg/day prevention	**Zinc**
1.0 mg/day for pregnant and lactating	For prevention only
women	Adults, and children 1 year and over—
Not to be used to treat deficiency	10 to 25 mg/day
Vitamin D	Pregnant and lactating women—
400 IU/day prevention, infants and	25 mg/day
growing children under 18 years of	
age	
200 IU/day prevention, adults	
Not to be used to treat deficiency	

Source: A. Hecht, "Vitamins Over the Counter: Take Only When Needed," *FDA Consumer* 13 (1979):17-19.

Conditioned Dependency. This is another hazard of taking large doses of some vitamins, particularly the water-soluble vitamins. Suppose you consume large amounts of a nutrient whose excess is excreted. Your body will increase the functioning of those elimination systems to protect itself from high levels of a chemical it does not

Figure 9.6.   Some women and children require an iron supplement to prevent anemia.

Figure 9.7.   Vitamin and mineral supplements are not an adequate replacement for a healthy, nutritious diet.

need. When you stop taking the supplements, your body continues to eliminate high levels of the vitamin. A deficiency occurs until your body adjusts to your new low intake.

Vitamin and Mineral "Insurance." Many people take vitamin and mineral supplements as "insurance." Some individuals may try to eat well, but want to be sure they get enough of the required nutrients. All the necessary nutrients can be obtained from food. Taking a simple supplement containing only 100% of the U. S. RDA of the nutrients will not cause nutrient toxicity or nutrient imbalances. Neither will it provide all the nutrients needed. Scientists still know very little about some of the vitamins and minerals necessary for human health. These nutrients are not yet added to supplements because the amount needed to prevent deficiency without causing toxicity is not known. A varied diet is still the best nutrient insurance.

Some people may be "at risk" for a nutrient deficiency. For example, some women and children may need iron supplements to prevent anemia. Supplementation should be based on a medically identified need. It is rarely necessary to take supplements of any more than 100% of the RDA. Use vitamin and mineral supplements cautiously. Over 4000 children are treated for poisonings related to an overdose of supplements each year. Always keep vitamins and minerals out of the reach of children.

Nutrition Misinformation: Consumer Risks

What are the consumer risks associated with nutrition misinformation? Nutrition misinformation can have financial and health consequences for the consumer. Excess doses of vitamin and mineral supplements may result in nutrient toxicity or imbalance. The risks to a person's health may be even greater if he or she uses supplements instead of seeking medical treatment for an illness. The misinformation may also instill false hope for a cure of a disease or chronic illness.

Nutrition misinformation is also expensive. Paperback books containing false or misleading information may sell for $5.00 or more. "Health" foods usually cost more—often twice as much as the usual supermarket brand. Vitamin and mineral supplements vary widely in cost. An annual supply often costs over a hundred dollars. Purchasing unnecessary nutrient supplements uses money that could be spent on nutritious foods and other needs. This fact is especially important to people with limited or fixed incomes.

Why Does Misinformation Abound? If nutrition misinformation is potentially harmful, why is there so much available? See Illustration 9.3. The First Amendment to the United States Constitution assures the right of free speech, even to those who misinform intentionally or by accident. People may write anything in a book or discuss the subject on a television or radio talk show. Authors are under no obligation to prove that their statements about nutrition are true. Sellers can be prosecuted for fraud only if false claims appear on the product's label or advertising. Misleading advertising is prosecuted only when it is grossly deceptive. Because the Federal Trade Commission has a limited staff and limited time, it concentrates on major abusers to curb false advertising. See Illustration 9.4.

The United States Post Office can prosecute nutrition fraud when the mail is used. The quantity of mail order health and nutrition frauds makes it difficult to handle all the cases. The Postal Department must first prove the sellers' intent to defraud the public, not just the inaccuracy of the advertising.

Illustration 9.3.   Nutrition Advice is Everywhere.

The FDA enforces labeling regulations that prohibit false nutritional claims. Unlike drugs, vitamins and minerals are not regulated by the FDA. A 1976 law prohibited the FDA from requiring that dietary supplements contain essential nutrients or from regulating the amount of nutrient a supplement could contain.

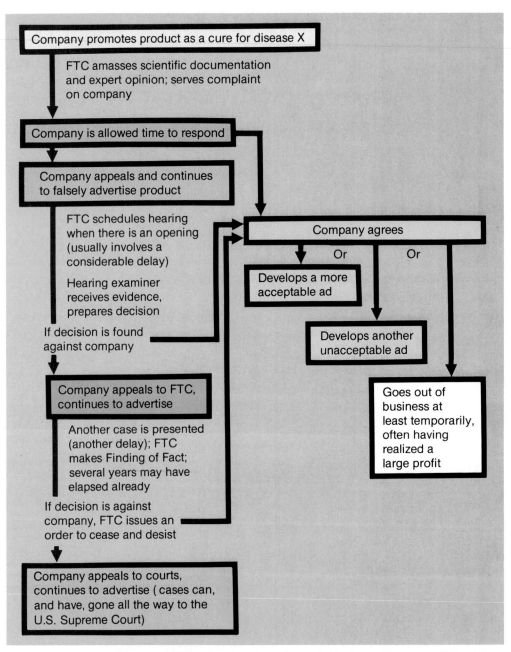

Illustration 9.4. The Food and Trade Commission Prosecutes False Advertising. Adapted from C. Suitor and M. Hunter, *Nutrition: Principles and Application in Health Promotion*, ed. 2 (Philadelphia: J.B. Lippincott Co., 1984), p. 196.

Of course, not all misinformation is deliberate. Responsible advertisers make efforts to avoid misinformation and overstatement that misleads the consumer. Some manufacturers have changed advertisements, corrected misinformation on labels, or recalled products to protect the consumer.

CRITICAL THINKING IS A CONSUMER SKILL

Recognizing nutrition misinformation is not always easy. Use your knowledge and common sense to evaluate nutrition claims. Shop as carefully for nutrition information as you do for the other things you buy. Consult a reliable source when you want to verify an answer to a nutrition question. If you feel a law is being broken, contact your state Attorney General's office, the Better Business Bureau, the FDA, your legislators, the state Health Department, or professional nutrition organizations. Protect your time, your money, and your health!

CHECK YOUR PROGRESS

1. List several biases you have as an information receiver. Why is it important for you to recognize your biases before making judgements about nutrition information?
2. What questions should you ask to evaluate the information giver?
3. Are personal testimonials reliable evidence of accurate information? Explain your answer.
4. Name several reliable professionals from whom you can obtain food and nutrition advice. Does the title "nutritionist" guarantee the person is a nutrition expert?
5. What is a placebo? How can the placebo effect cause false judgements to be made?
6. Describe the type of evidence required to assure that the information presented is factual. Where are nutrition research results published?
7. Describe the meaning of "organic," "natural," and "health" foods. What claims are made about these foods? Can these claims be supported by fact?

8. Identify the benefits and risks of taking vitamin and mineral supplements. Would you take a supplement? Why or why not?
9. Identify several risks associated with nutrition misinformation.
10. Describe the responsibilities of the Federal Trade Commission and the United States Post Office in curbing nutrition fraud.

10 WHAT'S IN THE PACKAGE?

John was looking closely at a package in the supermarket when Lonnie spotted him. "What are you doing?" Lonnie asked John. John explained that he was trying to determine which package of food to buy. His father had asked him to read the label and get the packaged item that is the "best buy."

John said to Lonnie, "Do you know anything about labels on food?"

"Sure," answered Lonnie. "Every package has the name of the food on it. Somewhere the ingredients are listed. But I just look at the price and get the cheapest one."

John and Lonnie are not alone in their lack of knowledge about food packages. Many consumers are unaware of the information that labels are designed to give them. Some people often purchase foods without reading labels. Likewise, some read only the brand name of a product, or look only at label pictures. Learn to understand and use label information to your best advantage. Labels are important tools to help you choose the food quality you need.

In this chapter your objectives will be to:

- *Name agencies that develop safety standards and control food industry processing and labeling activities*
- *Describe methods of food preservation*
- *List the positive and negative reasons for using food preservatives and certain additives*
- *Compare the nutritional value of processed foods using label information*

ENSURING A SAFE FOOD SUPPLY

Several agencies share responsibilities in making sure that Americans have safe food to buy. These agencies have been created through federal congressional or legislative state laws.

Federal Standards and a System of Control

A system of food safety control began with the passage of the Food, Drug, and Cosmetic (FD and C) Act of 1906. Since then, other laws have been passed establishing standards of food safety and a complex system for watching over the processing and handling of food, from the farm to your table. Table 10.1 summarizes the responsibility of federal agencies in assuring food safety.

The Food and Drug Administration (FDA), within the United States Department of Health and Human Services, oversees foods, drugs, and other substances that are used in food production. The agency evaluates substances that are intentionally added to foods to improve flavor, color, texture, and *shelf life* (the length of time a food can be kept or the date before which it should be eaten).

Table 10.1   Federal Agencies That Assure a Safe Food Supply

Agency	Unit	Responsibility
U. S. Department of Agriculture	Food Safety and Inspection Service Agricultural Marketing Service	Tests for chemicals in food Establishes standards for meat, poultry, egg, and milk inspection Oversees meat and poultry imports
U. S. Department of Human Services	Food and Drug Administration	Approves substances to be used in foods Enforces food labeling Oversees processed food inspection
U. S. Department of Commerce	National Marine Fisheries Service	Voluntary inspection and grading of fish

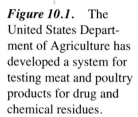

Figure 10.1. The United States Department of Agriculture has developed a system for testing meat and poultry products for drug and chemical residues.

Another federal agency, the United States Department of Agriculture (USDA), is responsible for inspecting and testing food for chemicals. In 1981 the USDA set up the Total Residue Avoidance Program to help reduce chemical residue in farm livestock. The USDA is responsible for testing meat and poultry products for drug and chemical residues. Products that have higher levels than permitted may not be processed for human food.

Other USDA food safety programs guard our food supply. The Food Safety and Inspection Service helps food processors set up tests for products as they are made. The Federal Meat and Poultry Inspection Program assures consumers that food products are safe to eat and are labeled correctly. Food may also be voluntarily graded for quality. Illustration 10.1 identifies the most common retail USDA grades for beef. The consumer can use food grading to purchase the level of quality needed for the intended purpose. Lesser grades are usually cheaper. The Food Safety and Inspection Service also oversees meat and poultry imports. The Federal Egg Production Inspection Program inspects the wholesomeness of dried, liquid, and frozen eggs.

Also at the federal level, the United States Department of Commerce has a role in monitoring food safety. The National Marine Fisheries Service, a unit within this department, monitors the safety of fish and shellfish.

The Environmental Protection Agency (EPA) is responsible for protecting the consumer from unnecessary exposure to agricultural chemicals. The EPA licenses the use of *pesticides* (chemicals used to

Illustration 10.1.
What the Grade of Beef
Means. Adapted from
United States Depart-
ment of Agriculture,
"Let the Grade be Your
Guide in Buying Food,"
*Food—From Farm to
Table; 1982 Yearbook
of Agriculture* (Wash-
ington, D.C.: United
States Government
Printing Office, 1982),
p. 312.

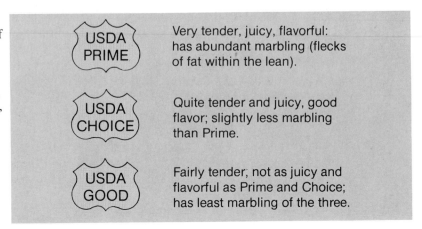

control insects) and *herbicides* (chemicals used to control weeds). The agency establishes limits on the amounts of chemicals allowed on food plants.

Food advertising is regulated by the Federal Trade Commission. This agency protects consumers from false or misleading advertising. The merit of nutrition claims made about certain food products was discussed in Chapter 9.

State Involvement

Each state has food inspection programs conducted by state agricultural and health agencies. Federal Standards often direct the state's programs, which are also designed to detect problems. One example is the Milk Inspection Program. Routine testing of cows is done to be sure that diseases such as *tuberculosis* and *brucellosis* are not present. These bacterial diseases can be transmitted through milk to humans. In addition to testing for disease, state and local inspectors inspect the cleanliness of dairy farms. Equipment must be sanitized. The water supply must be safe and the milking parlors must be clean.

THE INSIDE FACTS ON FOOD PROCESSING

Processing refers to the intentional altering of the properties of food by physical, chemical, and biological means. Heating and refrigeration (or freezing) are *physical* ways of altering food. The introduction of food additives is a *chemical* means of changing food. Fermentation is a *biological* method of processing.

Food Processing Changes Food

Foods are processed for three reasons:
1. To preserve food
2. To convert products into forms more suitable or desirable to eat
3. To obtain ingredients or nutrients from raw products not readily available in natural form

Examples of the first two reasons are more visible to consumers.

Processing as a Means of Preservation

Many people seem to be confused by the methods of food preservation because these may sound dangerous or harmful. Becoming knowledgable about the methods will permit you to decide the risks and benefits of each. *Preservation,* or adding certain substances to maintain product quality, has been practiced for centuries. Foods have been frozen, dried, salted, sugared, spiced, smoked, and pickled to prevent spoiling. Each of these is a method of preservation.

Food from both plant and animal origin begins to decompose immediately after harvest or slaughter. This breakdown of food can be caused by:
1. Natural chemicals in food that react with the air
2. Continued plant and animal cell activity
3. Growth of microorganisms such as bacteria, molds, and yeast

Left uncontrolled, these processes can ruin the quality and safety of food.

Various methods of food processing are used to stop or slow down food spoilage. These methods can be classed into five groups:
1. Heat processing
2. Dehydration
3. Refrigeration and freezing
4. Irradiation
5. Chemical control

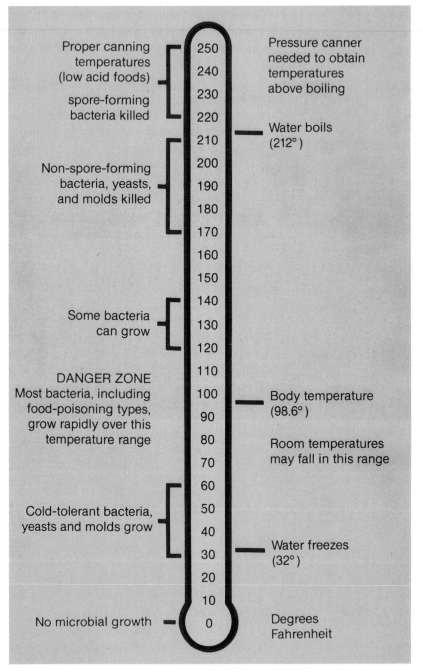

Illustration 10.2.
Effect of Temperature on Microorganisms. Adapted from United States Department of Agriculture, "Canning, Freezing, Storing Garden Produce" (Washington, D.C.: United States Government Printing Office, 1977), Agriculture Information Bulletin No. 410.

Heat Processing. Heat processing is used to increase the storage life of a food item and prevent the growth of microorganisms. See Illustration 10.2. Blanching, pasteurization, and sterilization are examples of heat processing.

Blanching. *Blanching* involves heating a product in steam or hot water at temperatures less than 212° F. It is commonly used to inactivate food enzymes before freezing or dehydration. Blanching before canning may also be used to soften tissue, remove tissue gases, and inactivate enzymes.

Pasteurization. This is a process designed to inactivate part but not all of the microorganisms present in a food. Because the resulting food product is not sterile, this method must be combined with another preservation process to assure food safety. For example, pasteurized milk must be refrigerated. Milk may be pasteurized by the hold method or by the high temperature, short-time method. In the *hold method,* milk is heated to 145° F, held at this temperature for 30 minutes, and then cooled to 45° F or lower. In the *short-time* method, milk is heated to 161° F for 15 seconds, and then quickly cooled to 50° F or lower.

Sterilization. *Sterilization* involves heat treatment to kill most of the microorganisms present. To achieve complete sterilization, every particle of food must be held at the killing temperature long enough to destroy all microorganisms. Such a process would have undesirable effects on nutritional value, flavor, color, and texture of food. Thus canning time and temperature combination charts have been developed to assure that the most microorganisms are killed with the least effect on food quality—in other words, an "acceptable" level of sterility.

The type and number of microorganisms present in the raw food affect the processing time. The time required also depends on the rate at which the heat can reach and raise the innermost particles to the killing temperature. Growing bacteria, for example, can be killed in just a few minutes at 212° F. Some bacteria, such as *Clostridium botulinum,* produce spores. Spores are very resistant to heat, and temperatures above the boiling point of water are required to kill them. To achieve these high temperatures, a pressure canner is required.

Acidity of a food is the most important factor in determining the length of time and temperature for safe processing. A method used for measuring the acid content is pH. A scale from 1 to 14 is used. A pH of 7 is considered neutral; below 7 is acidic, and above 7 is alkaline or basic. Foods with a pH below 4.6 are considered highly acidic; those with a pH greater than 4.6 are low-acid foods. See Illustration 10.3. To kill the *C. botulinum* spores, low-acid foods must be canned with a pressure cooker. For example, 10 pounds of pressure is used at sea level to achieve a temperature of 240° F.

Illustration 10.3.   pH Value of Various Foods. Adapted from United States Department of Agriculture, "Canning, Freezing, Storing Garden Produce" (Washington, D.C.: United States Government Printing Office, 1977), Agriculture Information Bulletin No. 410.

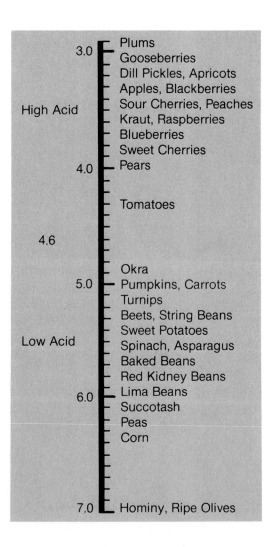

Figure 10.2. Today dried foods are popular "natural food" snacks.

Dehydration. Drying as a means of food preservation has been used for centuries. The increased interest in "natural foods" has revived its use. Foods may be dried by the sun, in an oven, or in a dehydrator. See Illustrations 10.4 and 10.5. Each of these methods removes water from the food. All living cells require water to carry on the process of metabolism. With the removal of enough water, cell functions and microorganisms become inactive. A temperature of 135° F to 140° F is desirable for drying. Moisture should be removed as fast as possible at a temperature that does not affect the food's quality. Fresh fruit, fresh vegetables, fish, and lean meats can be dehydrated. Drying times are affected by the moisture level of the food, humidity, and thickness of the slice being dried. Steps for drying fruit and vegetables are outlined in Table 10.2.

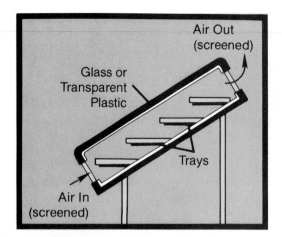

Illustration 10.4. Solar Drying Oven. Adapted from United States Department of Agriculture, "Canning, Freezing, Storing Garden Produce" (Washington, D.C.: United States Government Printing Office, 1977), Agriculture Information Bulletin No. 410.

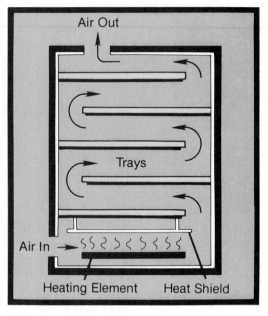

Illustration 10.5. Dehydration with Built-in Heater. Adapted from United States Department of Agriculture, "Canning, Freezing, Storing Garden Produce" (Washington, D.C.: United States Government Printing Office, 1977), Agriculture Information Bulletin No. 410.

Dried foods can be eaten as snacks, or *reconstituted* (rehydrated) for cooking or baking. The normal shelf life of dried fruits and vegetables is 1 year. Dried meats or jerky should be used in 1 to 2 months. Dehydrated foods should be stored in a clean, air-tight container at a temperature not exceeding 60° F. Dried foods may be frozen.

Refrigeration and Freezing. Refrigeration involves cooling a food product to a temperature below 45° F but above the freezing point of 32° F. This process is particularly important for short-term storage of foods. Refrigeration allows marketing of foods in their raw or fresh state. Maintaining this holding temperature also permits control of the ripening process. Most microorganism growth is slowed or stopped at temperatures below 45° F.

Table 10.2   Steps in Drying Fruits and Vegetables

Preparation	Drying
Wash	Oven
Sort	Sun
Peel	Dehydrator
Pit/Core	**Conditioning and Storage**
Slice	Equalize
Pretreatment	Pasteurize
Fruits	Package
Dip or Blanch	Store
Vegetables	
Blanch	

Source: United States Department of Agriculture, "Canning, Freezing, Storing Garden Produce (Washington, D.C.: United States Government Printing Office, 1977), Agriculture Information Bulletin No. 410.

Freezing, the lowering of the food temperature to below 32° F, preserves foods in two ways. First, like refrigeration, the lowering of temperature slows down cell activity and microorganism growth. Second, water is converted to ice and becomes less available for biological use (similar to the effect of dehydration). Not all water freezes when food is frozen, so chemical and microbial actions are slowed but not stopped. For best results, freeze food at 0° F or below for the maximum period as described in Table 10.3.

Irradiation. Over 30 years of research has gone into food irradiation. Irradiation involves the use of low doses of radiation to control insect and bacterial contamination in food. Irradiation doses are measured in rads. A low dose for food irradiation is in the range of 0 to 100 kilorads. The process involves exposing foods to gamma rays from cesium 137 for one to two minutes. Irradiation would most likely be used on fruits, vegetables, spices, and grains. The FDA has proposed regulations for the use of irradiation on any food in which insects may pose a problem.

Chemical Control: Natural and Added. *Fermentation* is a natural means of chemical preservation. In the fermentation process, food components are converted into related products that are more

Table 10.3   Recommended Frozen Storage Periods at 0° F

Fruits	Months
Berries, Cherries, Peaches	12
Fruit Juice concentrates	12
Vegetables	
Beans, Cauliflower, Corn, Peas, Spinach	8
Baked Goods	
Bread and Yeast Rolls	3
Cake	2-6
Fruit Pies (unbaked)	8
Meat	
Beef, Ground; Pork, Fresh Chops	4
Beef Roasts and Steaks	12
Lamb Roasts, Veal Chops	9
Pork, cured	2
Pork, Fresh Roasts	8
Cooked Meat	3
Poultry	
Chicken or Turkey parts	6-9
Chicken or Turkey, whole	12
Cooked Chicken and Turkey	4-6
Fish	
Cod, Flounder, Haddock, Halibut, Pollock Fillets	6
Clams, shucked; Oysters, shucked; and Dungeness Crabmeat	3-4
Shrimp	12
Cooked Fish and Shellfish	3
Frozen Desserts	
Ice Cream or Sherbet	1

Source: United States Department of Agriculture, "Consumer Guidelines for Food Safety," *Food—From Farm to Table; 1982 Yearbook of Agriculture* (Washington, D.C.: United States Government Printing Office, 1982).

Figure 10.3. Cheese is made by fermenting milk.

stable. For example, bacteria in milk can convert the lactose into lactic acid. The acid causes milk proteins to clot. This principle is applied in making cheese and yogurt. Sauerkraut, pickles, vinegar, and wine are made by fermentation. The end product is usually much different than the original food from which it was made.

It is sometimes desirable to preserve foods closer to their natural form. To achieve this goal, chemicals may be added to food. The most common chemicals added to inhibit microorganism growth are table salt (sodium chloride) and sugar (sucrose). These two chemicals bind with water, making the water less available for chemical and microbial action.

Acids lower the pH of the food to help retard microorganism growth. Acids often added to foods include citric, acetic, and phosphoric acids. Benzoic acid, which occurs naturally in cranberries, is used as a preservative in carbonated beverages.

Calcium propionate, a substance produced naturally by some molds in cheese, is used to prevent unwanted growth of mold on bread.

Synthetic compounds can also be used to preserve foods. For example, butylated hydroxyanisole (BHA) is used to prevent spoilage. Sulfites have been used to prevent the enzymatic browning of fruits and vegetables. Consumers often wonder why these and other compounds are added to food. Sometimes the compounds are added to foods for reasons other than preservation. Are you ready to take a more in-depth look at the issue of food additives?

FOOD ADDITIVES: EVALUATING THEIR USE

Misinformation or lack of information makes it easy to become confused when talking about food. Many people use the word additive without knowing its lawful meaning. Technically, anything added to food, such as baking soda, salt, or sugar, can be called an additive.

Types of Additives

Food additives are classified into three distinct groups:
1. Intentional additives

Figure 10.4. Any soap or detergent residue not completely rinsed off the plate will become an incidental additive at the next meal.

2. Incidental but anticipated additives

3. Incidental but not anticipated additives

Intentional additives have been discussed earlier. An example of incidental additives is the soap in which you wash your dishes. If the soap or detergent residue is not completely rinsed off, you will have an *incidental,* or unintended additive with your next meal. A similar addition occurs when you wrap a sandwich, preserve fruits, or freeze vegetables. Each package you use may add something to your food. These additives would be incidental but anticipated as a part of the food storage process. Unanticipated additives such as a button, human or animal hair, or insects occasionally get into the food supply by chance. These substances are *contaminants* and are not desired in food.

Incidental but anticipated additives used in the food industry, including ink, glue, and cardboard for packages, as well as detergents and sanitizers, are carefully researched. It is well understood by industry and by government personnel that these items get into the food. Therefore, incidental additives are evaluated and only those that are safe for people are allowed to be used.

Regulation of Additives

The FDA groups additives into two categories: *regulated* and *generally recognized as safe* (the GRAS list). Regulated additives are those that are tested and controlled. Specific usage levels are set for each food by the FDA. An additive on the GRAS list is defined as any substance generally recognized, by scientifically trained experts, as safe for the intended use in foods. Many GRAS additives used in or on food items have not been tested in the same way that new substances are tested. The FDA has compiled a list of over 700 substances assumed to be safe for use in foods. Casein is an example of an additive that is on the GRAS list. It is a protein found in milk and is often an intentional additive in other food products. Because it is part of a normally eaten food, it is considered safe.

Many people have said that absolute safety should be guaranteed for each GRAS list substance. While it is possible to scientifically study substances, it is impossible to guarantee 100% safety. Controlled studies can indicate the reasonable safety or harmfulness of a substance in normally consumed quantities.

Functions of Additives

There are many different functions of additives. These functions include:
1. Maintaining or improving nutritional value
2. Maintaining or enhancing product quality
3. Making food more appealing and acceptable
4. Aiding in processing or preparation
5. Reducing waste

Common additives used in homemade products include sugar, salt, baking soda, and various spices. A much larger variety of additives is used in commercial products that require periods of transportation and storage before being eaten.

Preservatives. The two classes of preservatives are antioxidants and antimicrobials.

Antioxidants. An *antioxidant* prevents discoloration or flavor change caused by the oxygen in the air. See Table 10.4. Ascorbic acid (vitamin C) is a naturally occurring antioxidant found in citrus fruits and plants of the cabbage family. Asparagus, onions, and red wine contain other natural antioxidants. *Tocopherols,* part of the vitamin E complex, are antioxidants found in vegetable oils.

Antioxidants are useful in preserving the flavor and wholesomeness of cake mixes, muffin mixes, and cereals. Without these compounds our food choices would be less varied. Most people have seen BHA, BHT, and PG on package labels. These are synthetic antioxidants. Butylated hydroxyanisole (BHA) and butylated hydroxytoluene (BHT) are more effective when used in combination. These compounds are used when fat is part of a product. Propyl gallate (PG) is used in products that do not contain fat. PG is easily dissolved in water, whereas BHA and BHT cannot be dissolved in water. BHA and BHT can be heated in baked goods and still be effective.

Antimicrobials. *Antimicrobials* are chemicals added to food to prevent spoilage. Table 10.5 lists some of the substances used to prevent spoilage. The safety of the preservative "nitrate" has frequently been questioned.

Nitrates have been used for centuries to cure meats. *Nitrate* is added to foods where, in the presence of an acid, it is converted to nitrite. It is the *nitrite* substance that preserves. Nitrites prevent

Table 10.4   Additives to Maintain Product Quality: Preservatives (Antioxidants)

Some Additives	Where You Might Find Them	Their Functions
Ascorbic Acid (Vitamin C)	Processed fruits, baked goods	Delay or prevent undesirable changes in color, flavor, or texture—enzymatic browning or discoloration due to oxidation; delay or prevent rancidity in foods with unstable oils
Butylated Hydroxyanisole (BHA), Butylated Hydroxytoluene (BHT)	Bakery products, cereals, snack foods, fats and oils	
Citric Acid	Fruits, snack foods, cereals, instant potatoes	
Ethylenediaminetetraacetic Acid (EDTA)	Dressings, sauces, margarine	
Propyl Gallate..............	Cereals, snack foods, pastries	
Tertiary Butylhydroquinone (TBHQ)..............	Snack foods, fats and oils	
Tocopherols (including Vitamin E)..............	Oils and shortening	

Source: P. Lehmann, *More Than You Ever Thought You Would Know About Food Additives . . . Part II* (Washington, D.C.: United States Government Printing Office, 1979), HHS Publication No. (FDA) 79-2118.

Table 10.5 Additives to Maintain Product Quality: Preservatives (Antimicrobials)

Some Additives	Where You Might Find Them	Their Functions
Ascorbic Acid (Vitamin C)	Fruit products, acidic foods	Prevent food spoilage from bacteria, molds, fungi, and yeast; extend shelf life; protect natural color or flavor
Benzoic Acid, Sodium Benzoate....	Fruit products, acidic foods, margarine	
Citric Acid............	Acidic foods	
Lactic Acid, Calcium Lactate.......	Olives, cheeses, frozen desserts, some beverages	
Parabens: Butylparaben, Heptylparaben, Methylparaben, Propylparaben.................	Beverages, cake-type pastries, salad dressings, relishes	
Propionic Acid: Calcium Propionate, Potassium Propionate, Sodium Propionate	Breads and other baked goods	
Sodium Diacetate.........	Baked goods	
Sodium Erythorbate.........	Cured meats	
Sodium Nitrate, Sodium Nitrite	Cured meats, fish, poultry	
Sorbic Acid: Calcium, Sorbate, Potassium Sorbate, Sodium Sorbate.........	Cheeses, syrups, cakes, beverages, mayonnaise, fruit products, margarine, processed meats	

Source: P. Lehmann, *More Than You Ever Thought You Would Know About Food Additives . . . Part II* (Washington, D.C.: United States Government Printing Office, 1979), HHS Publication No. (FDA) 79-2118.

microbes, such as *C. botulinum,* a food poisoning agent, from growing. Nitrites also delay spoilage, improve flavors, and keep the bright red color of meat products.

Nitrates and nitrites can occur naturally in food items. Green vegetables contain large amounts of nitrates. Spinach, which stores nitrates, may contain levels that are dangerous to infants less than 4 months old. Young infants do not have the ability to rid their bodies of nitrate. Young infants who ingest too much nitrate can develop a condition called *methemoglobinemia.* Their skin turns blue because their blood cannot carry adequate oxygen. Ground water, or water present in the soil, may contain high levels of nitrates. Nitrate levels can be increased by farm land runoff or frequent application of liquid lawn fertilizers. As a result, private wells should be tested for the presence of nitrate.

Nitrates and nitrites can also be toxic to adults. However, it is important to understand that it would take a lot of cured meat to kill you. A man weighing 154 pounds would have to eat 50 to 70 pounds of cured meat products at one meal to cause death.

Nitrates and nitrites have been called cancer-causing agents *(carcinogens).* This is not true. However, these compounds can be converted in the body to nitrosamines. Nitrosamines are carcinogenic; they have caused cancer in every animal species studied. Nitrosamines also cause defects in unborn animals and are able to change hereditary characteristics.

While nitrosamines are definitely unacceptable, nitrite is still the most effective way to prevent botulism food poisoning. Banning nitrite use could result in either an increase in botulism poisoning or the elimination of cured meat products. Do the risks outweigh the benefits?

Nutrients. Nutrients may be added to improve or maintain the nutritional value of a food. See Table 10.6. Foods to which vitamins and minerals are added back after processing are known as *enriched.* The nutrients are replaced at the level that naturally occurred before processing. Nutrients added at higher than natural levels or to foods not originally a source of the nutrient are known as *fortified.* Milk, for example, is fortified with vitamin D.

Flavors. Flavors are often added to food products. Whether the flavor is natural or manufactured artificially, the compounds are the same! In order to taste "apple," for example, similar compounds

Table 10.6 Additives to Improve or Maintain Nutritional Value: Nutrients

Some Additives	Where You Might Find Them	Their Functions
B Vitamins: Thiamine, Thiamine Hydrochloride, Thiamine Mononitrate; Riboflavin; Niacin, Niacinamide	Flour, breads, cereals, rice, macaroni products	*Enrich:* Replace vitamins and minerals lost in processing
Beta Carotene (Source of Vitamin A)........................	Margarine	*Fortify:* Add nutrients that may be lacking in the diet
Iodine, Potassium Iodide	Salt	
Iron	Grain products	
Alpha Tocopherols (Vitamin E)	Cereals, grain products	
Vitamin A	Milk, margarine, cereals	
Vitamins D, D_2, D_3	Milk, cereals	
Vitamin C (Ascorbic Acid)	Beverages, beverage mixes, processed fruit	

Source: P. Lehmann, *More Than You Ever Thought You Would Know About Food Additives . . . Part II* (Washington, D.C.: United States Government Printing Office, 1979), HHS Publication No. (FDA) 79-2118.

must be present. The tongue cannot differentiate between "natural" and "artificial" apple flavor because chemically there is no difference.

When natural flavors are extracted from whole foods (for example, lemon is extracted from lemons) and put into another product, these are declared *natural flavors* on labels. When a compound is made in a laboratory, but not found in nature, it is called *artificial*. For example, an artificial flavor can be made in a laboratory to taste or smell like lemon or apple. See Table 10.7.

Flavor Enhancers. A group of additives called *flavor enhancers* are important to food flavors. These substances do not give a flavor to a product. Instead, *enhancers* make the food's own flavor more noticeable. See Table 10.8. Two of the most common enhancers are salt and monosodium glutamate (MSG). Salt is used in amounts so small that you do not taste the salt. MSG was originally an extract from seaweed and has been used for centuries by the Japanese. MSG is also made in your body during normal digestion. Generally, substances made in the human body are used or eliminated safely from the body. This is an important fact when the safety of additives is considered.

Sweeteners. Although used for flavoring, sweeteners are usually considered a separate additive class. Sweeteners are classified as nutritive and nonnutritive. See Table 10.9.

Nutritive Sweeteners. These produce energy (Calories) when metabolized by the body. Nutritive sweeteners include sucrose, glucose, fructose, and sugar alcohols. Another nutritive sweetener recently made available to consumers is aspartame. *Aspartame* is composed of two amino acids and provides 4 Calories per gram. The amazing difference is that aspartame is 180 times as sweet as sugar! Sugar has 16 Calories per teaspoon. For the same sweetness, aspartame has one tenth of a Calorie.

Nonnutritive Sweeteners. Nonnutritive sweeteners, such as *saccharin,* are not metabolized by the body. Nonnutritive sweeteners provide no Calories and have been widely used in special diet foods for weight reduction and diabetes. Saccharin was originally on the GRAS list, but it was removed in the early 1970s when evidence of health risks surfaced. In the late 1970s the FDA proposed a ban on

Text continued on page 270.

Table 10.7   Additives to Affect Appeal Characteristics: Flavors

Some Additives	Where You Might Find Them	Their Functions
Vanilla (natural)	Baked goods	Make foods taste better; improve natural flavor; restore flavors lost in processing
Vanillin (artificial)	Baked goods	
Spices and other natural seasonings and flavorings, e.g., Clove, Cinnamon, Ginger, Paprika, Turmeric, Anise, Sage, Thyme, Basil	No restrictions on usage in foods—found in many products	

Source: P. Lehmann, *More Than You Ever Thought You Would Know About Food Additives . . . Part III* (Washington, D.C.: United States Government Printing Office, 1979), HHS Publication No. (FDA) 79-2119.

Table 10.8   Additives to Affect Appeal Characteristics: Flavor Enhancers

Some Additives	Where You Might Find Them	Their Functions
Disodium Guanylate	Canned vegetables	Substances that supplement, magnify, or modify the original taste or aroma of a food—*without* imparting a characteristic taste or aroma of their own
Disodium Inosinate	Canned vegetables	
Hydrolyzed Vegetable Protein	Processed meats, gravy/sauce mixes, fabricated foods	
Monosodium Glutamate (MSG)	Oriental foods, soups, foods with animal protein	
Yeast-Malt Sprout Extract	Gravies, sauces	

Source: P. Lehmann, *More Than You Ever Thought You Would Know About Food Additives . . . Part III* (Washington, D.C.: United States Government Printing Office, 1979), HHS Publication No. (FDA) 79-2119.

Table 10.9   Additives to Affect Appeal Characteristics: Sweeteners

Some Additives	Where You Might Find Them	Their Functions
Nutritive Sweeteners: Mannitol—Sugar Alcohol, Sorbitol—Sugar Alcohol	Candies, gum, confections, baked goods	Make the aroma or taste of a food more agreeable or pleasurable
Dextrose, Fructose, Glucose, Sucrose (table sugar)	Cereals, baked goods, candies, processed foods, processed meats	
Corn Syrup/Corn Syrup Solids, Invert Sugar	Cereals, baked goods, candies, processed foods, processed meats	
Nonnutritive Sweetener: Saccharin	Special dietary foods, beverages	

Source: P. Lehmann, *More Than You Ever Thought You Would Know About Food Additives . . . Part III* (Washington, D.C.: United States Government Printing Office, 1979), HHS Publication No. (FDA) 79-2119.

Table 10.10 Additives to Affect Appeal Characteristics: Natural/Synthetic (N/S) Colors

Some Additives	Where You Might Find Them	Their Functions
N Annatto Extract (yellow-red)	No restrictions	Increase consumer appeal and product acceptance by giving a desired, appetizing, or characteristic color; any material that imparts color when added to a food, generally *not* restricted to certain foods or food classes; may *not* be used to cover up an unwholesome food or used in excessive amounts; *must* be used in accordance with FDA Good Manufacturing Practice Regulations
N Dehydrated Beets/Beet Powder..	No restrictions	
S Ultramarine Blue....................	Animal feed only 0.5% by weight	
N/S Canthaxanthin (orange-red) ...	Limit 30 mg/lb of food	
N Caramel (brown).....................	No restrictions	
N/S Beta-apo-8′ Carotenal (yellow-red)	Limit 15 mg/lb of food	
N/S Beta Carotene (yellow).........	No restrictions	
N Cochineal Extract/Carmine (red)	No restrictions	
N Toasted Partially Defatted Cooked Cottonseed Flour (brown shades)......................	No restrictions	
S Ferrous Gluconate (turns black)..	Ripe olives	
N Grape Skin Extract (purple-red).	Beverages only	
S Iron Oxide (red-brown)	Pet foods only 0.25% or less by weight	

N Fruit Juice/Vegetable Juice	No restrictions
N Dried Algae Meal (yellow).........	Chicken feed only
N Tagetes (Aztec Marigold)..........	Chicken feed only
N Carrot Oil (orange)	No restrictions
N Corn Endosperm (red-brown) ...	Chicken feed only
N Paprika/Paprika Oleoresin (red-orange)......................	No restrictions
N/S Riboflavin (yellow)	No restrictions
N Saffron (orange)	No restrictions
S Titanium Dioxide (white).........	Limit 1% by weight
N Turmeric/Turmeric Oleoresins (yellow).......................	No restrictions
S FD&C Blue No. 1	No restrictions
S Citrus Red No. 2	Orange skins of mature, green, eating-oranges. Limit 2 ppm
S FD&C Red No. 3	No restrictions
S FD&C Red No. 40................	No restrictions
S FD&C Yellow No. 5	No restrictions

Synthetic color additives subject to certification: inspected and tested for impurities

Source: P. Lehmann, *More Than You Ever Thought You Would Know About Food Additives . . . Part III* (Washington, D.C.: United States Government Printing Office, 1979), HHS Publication No. (FDA) 79-2119.

Table 10.11   Additives to Aid in Processing or Preparation: Emulsifiers

Some Additives	Where You Might Find Them	Their Functions
Carrageenan...............	Chocolate milk, canned milk drinks, whipped toppings	Help to evenly distribute tiny particles of one liquid into another, e.g., oil and water; modify surface tension of liquid to establish a uniform dispersion or emulsion; improve homogeneity, consistency, stability, texture
Lecithin	Margarine, dressings, chocolate, frozen desserts, baked goods	
Mono/Diglycerides.......	Baked goods, peanut butter, cereals	
Polysorbate 60, 65, 80............	Gelatin/pudding desserts, dressings, baked goods, nondairy creams, ice cream	
Sorbitan Monostearate...........	Cakes, toppings, chocolate	
Dioctyl Sodium Sulfosuccinate......	Cocoa	

Source: P. Lehmann, *More Than You Ever Thought You Would Know About Food Additives . . . Part III* (Washington, D.C.: United States Government Printing Office, 1979), HHS Publication No. (FDA) 79-2119.

Table 10.12   Additives to Aid in Processing or Preparation: Stabilizers, Thickeners, and Texturizers

Some Additives	Where You Might Find Them	Their Functions
Ammonium Alginate, Calcium Alginate, Potassium Alginate, Sodium Alginate	Dessert-type dairy products, confections	Impart body, improve consistency, texture; stabilize emulsions; affect appearance and feeling of the food in the mouth; many are natural carbohydrates that absorb water in the food
Carrageenan	Frozen desserts, puddings, syrups, jellies	
Cellulose Derivatives	Breads, ice cream, confections, diet foods	
Flour	Sauces, gravies, canned foods	
Furcelleran	Frozen desserts, puddings, syrups	
Modified Food Starch	Sauces, soups, pie fillings, canned meals, snack foods	
Pectin	Jams/jellies, fruit products, frozen desserts	
Propylene Glycol	Baked goods, frozen desserts, dairy spreads	
Vegetable Gums: Guar Gum, Gum Arabic, Gum Ghatti, Karaya Gum, Locust (Carob) Bean Gum, Tragacanth Gum, Larch Gum (Arabinogalactan)	Chewing gum, sauces, desserts, dressings, syrups, beverages, fabricated foods, cheeses, baked goods	

Source: P. Lehmann, *More Than You Ever Thought You Would Know About Food Additives . . . Part III* (Washington, D.C.: United States Government Printing Office, 1979), HHS Publication No. (FDA) 79-2119.

saccharin. The ban was halted because of public pressure for the continued availability of diet products containing saccharin.

Food Colors. The safety of food colorings as additives has been of concern since the early 1970s. Are they safe?

Food colors are separated into three groups:

1. *Synthetic organic compounds* (FD and C colors)
2. *Mineral or synthetic inorganic colors* (rust from iron oxide, for example)
3. *Natural* colors from either plants or animals (chlorophyll from green plants, for example)

When describing food coloring, the term *artificial* means that color has been added. This color could be synthetic or natural. Unless the color is listed on a label, you would not know which it was. Table 10.10 lists common food colors.

Synthetic colors are made from *coal tar.* Ten of the 695 coal tar dyes are legally used in food. Two of the ten are the most frequently used. These dyes are tartrazine (FD and C Yellow No. 5) and sunset FCF (FD and C Yellow No. 6). Amaranth (FD and C Red No. 2) was banned for use in food in 1976. These three dyes could be blended to create a number of other colors because each one is a primary color. With the banning of amaranth, other ways to achieve certain colors had to be evaluated.

It is important to realize that most food are not colored. Bread, meat, potatoes, most fruits and vegetables, and fluid milk products are not colored. Below are food items ranked in order of the amount of coloring used. The items listed first contain the most and items listed last contain the least food colors:

1. Beverages
2. Candy and confections
3. Dessert powders
4. Bakery goods (including salad dressing, nuts, gravies, spices, jam, jelly, and food packaging material)
5. Sausage (casing color)
6. Cereals
7. Ice cream, sherbets, butter, and cheese
8. Snack foods
9. Maraschino cherries

You can see that someone who drinks a lot of carbonated drinks could get more color in his or her diet than a milk drinker.

Much research has been conducted to learn more about food colors. Excessive intake of foods containing artificial colors has been blamed for hyperactivity in children. However, carefully controlled scientific research has not shown this to be true. The best way to avoid problems is to eat a wide variety of foods. It's also more fun!

Emulsifiers. Oil and water normally separate after mixing stops. An *emulsifier* is used to help the ingredients stay mixed longer. Lecithin is a naturally occurring emulsifier present in milk and egg yolk. Table 10.11 identifies foods to which emulsifiers are commonly added.

Stabilizers. *Stabilizers* cause foods to thicken by absorbing water. The result is a uniform product texture. Stabilizers add "body" to puddings, sauces, gravies, jams, jellies, and other toppings. Most stabilizers are found in nature. Table 10.12 lists common stabilizers commercially used in food. *Arabinogalactan* comes from larch trees, *gum arabic* is from acacia trees, *pectin* occurs in fruits, and seaweed provides *agar, algin, carrageenan,* and *furcelleran.*

pH Control Agents. Substances are also added that affect the texture, taste, and safety of foods by controlling acidity or alkalinity. See Table 10.13. Acids give the tart taste to soft drinks and sherbets. Acids are also added to low-acid foods, eliminating the need for higher temperatures and longer processing required to kill bacteria. A more acceptable quality of product is the result. Alkalizers are added to cocoa beans during processing to neutralize acids that are produced during fermentation. The result is a darker, milder flavored chocolate.

Leavening Agents. Carbon dioxide is required to raise cakes and breads to produce a light-textured product. *Leavening agents* are natural or chemical substances that react in the presence of heat or water to release carbon dioxide. See Table 10.14. *Baking soda* (sodium bicarbonate), for example, releases carbon dioxide when heated. *Yeast,* a one-celled plant, is a natural leavening agent. Yeast plants feed on sugar and release carbon dioxide, water, and alcohol as the sugar is broken down.

Maturing and Bleaching Agents. Milled flour has a natural yellowish color and lacks qualities needed to make an elastic, stable dough. Aging is one way to make the flour ready for use in baking. Chemicals can be added to hasten the process of maturing and whitening the flour. See Table 10.15.

Table 10.13   Additives to Aid in Processing or Preparation: pH Control Agents

Some Additives	Where You Might Find Them	Their Functions
Acetic Acid/Sodium Acetate........	Candies, sauces, dressings, relishes	Control (change/maintain) acidity or alkalinity; can affect texture, taste, wholesomeness
Adipic Acid	Beverage/gelatin bases, bottled drinks	
Citric Acid/Sodium Citrate..........	Fruit products, candies, beverages, frozen desserts	
Fumaric Acid.......	Dry dessert bases, confections, powdered soft drinks	
Lactic Acid	Cheeses, beverages, frozen desserts	
Calcium Lactate	Fruits/vegetables, dry/condensed milk	
Phosphoric Acid/Phosphates........	Fruit products, beverages, ices/sherbets, soft drinks, oils, baked goods	
Tartaric Acid/Tartrates	Confections, some dairy desserts, baked goods, beverages	

Source: P. Lehmann, *More Than You Ever Thought You Would Know About Food Additives . . . Part III* (Washington, D.C.: United States Government Printing Office, 1979), HHS Publication No. (FDA) 79-2119.

Table 10.14   Additives to Aid in Processing or Preparation: Leavening Agents

Some Additives	Where You Might Find Them	Their Functions
Yeast............	Breads, baked goods	Affect cooking results; texture and increased volume; also some flavor effects
Baking Powder, Double-Acting (Sodium Bicarbonate, Sodium Aluminum Sulfate, Calcium Phosphate)........	Quick breads, cake-type baked goods	
Baking Soda (Sodium Bicarbonate)........	Quick breads, cake-type baked goods	

Source: P. Lehmann, *More Than You Ever Thought You Would Know About Food Additives . . . Part III* (Washington, D.C.: United States Government Printing Office, 1979), HHS Publication No. (FDA) 79-2119.

Table 10.15   Additives to Aid in Processing or Preparation: Maturing and Bleaching Agents, Dough Conditioners

Some Additives	Where You Might Find Them	Their Functions
Azodicarbonamide	Cereal flour, breads	Accelerate the aging process (oxidation) to develop the gluten characteristics of flour; improve baking qualities
Acetone Peroxide, Benzoyl Peroxide, Hydrogen Peroxide	Flour, breads, and rolls	
Calcium/Potassium Bromate........	Breads	
Sodium Stearyl Fumarate	Yeast-leavened breads, instant potatoes, processed cereals	

Source: P. Lehmann, *More Than You Ever Thought You Would Know About Food Additives . . . Part III* (Washington, D.C.: United States Government Printing Office, 1979), HHS Publication No. (FDA) 79-2119.

Anticaking Agents. In humid weather, grains of table salt would naturally stick together. To keep salt, baking powder, and powdered sugar flowing freely, anticaking agents are added. Certain chemicals, such as calcium silicate, absorb moisture and prevent lumping of powdered products. See Table 10.16.

Humectants. Substances added to food to retain moisture are known as *humectants*. Humectants such as glycerine are added to shredded coconut and marshmallows to keep them soft and moist. See Table 10.17.

TOXIC SUBSTANCES IN OUR FOOD SUPPLY

Yes, some foods can be dangerous. Certain foods contain compounds that are *toxicants,* or poisonous agents. Some minerals and metals are toxic.

Some Minerals Can Be Toxic

Every food contains tiny or trace amounts of many minerals. Eating a wide variety of food helps to prevent overloads of toxic minerals. Occasionally, large quantities of toxic metals get into our food. The most toxic metals, referred to as "heavy metals," are lead, cadmium, and mercury.

Lead. Lead has been a health hazard in the past because cans for food were soldered with lead. Toothpaste was sold in lead-containing tubes. Plumbing pipes were soldered with lead. These practices of using lead have now been eliminated.

Any intake of lead is too much. Lead is not readily excreted from the body. Lead toxicity occurs more quickly in children than adults. Lead poisoning causes damage to the nervous system and kidneys. Blood cells are not produced correctly and hyperactivity may occur. Damage caused by lead poisoning may be irreversible.

Cadmium. Cadmium is found everywhere. It is in tools, equipment, plastic coloring, paint, rubber, ink, glass, and ceramics. It is used in medicine and has a primary function in batteries.

Table 10.16   Additives to Aid in Processing or Preparation: Anticaking Agents

Some Additives	Where You Might Find Them	Their Functions
Calcium Silicate	Table salt, baking powder, other powdered foods	Help keep salts and powders free-flowing; prevent caking, lumping, or clustering of a finely powdered or crystalline substance
Iron Ammonium Citrate	Salt	
Silicon Dioxide	Table salt, baking powder, other powdered foods	
Yellow Prussiate of Soda	Salt	

Source: P. Lehmann, *More Than You Ever Thought You Would Know About Food Additives . . . Part III* (Washington, D.C.: United States Government Printing Office, 1979), HHS Publication No. (FDA) 79-2119.

Table 10.17   Additives to Aid in Processing or Preparation: Humectants

Some Additives	Where You Might Find Them	Their Functions
Glycerine	Flaked coconut	Retain moisture
Glycerol Monostearate	Marshmallow	
Propylene Glycol	Confections, pet foods	
Sorbitol	Soft candies, gum	

Source: P. Lehmann, *More Than You Ever Thought You Would Know About Food Additives . . . Part III* (Washington, D.C.: United States Government Printing Office, 1979), HHS Publication No. (FDA) 79-2119.

Plants absorb cadmium. Because cadmium is used in so many products, including fertilizer, it occurs in our food supply. Humans absorb cadmium through the stomach or the lungs. Symptoms of poisoning include shortness of breath, bronchitis resulting from bronchial tube infections, and abnormal kidney function. Overaccumulation may cause death in some cases.

Cadmium is a serious threat in our food supply. It does not break down into harmless compounds. The production and use of cadmium are increasing; thus the risk to our food is increasing.

Mercury. A disaster occurred in Minimata Bay, Japan, early in the 1950s. People began to complain of vision problems, hearing loss, headaches, dizziness, depression, sleeplessness, and irritability. Because all of us suffer from these conditions at one time or another, people were not alarmed by the symptoms. As time passed, however, more people went to physicians with these problems. Eventually people began losing their balance. They stumbled around. Mental derangements occurred. Before the cause was found 111 people were poisoned; 27 of these were unborn infants and 41 people died. In another part of Japan, 5 other people died and 47 more were sick. What was the cause?

Figure 10.5. Cadmium, as used in fertilizers, batteries, plastic coloring, paint, and many other products, is a dangerous threat in our food supply.

The problem was that their limited basic food supply was contaminated with mercury. Large intakes of mercury were possible because their meals had little or no variety. Unfortunately, the puzzle took 7 years to solve. Variety in food choices could have prevented this from happening.

Natural Toxicants

Toxicants can have a number of different effects on people. The symptoms of ingesting too much of a toxicant vary. Several specific toxicants and their effects are described in the following paragraphs. Foods containing large amounts of a toxicant are listed. The quantity eaten of most of these foods would not provide enough toxicant to be harmful. Once again, eating a wide variety of foods is of value in avoiding toxic reactions.

Goitrogens. These substances can cause a *goiter,* which is an enlargement of the thyroid gland. The enlargement may occur because goitrogens can prevent the thyroid gland from using iodine. The use of iodized salt will probably be enough to prevent this problem. A diet that is very low in iodine and that includes a lot of the plants that contain goitrogens could cause a goiter to develop.

Cabbage, turnips, cauliflower, brussels sprouts, kale, and rutabagas are rich sources of goitrogens. It is estimated that a person would have to eat 22 pounds of cauliflower in order to have a problem. Cows can eat that much, but humans cannot. Unless a person eats only cauliflower, the problem exists in theory, but probably not in practice.

Aflatoxin. Aflatoxin is a potent cancer-causing substance. As mentioned in Chapter 6, it is a compound that you should not consume.

Aflatoxin is produced by a fungus. It occurs when corn, peanuts, and wheat are stored improperly. In the United States, producers of peanut butter use very sensitive instruments designed to find minute amounts of aflatoxin. Peanut butter that is contaminated cannot be sold.

Selenium. Selenium is an essential trace mineral that can be toxic (see Chapter 4). The margin of safety between its usefulness and toxicity is small. Milk, meats, seafood, and egg yolk are food sources

Figure 10.6.
Aflatoxin, a potent
cancer-causing sub-
stance, can develop
when corn, peanuts,
and wheat are stored
improperly.

of selenium. Normal food intake usually does not cause any trouble. Supplements with selenium have caused a number of symptoms, such as rashes, headaches, and nausea.

Antivitamins. Antivitamins are substances that can interfere with the body's use of vitamins. Raw egg white contains avidin. *Avidin* makes biotin, a B vitamin, unavailable to the body. Cooking egg white destroys the avidin. Linseed and flaxseed meal contain a substance that interferes with pyridoxine (vitamin B_6). *Thiaminase* is an enzyme that destroys thiamin (vitamin B_1). Foods rich in thiaminase are raw fish, blackberries, black currants, red beets, brussels sprouts, and red cabbage. Heat can destroy some types of thiaminase, but others are not changed by heating.

Vitamin Interactions. Excess doses (more than 10 times the Recommended Dietary Allowances) of some vitamins can interfere with other vitamins. Vitamin E in large amounts will prevent vitamin K from working. This can result in hemorrhages. Supplementary iron, in a mineral tablet form, can interfere with vitamin E. Every food provides both helpful and potentially harmful compounds. Eating many different foods in balanced amounts keeps us safer and healthier.

Oxalates. Oxalic acid is found in spinach, swiss chard, rhubarb, beet greens, and cocoa. Oxalic acid combines easily with calcium found in other foods. When this occurs, the body cannot use the calcium because it is attached to the oxalic acid. Someone who eats very few calcium-containing foods could develop a deficiency if he or she eats a lot of foods containing oxalic acid.

Phytates. Phytates are found in cereal grains. Phytates can prevent the body from absorbing calcium, zinc, iron, and magnesium. Yeast, commonly used in baked goods, seems to reduce this problem.

Summary. Problems related to a person's diet are not always identified easily. Many isolated symptoms caused by food content may be viewed as incidental or coincidental. Yet the Japanese experience at Minimata Bay provides a memorable example. The problem was identified in 1953, but not solved until 1960! Physicians or nurses are less familiar with food-related toxic reactions than are specialists such as dietitians. Dietitians and nutritionists are usually the best sources of advice about diets and foods. Avoid problems by including a wide variety of foods in your meals.

LABELING: HOW TO UNCODE THE PACKAGE

With the exception of fresh produce and possibly bulk foods, everything in a supermarket is packaged. The shelves are lined with jars, cans, boxes, and bags that display vivid colors and patterns. The package is often more exciting than the food inside! It also may cost more. Packages are designed to attract your attention. For example, marketing research studies have shown that bold yellow attracts people to packages.

Labeling requirements are controlled by Federal regulations and enforced by the FDA.

In 1966, the "Fair Packaging and Labeling Act" was enacted. This act made it mandatory for specific information to appear on each food label. Standard placement of each piece of information was required. In addition, the sizes of letters and pictures were specified.

On January 12, 1973, a document entitled "Regulations for the Enforcement of the Federal Food, Drug, and Cosmetic Act and the Fair Packaging and Labeling Act" was signed by the FDA commissioner. This regulation was the beginning of regulated nutrition labeling. However, this regulation does not require nutrition information to be on all labels. The listing of certain nutrients is required if

Figure 10.7. Package coloring, design, and placement on shelves are all geared toward one goal: enticing the consumer to buy the product.

any nutrition claim is being made for the product or if any nutrients are being identified.

The Food Label

In order to really understand labeling, you need to read a label. In the United States, all information must be in English and located in a specific place on the label. To interpret the label, you will need to know the meaning of several labeling terms. The following definitions will help you uncode the label.

Principal Display Panel. Let's assume you are facing a package, can, or pouch. The product name must appear prominently on the upper half of the Principal Display Panel (front). The weight in pounds and ounces (may also be in kilograms and grams) must appear in the lower third of this panel.

Pictures. Any picture used must show the actual product. If it shows other foods that are not in the package, the picture must be labeled "serving suggestion."

Information Panel. The information panel is on the side adjacent and to the right of the Principal Display Panel.

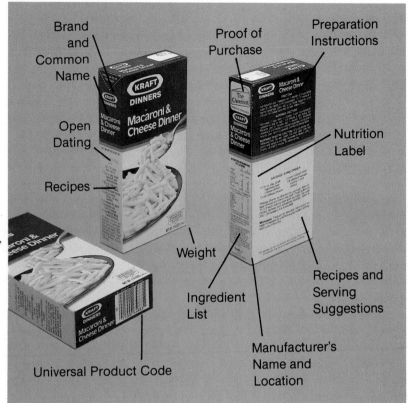

Figure 10.8. Understanding the package label will help you uncode the product information. Adapted from "Learning from Labels" (Glenview, Ill.: Kraft, Inc.).

Universal Product Code (UPC). The UPC is a series of lines, bars, and numbers that contains information about the product and manufacturer. It is used in stores in which computer-assisted checkouts read the UPC. Some of the information from the UPC label is printed on the cash register receipt.

Common Name. Trademark names are on the package front. The common name, such as gelatin dessert, must also be included. Generic foods usually use the common name.

Grade. Each food product has a unique grading system. USDA has specified grades for meat, poultry, and processed fruits and vegetables. Grades are not required on labels.

Weight. The total product weight, both liquids and solids, must be stated in usual terms (for example, pounds and/or ounces). This weight does not include the weight of the package. It is the weight of the product only.

Nutritional Information. Nutrition labeling is required for products that: (1) are fortified, (2) make a nutrition claim (for example, "one glass provides all you need each day"), or (3) are labeled "low calorie," "reduced calorie," "diet," "sugar free," or "dietetic." See Table 10.18. This labeling must be on the information

Table 10.18   Consumers Guide to Lower Calorie Products

Label Terms	Requirement
Low Calorie	No more than 40 Calories/serving and no more than 0.4 Calories/gram
Reduced Calorie	One-third lower in Calories than similar product in which Calories are not reduced
Diet or Dietetic	Must meet the requirements of either low Calorie or reduced Calorie; or for dietary use other than weight control (i.e., low sodium)
Lite or Light	May mean reduced or low Calorie, but can also describe other properties (i.e., light cream, light salt); read label carefully for Calorie/serving information
Sugar Free or Sugarless	Usually means reduced or low Calorie; label must say if not a reduced Calorie food or not intended for weight control

Source: Adapted from L. Fenner, *That Lite Stuff* (Washington, D.C.: United States Government Printing Office, 1982), HHS Publication No. (FDA) 82-2166.

panel adjacent and to the right of the Principal Display Panel. If a nutritional claim is made about the product, the specific nutrients must be listed. If a manufacturer wants to list a specific nutrient, all other nutrients required by the FDA labeling law must also be stated. The format must include serving size, number of servings per container, Calories per serving, and the following nutrients per serving: protein, carbohydrates, fat, vitamins A and C, thiamin, riboflavin, niacin, calcium, and iron. These nutrients must be given as a percentage of the RDA (discussed in Chapter 5). A serving size is defined by the FDA as an amount that would be reasonable to consume during a meal.

Ingredients. All items found in the product must be listed, including preservatives, additives, and spices (unless the product has a Standard of Identity registered with FDA, which will be discussed later). The ingredients are listed on the label in order of their product weight. The ingredient with the most weight is listed first. The last ingredient listed contributes the least weight in the product. Ingredients are always listed on the information panel.

Supplementary Information. Recipes or serving suggestions may be found on either the back panel or to the left of the Principal Display Panel.

Using Label Information

Similar products can be compared by using the information provided on labels. Since ingredients are listed by order of weight in the product, it is easy to compare the first ingredients. For example, two chicken soups can be compared. If one lists water first and the other lists chicken, then the one with chicken first has more chicken. The other one might be priced lower, but that is probably because it contains more water. If both list chicken first, then price could be used in making a selection.

Product names are descriptive. If a package says "chicken with gravy," then chicken is the primary ingredient. When the label states "gravy and chicken," then gravy outweighs the chicken.

Nutrition labeling information can assist you to make the appropriate choices. You may want a product with 50% of the RDA for iron. If you check the label, you can select one that meets your

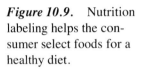**Figure 10.9.** Nutrition labeling helps the consumer select foods for a healthy diet.

needs. You can also determine the relative nutrient density by looking at the Calories and nutrients per serving. You can determine if the Calories are from proteins, fats, or carbohydrates. All of this information is available to you when you read the label information.

Labeling Standards

Some products use labels to state only the common name, UPC, manufacturer or distributor, and weight, while the ingredient listing is absent. This occurs when a product has a registered *standard of identity*. The standard is similar to a recipe. It states which ingredients, and the amounts or proportions, *must be included* in the product. Optional ingredients are also listed. Thus a product such as mayonnaise, no matter who makes it, will have basically the same composition. It may taste different because of the optional ingredients used or the amounts of required ingredients used.

Both the FDA and the USDA have established standards of identity for products that they regulate. The FDA has standards for over 200 products, such as enriched bread, margarine, mayonnaise, and ice cream. Standards change as improvements or problems are identified. The latest code of federal regulations lists the current standards of identity.

Other standards that affect products include the FDA's standards of quality and standards of fill for containers. The standards of fill are designed to assure you of getting a reasonable amount of a product you expect in a container size. Imagine your surprise if you opened a large can of green beans and found it to be half full, and the beans had long strings or leaves attached!

Standards of fill set requirements for the amount of product in a container. The requirements differ slightly for each food type. Some standards may specify a *solid weight* per container (or the product weight after the liquid is removed). Other standards may specify that the container be as full as possible without interfering with the lid.

Standards of quality limit the types of defects that are allowed. Minimum specifications for tenderness, color, and freedom from defect are established. These standards are mandatory. Products that do not meet these must state on the label "substandard for quality."

FOOD SELECTION

A basic understanding of food processing and labeling helps people to make satisfying choices. Your understanding of labeling information will help you to be satisfied with the choices you make. Reading labels is important. You can compare nutrient content with price to determine the best buy. You can identify the source of Calories. You can compare specific nutrients to select a product that best meets you needs. The ingredient panel will now make sense to you. The inclusion of additives won't distress you unnecessarily. You will know why some additives are used as preservatives. "Artificial" and "natural" now have meanings that are clear and make sense. Foods labeled with the word "artificial" should not alarm you. Being informed prepares you to be responsible for the food choices you make.

CHECK YOUR PROGRESS

1. Name two federal agencies that have a responsibility for assuring a safe food supply.
2. Describe a state-level responsibility for food safety.
3. What does food processing mean? Why are foods processed?
4. Name three methods of preserving food by the use of heat.

5. How does temperature affect bacterial growth? At what temperature are most non-spore-forming bacteria killed? At what temperature are spore-forming bacteria killed?
6. Why is acidity an important factor to consider in canning foods?
7. Identify two methods for dehydrating foods. How does dehydration prevent spoilage?
8. Explain the process of irradiation. Which foods are most likely to be preserved using irradiation?
9. Identify a natural chemical means of food preservation. List several foods that are commonly preserved by this method.
10. Name the two most common chemicals added to food to inhibit microorganism growth.
11. Define the term "additive." List the function of intentional additives.
12. What is the GRAS list?
13. Describe the function of an antioxidant. Name a natural and a synthetic antioxidant.
14. What is the function of an antimicrobial agent? Name an antimicrobial agent and a food frequently containing the agent.
15. What are the risks and benefits involved in the use of nitrates?
16. Define enriched and fortified.
17. What is the difference between natural and artificial flavors?
18. Describe the use of flavor enhancers. Name one substance in this category.
19. Describe the difference between nutritive and nonnutritive sweeteners. Identify a sweetener in each group. What is aspartame?
20. Identify the most common foods to which colors are added.
21. What are the functions of emulsifiers and stabilizers? Name one of each.
22. Why are substances added to control food pH?
23. Name a natural leavening agent and a chemical leavening agent.
24. Why are maturing and bleaching agents added to flour?
25. Describe the functions of anticaking agents and humectants.
26. Identify three minerals that can be toxic in large amounts.
27. What is a toxicant? Name two.
28. Describe the information you would expect to find on a food label. When is nutrition information required?
29. Define a standard of identity. Name a food for which the FDA has a standard of identity.
30. How do standards of quality and fill protect the consumer?

OUR FOOD RESOURCES

John lives on a farm that his great-grandfather homesteaded in the late 1800s. He wonders what his ancestors would think of farming today. Each day 80 cows are mechanically milked, and the volume and quality of milk from each cow are analyzed by computer. More than 500 acres are planted and harvested by use of the latest in farm machinery. How has our food supply been affected by modern farming methods?

The grocery store produce display case is filled with an array of fresh fruits and vegetables. Amazed at the selection, Sarah wonders where all the items come from. Bananas and pineapples need a tropical climate to grow. Green peppers and broccoli grow locally in the summer, but where do they come from in December? How has contemporary food marketing made delivery possible, regardless of the season?

Sue is moving into her own apartment and needs to stock her kitchen shelves and refrigerator. She knows there are several food stores in the city. One food warehouse advertises the lowest prices, but customers must bag and carry their own groceries. Another store claims to offer a variety of specialty bakery and delicatessen items. A nationwide chain supermarket claims the largest selection of food items plus a variety of consumer services, including a postal station, a savings and loan office, and an outdoor nursery. What features would you look for in a grocery store?

Attending school and working part-time doesn't leave much time for food preparation. As a result, Sam eats away from home several times each week. He often stops at one of the fast-food chains, as the choices in eating places and types of food are numerous. What factors have fostered the growth in the food service and hospitality industry?

Your objectives in this chapter will be to:

■ *Describe the historical and current trends in food production in the United States*

■ *Identify the steps in food production, from planting through processing to distribution and service outlets*

■ *Examine the costs involved in producing and distributing food*

■ *Describe the factors that affect food prices*

■ *Identify the specialized jobs available within the food-marketing system*

■ *Discuss the influence of the farmer, government, food industry, and the consumer on food availability and the marketplace*

FOOD PRODUCTION NOW AND THEN

Many of us take our meals and food for granted. Grocery stores stock hundreds of items, while fast-food chains punctuate the highways. Where does the food we buy come from? There are many steps to be performed before food from the farm becomes part of a nutritious meal on the dinner table. How has American food production evolved over the years?

Looking Back at American Agriculture

At the time of the American Revolution, the U.S. economy was almost totally based on farming. Because transportation and food preservation methods were limited, food needed to be produced locally for survival. Not surprisingly, then, more than 90% of the population was involved in farming. Colonial agriculture was a labor-intensive process, as one farmer provided enough food for four people. About 60% of a family's income went for food. What extra food could be produced was used to trade for other goods and services. Farm products were the major export of the New World.

Corn was the main staple crop produced in the Colonies. Tobacco was raised for export to Europe. Later, rice and cotton were produced for export. Farmers also began raising other cereal grains and livestock to complement their local diet. As the American population grew, people moved westward, clearing and breaking more land for food production.

In the 1800s, the development of the plow signaled the beginning of increased farm productivity. By the mid-1900s, mechanical planters, reapers, and threshers had replaced the hoe and scythe. Animal power was combined with human labor to produce more food. During this era, farmers used 180 man-hours of labor to produce 100 bushels of corn and 373 man-hours for 100 bushels of wheat. As Americans settled the West, additional land was brought into production. In 1880 the farming population in the United States was 22 million, or about 44% of the total population. At the same time, new nonfarming jobs were being created as a result of the industrial revolution. With the growth of industry in cities, the need to supply food to the urban population grew. Railroads provided a system for the transportation of agricultural products to distant markets for sale or storage. Special price breaks, known as milling in transit billing, provided economic incentive to ship by rail. The development of refrigeration made longer, safe food storage possible.

Prior to 1900, farmers were largely self-sufficient. The use of mechanical power to operate tractors began in the early 1900s. Farm products produced doubled between 1880 and 1930, and by 1910 there were 32 million people working on 6.4 million farms. As a comparison, in 1900 each farmer produced enough food to feed seven people. By the early 1970s, each farmer produced enough food and fiber to feed 47 people. New technology and education were forces in

Figure 11.1. As cities became industrialized, the need to supply food to the urban population began to grow.

achieving increased productivity. Federal funding of the Land Grant Colleges in the 1860s provided for research and education in agriculture and home economics. Establishment of the Cooperative Extension Service offered the means for distributing this knowledge to farmers in every county in the United States.

Current Agricultural Trends

Farming in the United States has shown continual growth in productivity. See Illustration 11.1. The increase in productivity is measured as the rise in *output* (bushels of grain, gallons of milk, and so forth) per unit of *input* (labor, animal power, machines, or chemicals). Today only 3% of the labor force is involved in farming, but each farm worker produces enough food for 78 people. Over 367 million acres are cultivated cropland. Agricultural products today account for 20% of U.S. exports. Today consumers spend less than 17% of their family income on food.

AN OVERVIEW OF OUR FOOD SYSTEM

Production and distribution of food have evolved into a highly complex process known as *agribusiness*.

Illustration 11.1.
Agricultural Productivity Growth throughout American History. Adapted from Zellner, J., and Lamm, R., "Agriculture's Vital Role for Us All," in United States Department of Agriculture, *Food—From Farm to Table* (Washington, D.C.: United States Government Printing Office, 1982), p. 3.

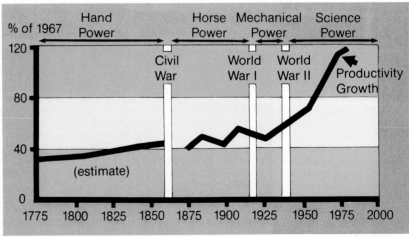

Figure 11.2. Today each farm worker produces enough food for 78 people.

Farmers: The Food Producers

The backbone of our agricultural system is the farmer. The farmer determines what to produce based on available resources and demand for a given product. The products, or output, of farming include food crops, feed crops, industrial crops, livestock, and livestock products. The economic incentive to produce a given product changes with consumer demand and government policy. Geography is a major factor that influences what a farmer produces in a given region. Compare, for example, the climate and soil of Wisconsin with those of Florida. Would oranges grow in Wisconsin?

A farmer's inputs, or resources, include land, machinery, buildings, seed, livestock, energy, fertilizers, and labor. Resource needs vary with the type of food produced. Some resources permit changes in methods of production and improved efficiency. Farmers have become more dependent on products and services purchased from nonfarm sources. Today 80% of animal feed and all seed are purchased from commercial sources. Farmers are the third largest group of buyers of chemical products and the sixth largest users of petroleum. See Illustration 11.2.

The cost of these resources is often a limiting factor for individual farmers. Farmers need to select and expend resources

Figure 11.3. As a result of modern farming methods, farmers have become the nation's third largest buyers of chemical products.

wisely to earn a livelihood and avoid losing money. If a crop costs more to produce than what it can be sold for, the farmer must change inputs or produce something different. An element of risk is always present in producing food. Natural and human-made disasters can erase expected outputs, resulting in loss of crops and income. Large-scale disasters affect the amount of food available to consumers.

Illustration 11.2. Energy Used in Agricultural Production. Adapted from United States Department of Agriculture, *Handbook of Agricultural Charts* (Washington, D.C.: United States Government Printing Office, 1983), p. 17.

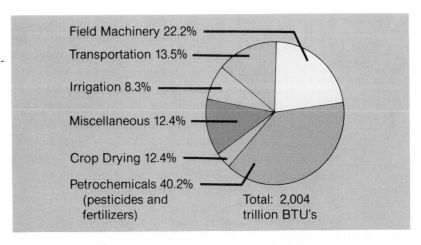

Field Machinery 22.2%
Transportation 13.5%
Irrigation 8.3%
Miscellaneous 12.4%
Crop Drying 12.4%
Petrochemicals 40.2% (pesticides and fertilizers)
Total: 2,004 trillion BTU's

Until recently, input or resource management has focused on short-term productivity and profit. The long-term effects of using inputs such as fertilizers, pesticides, and irrigation on land ecology are now being debated.

Farms vary widely in size, with an average of 450 acres. The "typical" farm is fading, while there is an increase in very small farms and very large farms. Only 5% of all farms had sales greater than $200,000, but these farms accounted for one fifth of the U.S. farm income. More than half of all farms had sales less then $20,000, but together these smaller farms represented only 15% of the net farm income. Agricultural specialists have classified farms by type and size. See Table 11.1.

The Food-Marketing Chain

The demand for farm products is stimulated by consumer purchases. See Illustration 11.3. Money and information flow backward through the food system. A consumer's food purchase causes *retailers* (who sell to individuals) to buy from *wholesalers* (who supply the retailers). In turn, wholesalers place orders with manufacturers. Finally, the demand for the raw product reaches the farmer. As this information is received, food products again move forward toward the consumer.

Table 11.1   Types of Farms in the United States Today

  I. Linked to local market
     A. Smaller than family size
     B. Family size
        1. Primarily owner operated
        2. Primarily tenant operated
 II. Not linked to local market
     A. Larger than family size
     B. Contractually integrated
     C. Larger corporation

Source: Breimeyer, H., and Schertz, L., "Profile of Farming and Rural America," in United States Department of Agriculture, *Food—From Farm to Table* (Washington, D.C.: United States Government Printing Office, 1982), p. 10.

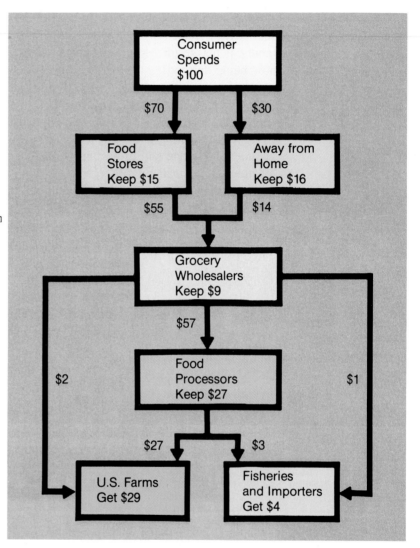

Illustration 11.3.
What Happens to $100 of Consumer Food Spending. Adapted from Harp, H., and Connor, J., "Tracing Your Food Dollar Back to the Farm," in United States Department of Agriculture, *Food—From Farm to Table* (Washington, D.C.: United States Government Printing Office, 1982), p. 120.

Products pass through a series of *markets,* or voluntary exchanges between buyers and sellers, to move food from farm to table. Buyers and sellers interact to set the conditions for exchange—including price. Usually, the buyer will purchase more of a product as the price decreases and less as the price increases. Sellers prefer to supply more of a product for sale as the price rises and less as the price drops. Buyers and sellers must negotiate to find a price that is acceptable to both parties.

Figure 11.4.
Wholesalers are an important link in the food-marketing chain.

In addition to price, the demand for a product is influenced by the costs of related products, buyers' tastes and preferences, money available, and market price trends. Food products change hands for specific purposes enroute to the consumer. The marketing chain may be short and simple, involving only the farmer and consumer. However, the chain may also be complex, involving many steps and people.

The three major marketing functions are *assembly, processing,* and *distribution.* See Illustration 11.4. These marketing functions are directed by a variety of food marketing institutions or agencies directly involved in the marketing process. People involved in the process include brokers, wholesalers, processors, grocers, and food service personnel.

Assembly. The assembly stage involves collecting raw products from individual farmers and bringing the products together in a central location. Transportation from farm to buyer is the primary feature of this marketing stage. Examples of assembly functions include the livestock auction market and farm cooperative organizations. Today local assembly steps are being eliminated, with more direct transportation to regional markets or to the processor. This trend often means that foods produced in a certain geographical region are

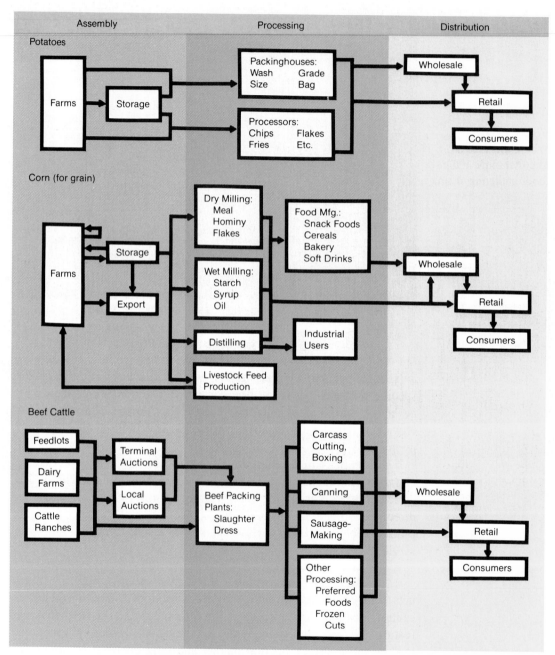

Illustration 11.4. Marketing Chains for Selected Farm Commodities.
Adapted from Jesse, E., "Links That Make Up the Marketing Chain,"
in United States Department of Agriculture, *Food—From Farm to Table*
(Washington, D.C.: United States Government Printing Office, 1982),
p. 144.

Figure 11.5. Before a consumer can buy broccoli on the grocer's shelf, the broccoli must travel through many different marketing stages. Which stages do you see here?

not sold to consumers in that region. Instead, products are shipped to a market several hundred miles away.

Storage is another feature of the assembly stage. Products may be collected, stored, and released for sale over a period of time. Grain products, for example, may be stored in an elevator and sold as demand and price influence the exchange between buyer and seller. The supply of grain can be released into the market gradually over a year, to ensure a constant supply and to keep prices under control.

Processing. Food processing and manufacturing account for about 15% of all manufacturing in the United States. Many processing firms buy directly from farmers, and some firms own their own farm operations. More than 1 million workers are involved in producing foods and beverages. More than 50% of our food is processed by the 100 largest food and tobacco companies, such as Kraft, Kelloggs, Pillsbury, General Foods, and Reynolds Tobacco Company.

Processing involves the activities that prepare food to be sold as a finished product. Processing can be as simple as sorting and packaging fresh strawberries or as complex as changing a food's shape and content to make breakfast cereals. For example, wheat can be sold as flour for home baking or as a finished loaf of bread. See Illustration 11.5. Potatoes can be marketed raw by the pound or as dehydrated flakes, frozen precut fries, and ready-to-eat chips.

Consumer demand and available technology influence the creation of new food products. Food-manufacturing companies em-

Illustration 11.5. Profile of Costs for a One-Pound Loaf of White Bread. Adapted from *Who Makes the Dough?* (Bismarck, N. D.: North Dakota State Wheat Commission).

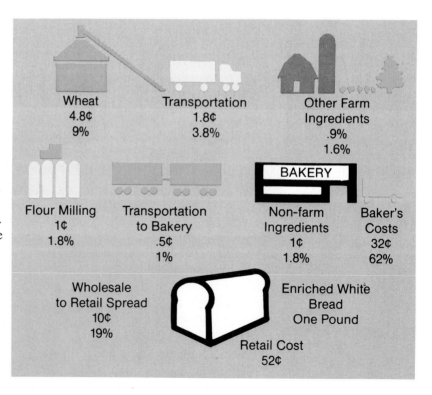

Wheat
4.8¢
9%

Transportation
1.8¢
3.8%

Other Farm Ingredients
.9%
1.6%

Flour Milling
1¢
1.8%

Transportation to Bakery
.5¢
1%

BAKERY

Non-farm Ingredients
1¢
1.8%

Baker's Costs
32¢
62%

Wholesale to Retail Spread
10¢
19%

Enriched White Bread
One Pound

Retail Cost
52¢

ploy market research techniques to identify new product needs and consumer preferences. Companies have responded to consumer desire for health and diet foods. Ethnic foods have also been marketed to meet consumer demand. Offering the consumer more convenience has become a major theme for companies that produce highly processed foods.

Companies need new products to compete in the marketplace. One way to compete is to use processing techniques to create differences among products to increase sales. For example, raisins are added to a bran cereal, a spreadable cheese is developed, or a liquid margarine is produced. Brand names are advertised to develop consumer identification and loyalty with a given product and the manufacturer or processor. New brand names are introduced, established brands bring out allied products or enter a new field, and local producers adapt products to a regional market.

Advances in food science and packaging have changed the

Figure 11.6. Many different types of packaging are used to display food on the grocer's shelves.

form and variety of food available. Food *shelf life,* or the period of a food's peak quality, has been extended for many items. Cans and bottles are being replaced by plastic and foil pouches, bag-in-the-box containers, and brick-shaped plastic and foil cartons. How do processing and packaging affect a product's cost?

Distribution. Food products in their final form must be distributed to the consumer. Distribution includes wholesale and retail sales of food products. Approximately 8.2 million workers are employed in the distribution of food products. Transportation and product storage are major activities in the distribution of food to retail outlets for consumer purchase. Over $15 billion is spent annually to transport food to the table. Food distribution requires energy and labor, which add cost to food products. Thus the cost of marketing food exceeds the cost of the raw food. See Illustration 11.6.

Wholesalers buy products in volume, store and break down large quantities, accept orders from retail buyers, and deliver smaller quantities to retail outlets. Food wholesalers may carry a complete line of food products, or they may specialize only in certain foods. For example, one wholesaler may handle only fresh produce, while another may distribute only meat, fish, and poultry. A wholesale business may operate independently, as a cooperative, or as a part of a

Illustration 11.6. Components of the Food Dollar Spent for Consumption at Home and away from Home. Adapted from United States Department of Agriculture, *Agricultural Chartbook* (Washington, D.C.: United States Government Printing Office, 1985), p. 39.

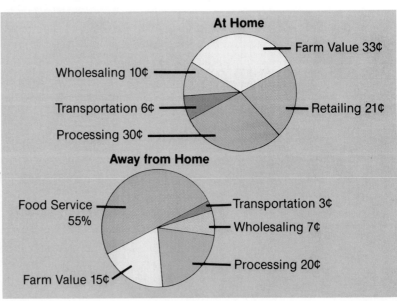

Figure 11.7. Americans spend 35% of their food dollar on food that is eaten away from home.

large retail food corporation. People employed in food wholesaling include commission agents, brokers, receivers, and jobbers. *Brokers,* for example, line up buyers and sellers and arrange for shipments of food products. *Jobbers* represent two or more smaller companies that deal in different types of food products.

Consumers are most familiar with food retailers as the last stage in the marketing process. Food is available to consumers through a variety of retail outlets. Food may be purchased from a food warehouse, small grocery store, or supermarket. The store manager, stock clerks, checkout clerks, and butchers are all part of the retail organization. Some supermarkets also employ home economists.

Only about half of the American consumer food dollar is spent in grocery stores. Specialty shops, convenience stores, and farmer's markets account for another 15%. The remaining 35% is spent on food eaten away from home. Consumers have many choices in eating away from home, including sit-down restaurants, fast-food operations, school and other cafeterias, and vending machines. Restaurant or cafeteria managers, cooks, bakers, hosts or hostesses, and waitresses are retail positions in the rapidly growing food service and hospitality industry. See Table 11.2.

Government Involvement in the Food System

The United States' farm policy has generally encouraged food production. Attention is now being given to the need to balance

| Table 11.2 | Employment Trends in the Food System, 1950-1980 | | | |

| | Year | | | |
Sector	1950	1960	1970	1980
	Thousands[a]			
Agriculture............................	7,160	5,458	3,463	3,364
Food and Tobacco Manufacturing	1,893	1,884	1,866	1,780
Wholesale Grocery	206[b]	494	550	674
Retail Food and Grocery...........	1,478[b]	1,356	1,731	2,386
Eating and Drinking Places........	1,228[b]	1,654	2,488	4,666
Total Food System	11,965	10,846	10,098	12,780
Total Civilian Employment.....	58,918	65,778	78,678	99,303

Source: U.S. Bureau of the Census.
[a]Average annual full-time equivalent persons.
[b]1948-54 average.

production with consumption. Three types of governmental policy affect the availability and price of food: (1) domestic production subsidies, (2) import controls, and (3) export subsidies.

Domestic Production Subsidies. A *subsidy* is a grant of public money to a private enterprise that produces a needed item for the public in general. Policies that subsidize domestic food production are developed to guarantee a self-sufficient food supply or to cover the cost of production. Policies in this category include production quotas, government purchase of commodities, and price supports. A *production quota* establishes a ceiling on how much can be produced. For example, the growing of tobacco has been limited by government policy.

Commodity purchase, under the Agriculture Act of 1935, authorizes the United States Department of Agriculture (USDA) to buy surplus perishable commodities such as meats, poultry, fruits, and vegetables. The Secretary of Agriculture determines what food is considered to be surplus. Then the USDA purchases the commodities, resulting in a decrease in market supply. The law is designed to support farm incomes when market prices are low and to encourage product export.

The Agriculture Act of 1949 established the *price support* programs, which allow Congress to determine prices at which the

USDA will buy wheat, corn, rice, dairy products, soybeans, peanuts, and vegetable oils. When farm prices for these basic items fall below levels set by Congress, a quantity of the product is purchased by the USDA to stabilize or reverse the falling price.

In the dairy industry, excess fluid milk is made into cheese, butter, and other milk products. Farmers usually receive less money when milk is used to produce these products. If the market price for milk falls below the set minimum, the USDA purchases quantities of cheese, butter, and powdered milk. This purchase tightens the supply and raises the price.

These policies, combined with a change in consumer demand, have led to a large government surplus of milk products and other commodities. The purchase, transportation, and storage of these products have become very costly to taxpayers. However, consumers have also benefitted from the distribution of commodities through the National School Lunch Program, Nutrition Program for the Elderly, and other food programs. See Illustration 11.7.

Import Controls. Import controls such as import quotas and tariffs have been used to restrict the flow of foreign food products into the country. Unrestricted flow could lower prices and negatively affect domestic production. *Import quotas* establish ceilings on the amounts

Figure 11.8. Surplus dairy products purchased by the USDA have been redistributed through the National School Lunch Program.

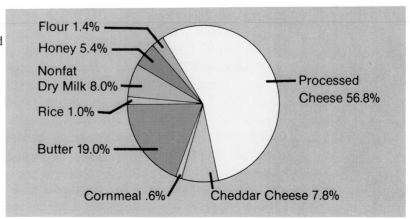

Illustration 11.7.
Commodities Distributed under the Temporary Emergency Food Assistance Program. Adapted from United States Department of Agriculture, *Agricultural Chartbook* (Washington, D.C.: United States Government Printing Office, 1985), p. 55.

of an item that can be brought into the country. For example, import quotas have been set on dairy products, sugar, and beef.

The establishment of a quota limits the supply from foreign sources and protects domestic producers from price competition. *Tariffs,* or taxes, may also be imposed on imported products. The tariff increases the price of foreign products, giving the price advantage to domestic producers. Foreign wine is an example of a product that is taxed.

Export Subsidies. The total demand for agricultural products includes domestic and foreign demand. Prices generally rise as export demand increases. To increase export sales, a form of *export subsidy* may be used. The United States offers government credit to foreign purchasers of agricultural products. The credit is extended at interest rates below the market level or as a blend of no-interest, market-rate, and government credit.

Exports account for about one fifth of farm income. For example, the value of U.S. farm exports in 1984 was $37.8 billion. However, export levels rise and fall as other nations compete for export markets. See Illustration 11.8. Because of overproduction, the American farmer is unable to sell products at a profit.

Issues in Food Production and Marketing

In recent years the mass media have brought the economic plight of the American farmer to the attention of consumers. Product

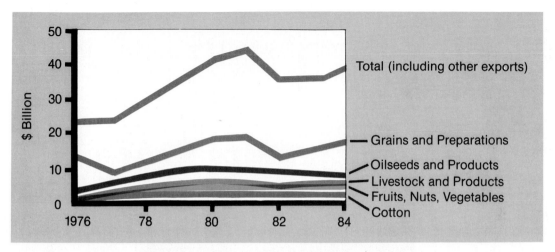

Illustration 11.8.   Value of U. S. Agricultural Exports by Commodity. Adapted from United States Department of Agriculture, *Agricultural Chartbook* (Washington, D.C.: United States Government Printing Office, 1985), p. 63.

surpluses resulting in low farm prices have left many farmers deeply in debt. Several forces have contributed to the farmers' economic crisis, including government policies, changing dietary patterns, high interest rates, and declines of export sales and farm land values. In addition, the use of expensive inputs such as equipment, energy, and fertilizer has raised production costs.

As noted earlier, the trend is toward fewer and larger farms with more operating capital. Farmers are also selling to larger and more powerful buyers. As a result, issues surface regarding farmers' bargaining power, market information, and price agreements. Such changes in production are having an impact on the assembly, processing, and distribution of food.

Conglomerates and Controls. There is a trend to fewer and larger marketing firms. The number of food-marketing companies has declined from 725,000 in 1947 to about 540,000 today. Corporations have concentrated ownership and control of our food system through (1) diversification, (2) vertical integration, and (3) horizontal integration. Corporations *diversify* by buying a business that manufactures other products.

Figure 11.9. The current trend is toward fewer and larger farms.

A *conglomerate* is a company that operates two or more industries. Many consumers are not aware of the relatively few corporations that control the food system. For example, Nestlés owns Libbys and Stouffers. General Foods owns Oscar Meyer, and Pillsbury owns Green Giant. Company mergers have built conglomerates with a wide range of interests. One conglomerate, Beatrice Foods Company, now produces La Choy Chinese foods, Meadow Gold Milk, Sunbeam bread, Samsonite luggage, Airstream trailers, and Hart sports equipment.

Buying and controlling several steps in production and marketing is known as *vertical integration*. An example is a turkey-processing plant that also owns a breeding operation, feed mill, turkey farms, and a wholesale firm for marketing processed turkey products. *Horizontal integration* occurs when a company increases production of a product and captures a greater market share. This increase can be achieved by expanding the company's own plant and production or by purchasing a business that produces the same product.

In addition to control by ownership, food manufacturers have gained power and control through contracts with producers, especially fruit and vegetable producers. Advertising is also a powerful avenue of control. Corporate expansion helps firms obtain a larger share of the market. The concentration of control may have negative effects, including price fixing and excess profits because of a lack of competition. Control by large corporations also makes it difficult for smaller manufacturers, wholesalers, and retailers to compete in the marketplace.

Retailing Chains. Concentration of ownership has also occurred in retailing operations. Prior to the 1920s, food was distributed locally by small, family-owned stores. Today, supermarkets with annual sales of greater than $1 million are the major food retailers. Sixty percent of the supermarkets are owned by chains that control 11 or more stores. Many large supermarkets operate their own bakeries and fluid milk–processing plants. In addition, chains often contract with processors to provide private-label food products. The trend is for supermarkets to offer more services, such as a pharmacy, deli, and flower shop. Stores promote one-stop shopping to secure their food dollar. Specialty items also command higher profits. The average food product markup is 20%. Cosmetics have a markup of 30%, deli products 40%, and flowers 45%.

Chains frequently operate their own warehouse that combines both wholesale and retail functions. Some independent retailers have linked up with wholesale suppliers to take advantage of quantity purchasing power. It is not uncommon to discover that the largest four stores in a metropolitan area do more than half the food retail business. In smaller communities one or two stores may do most of the business. What issues of control does this concentration of ownership raise?

Figure 11.10.
Many supermarkets offer diverse services to attract customers.

A limited number of food retailers determine which food products are given shelf space. Price competition is limited by concentration of the market. Nonprice competition and promotional advertising may raise food prices. Stores battle for market share by opening different types of outlets, such as warehouse stores, gourmet markets, and superstores. The average store size continues to increase. Rural communities and low-income urban neighborhoods are not as profitable, so residents may be underserved.

Price may be used as a merchandising tool, with some products sold at cost and others sold much higher to obtain the desired profit margin. The use of the Universal Product Code (UPC) scanning system has provided large retailers with an information advantage on buying trends and inventory. In addition, the computerized Uniform Communications System that links manufacturers, brokers, and distributors is a powerful tool in limiting or controlling consumer choices in the food system.

The supermarket industry has identified recent consumer trends that include greater use of coupons, more one-stop shopping (less comparison shopping), increased purchasing of generic and store brands, and less brand loyalty. Is the industry responding to the consumer, or is the consumer being molded by the industry?

Food Service and Fast Food Chains. In a recent year, Americans spent over $170 billion to eat away from home. A variety

Figure 11.11. The Universal Products Code scanning system provides retailers with product inventory and sales information.

of social and economic factors that support this trend are outlined in Chapter 12. The away-from-home eating market continues to expand rapidly. Much of the growth has been in the fast-food industry, including hamburger stands, fried chicken stores, and pizza parlors. The number of fast-food outlets has tripled since 1963, to more than 122,000. Concentration of the food service industry has also occurred, with ownership of individual outlets by chains and through franchise agreements.

Key factors in the growth of the food service chains have been price competition and service. National advertising budgets have assisted local outlets in capturing a greater portion of the market. At one time it was easy for an individual to open and operate an eating establishment. Today the market is fiercely competitive, with chains offering centralized food buying and distribution as well as training programs for managers and employees. Convenience stores, traditional restaurants, and supermarkets are also competing for a share of the take-out market. The institutional food service market is also experiencing a similar trend in concentrated ownership and fierce competition.

YOUR ROLE IN THE FOOD SYSTEM

As you can see, the delivery of food to your table is a complex process. An elaborate marketing system has brought consumers an abundance of food choices. Computer technology permits the collection of vast amounts of information on consumers' buying habits. Mass advertising is a powerful tool in influencing what and where food is purchased. An understanding of the marketing system can assist you in effectively meeting your food needs. You, the consumer, are also a powerful force in the marketing system. Your power is exhibited through the purchases you make. The remaining chapters will examine forces that shape food patterns and worldwide food distribution.

CHECK YOUR PROGRESS

1. Identify key factors that have led to the increase in farm productivity in the United States.

2. Describe current trends in food production in the United States.
3. Define the economic terms input, output, and market.
4. How have farmers' inputs changed over the past 100 years?
5. List and describe the three major steps in food marketing.
6. What impact does each step in food marketing have on food prices?
7. Identify employment opportunities in the food production and distribution systems. Where is the greatest growth in jobs occurring?
8. Describe the effect of each of these government policies on food availability and price: production quota, commodity purchase, price support, import quota, tariff, and export subsidy.
9. Identify the factors that contribute to the American farm economic crisis. How is farming changing as a result?
10. Define conglomerate.
11. Identify and describe the three methods by which corporations have concentrated ownership in the food system.
12. Describe the effect of supermarket chains on the food retailing business.
13. How have chains and franchises affected the food service industry?

FOOD CHOICES

3

HEALTHY EATING PATTERNS

AND WHAT DID YOU EAT FOR LUNCH?

The cafeteria is crowded and bubbling with activity. Groups of friends are talking and laughing as they eat. Others are reading magazines, playing cards, and studying while they eat. Let's take a closer look at what everyone is eating for lunch.

Maria is enjoying a bean burrito, the school lunch feature for Mexican heritage day. Carol, in an effort to save money, is munching a homemade sandwich, while her best friend, Allison, sips a diet cola. Sammy, an athlete, is consuming his second hamburger and his third carton of milk. Sue nibbles on carrot sticks and green pepper strips while reading the latest fashion magazine. Luanne, running late for class, stops at a vending machine for a candy bar. Bill is skipping lunch to study for a chemistry test. Sarah is sharing her birthday cake with a group of friends.

Many factors motivate our food choices. Can you identify student choices that may have been influenced by cost? Time available? Heritage? Physical activity requirements? Body image? Personal priorities or values? Special social occasions? Advertising?

Your objectives in this chapter will be to:

- *Identify trends in food consumption*
- *List factors that influence your food choices*
- *Explain how your life-style affects your food pattern*
- *Evaluate the effect food advertising has on you*

TRENDS IN FOOD CONSUMPTION

In the United States the array of foods to choose from is almost endless. There are over 10,000 food items on most supermarket

313

shelves. However, the nutritional quality of available foods varies greatly. Since the turn of the century, technology, mobility, and affluence have dramatically altered the American way of living.

The food industry has responded to the needs of the always-on-the-go consumer by developing processing and packaging methods that offer convenience. Warm-and-serve and ready-to-eat products contribute to a significant portion of the American diet. Eating outside the home has become more frequent. It is difficult to describe the "typical" American eating pattern. Today's array of lifestyles and food choices have created consumer markets with different eating patterns. Marketing surveys have classified consumers by their nutrition attitudes and practices. These eating practices range from the health-conscious dieter to the always-on-the-go snacker. See Table 12.1.

Many consumers, striving for health and fitness, acknowledge the importance of nutrition. More than 90% of those surveyed in a Louis Harris poll responded that they were "very concerned" or "somewhat concerned" about nutrition. A 1980 United States Department of Agriculture survey also revealed that 3 out of 5 households had made a dietary change for health reasons within the preceding 3 years.

Figure 12.1. Food is an expression of life-style.

Table 12.1   Profile of American Eating Patterns

Meat Eater Households:
- Skip meals and eat out no more than others, but spend less on food than the average;
- Watch mysteries and hospital shows on TV, and read the Reader's Digest. They read women's and food pages in newspapers as much as national news;
- Like to cook and entertain, and use recipes from friends and family more so than from magazines;
- Use convenience foods more often;
- Try new foods reluctantly;
- Rate their nutrition performance as average;
- Lack confidence in their nutrition knowledge;
- Grasp nutrition information poorly, and are indifferent to information on fat and sodium.

On the Go Households:
- Enjoy eating out and do so often. They spend the most on food of any profile;
- Listen heavily to radio, especially rock stations, and news. They read newspapers in preference to magazines;
- Use microwave ovens more than most, but probably to prepare meals quickly from scratch;
- Like cooking and using new recipes, mostly to try new foods for festive occasions or entertaining;
- Don't see cholesterol as a problem, although they consume more than average amounts;
- Lack confidence in their nutrition knowledge;
- Recognize they should eat more fruits and vegetables;
- Dislike junk food, but don't want to bother with good nutrition.

In a Dither Households:
- Skip more meals and eat away from home more often than any other profile household;

(Continued)

Source: Leonard, R., "Nutrition Profiles: Diet in the '80's," *The Community Nutritionist* (September-October, 1982), p. 13.

Table 12.1 (cont'd)

In a Dither Households (cont'd):
- Spend the least on food at home;
- Own more microwave ovens and use them to cook convenience foods;
- Read TV Guide and women's magazines, particularly Good Housekeeping and Women's Day;
- Believe their spouse is overweight;
- Won't change eating habits if lifestyle changes occur;
- Dislike cooking, baking, trying new recipes, or entertaining;
- Complain their children ask for foods they see on television;
- Resist trying new foods;
- Lack confidence in nutrition, and acknowledge the need for improvement, but are unconcerned about sugar, sodium, or food additives;
- Worry about the safety and wholesomeness of the food they eat.

Conscientious Households:
- Eat more meals at home than most, even though the spouse may have an irregular eating pattern;
- Spend less on food than other profiles;
- Prefer television news and documentaries, radio news and "pop" music stations;
- Read Time and professional magazines, as well as Women's Day and Reader's Digest;
- Say their spouse is not overweight;
- Alter diets more often in response to life change events—i.e., exercise, going to the dentist;
- Enjoy cooking, baking and trying new recipes; when they try new recipes, however, they prepare fancy, high calorie foods;
- Try new foods;
- Feel confident about their nutrition knowledge, and believe they are doing well;
- Score highest in nutrition knowledge;
- Worry about sugar and protein, and say they should eat more fish and less white bread.

Table 12.1 (cont'd)

Healthy Eater Households:
- Skip few meals, and spend more on food than most;
- Watch health programs on television, but don't read magazines or listen to radio as much as others;
- Say their spouse's weight is just right;
- Do not worry about food budgets, but are careful shoppers and use leftovers;
- Enjoy entertaining and cooking. They try new recipes, especially healthful ones;
- Rate their nutrition performance high and feel well informed, but are only average in nutritional knowledge;
- Want to cut down on cholesterol, salt, preservatives and worry about getting enough fiber.

Food consumption survey trends support consumers' claims that their dietary practices are changing, but take a closer look! Aware of the need to lower fat and cholesterol intake many consumers changed their usual beverage. Over the past 20 years there has been a steady decline in whole milk consumption with a dramatic increase in the use of low-fat milk. See Illustration 12.1. However, total milk consumption dropped by one-half. This decline raises a concern for adequate calcium intake.

Sparked by health concerns fruit juice consumption has increased, but not nearly as much as soft drinks. Soft drink consumption has increased by 300% since 1950. Today sugar-free and decaffeinated soft drinks are even capitalizing on the "health" image.

Heart-health concerns have prompted consumers to change table spreads. Today twice as much margarine is used as butter. Likewise, egg consumption has declined. Ironically, cheese consumption has tripled. Many perceive the calcium and protein value of cheese, but may not recognize cheese as a major source of saturated fat, cholesterol, and sodium. Red meat consumption has continued to decline with the increased use of poultry and fish. In particular, consumers reported a decline in the use of sausage, bacon, and luncheon meats. Both cost and health concerns may be responsible for this trend.

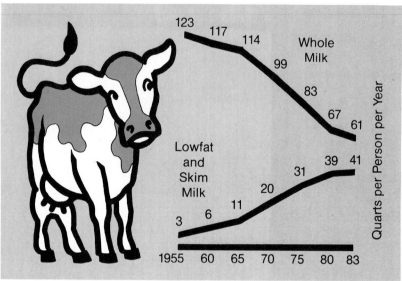

Illustration 12.1.
Changes in Milk Consumption. Adapted from Food and Drug Administration, "America's Changing Diet," *FDA Consumer* (Washington, D.C.: United States Government Printing Office, October, 1985).

Another important trend is the continued rapid growth in the consumption of fresh fruit and vegetables. It is believed the switch to fresh is a direct result of consumer concerns about nutrition. However, the consumption of one vegetable, the potato, has declined. Many consumers incorrectly associate starches with being fattening.

The trends reveal that consumer food choices have been altered by health and nutrition information. However, some trends may not be as nutritionally sound as others. Can eating be enjoyable and healthful? The answer is up to each individual. The first challenge is to understand what motivates you to choose the foods you do.

THE DEVELOPMENT OF FOOD PATTERNS

Food choices and their consequences have been used to describe individuals or groups of people. Nutritionists have traditionally studied people's diets as they relate to health and disease. On the other hand, social scientists have focused on factors that affect the formation and change of food patterns. *Food patterns* represent a composite of foods typically selected by an individual or group. Patterns continue to evolve as influencing factors change. See Illustration 12.2.

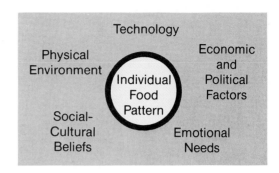

Illustration 12.2.
Factors That Influence
Your Food Choices.

Eating is a social experience. Rarely do people stop to think about the food patterns they have acquired. Nutritional well-being is the result of food decisions made over time. Most food choices, however, are made for reasons other than nutrition. Food patterns develop based on what foods are available and preferable to eat. These patterns are learned and reinforced by experience.

Figure 12.2. What
food pattern does this
man establish when
he buys lunch every
day from this lunch
truck?

Figure 12.3. Lobster is a food associated with the New England region.

Access to Food

A food must be readily available in order for it to become part of our diet pattern. The physical environment plays a major role in determining what foods are present. The quality of soil, land contour, location of waterways, and climate affect the kind of food produced in an area. For example, cereal grains grow well in dry climates, whereas rice grows well in wet areas. Soybeans and other legumes become *staples,* or main food products, where land is less fertile. Fish is a major food item for people living along a coastline or river, whereas beef cattle adapt well to grasslands.

United States regional eating patterns have also evolved around foods available in a geographic area. Fish are abundant in coastal areas and cattle plentiful in the western plains. Thus, New England is known for clam chowder, Louisiana for shrimp jambalaya, and Texas for barbequed ribs.

In many parts of the world one or two foods are the main dietary staple. Historically, corn is the staple food in the diet of the

Indians of the southwestern United States and Mexico. In southeast Asia rice is dominant, whereas wheat is the main food of the Middle East and Europe.

Food Preservation. Food availability often varies with the season of the year. Fall is associated with the harvest of many cereal grains and vegetables. In the past, people found that the supply of meat and fish was not always constant. Methods of food preservation evolved out of the need to ensure an adequate food supply all year. Drying, salting, and smoking were among the first methods used. Today's consumer has a choice of buying food fresh, canned, frozen, dehydrated, irradiated, freeze-dried, or vacuum packed. Many consumers are returning to home food preservation as a way to assure food quality. Consider time, energy, and material costs when evaluating home food preservation options. See Table 12.2.

Table 12.2   Costs of Home Food Preservation

| Method | Time | Energy | | Dollar Cost from Kitchen to Table | Quality Satisfaction |
		Fuel	Human Effort		
Freezing	Minimal to low	High	Low	Very high	Very high
Canning	Moderate	Moderate	High	Moderate	Moderate to high
Drying	High	Moderate to high	Moderate	Moderate to high	High (specialty items) Low, if only method available
Pickling	High	Low	Moderate	Depends on type chosen[a]	High
Storage (unprocessed)	Low to moderate	Low	Moderate (checking/ culling)	Low	Moderate to high

Source: United States Department of Agriculture, *Canning, Freezing, Storing Garden Produce* (Washington, D.C.: United States Government Printing Office, 1977), Bulletin No. 410.

[a]Some (such as quick dill pickles) are quick to make, take little effort, and use inexpensive ingredients. Others require prolonged brining over several days, plus expensive sugar and other ingredients.

Figure 12.4. Home canning can be time consuming, but many people like to control the quality of their processed foods.

A Supermarket of Choices. Technology has expanded the quantity and variety of foods available. Just imagine, in 1900 the general store carried about 500 food items. These foods were primarily staple items, such as flour, sugar, salt, and spices. The population of the United States was primarily rural, and most families raised the other foods they needed.

Advances in agricultural technology dramatically increased the quantities of food that could be raised. Modern food production and processing, combined with an elaborate transportation system, provide Americans with some 60,000 different brand name processed foods. Growth of national supermarket chains has increased individual access to these foods. Today Americans enjoy the most abundant and varied food supply in the world.

The Cost of an Adequate Diet. Money is the most limiting factor in obtaining a nutritionally adequate diet for many consumers. The ability to purchase food is directly related to a person's income and the cost of the items. In the United States, government food programs attempt to lessen the impact of a low income on a person's access to food. Low-income participants in the Food Stamp Program have better quality diets than their nonparticipating counterparts. See Table 12.3.

The percent of money spent for different food groups varies with income. Lower-income groups tend to purchase more bread and cereal products. See Illustration 12.3. As income rises, the selection of more expensive animal and vegetable products increases. Also, there is a tendency to increase consumption of refined, processed foods as income goes up. The "health food" movement may be the

Table 12.3	Diet Quality and Effects of Money Available for Food	
	Value per Person	**Diets Meeting RDA for 11 Nutrients**
All Households		
1977-1978[a]	$17.21	42%
1979-1980[b]	$16.12	39%
Food Stamp Program Participants		
1977-1978[a]	$17.85	48%
1979-1980[b]	$16.57	46%
Nonparticipants		
1977-1978[a]	$16.79	38%
1979-1980[b]	$15.82	34%

Source: United States Department of Agriculture, *Surveys of Food Consumption in Low-Income Households* (Washington, D.C.: United States Government Printing Office, 1981).
[a]1977-1978 values adjusted to 1979-1980 dollars.
[b]Preliminary data.

exception to this trend, as foods purchased in health food stores often cost more than their refined, processed counterparts.

Limited Selection. Food selection is also influenced by the decisions of others. The grocer makes decisions about what foods will be stocked in a store. The manager of a restaurant designs a menu, which determines the foods sold. Government regulation and the food service manager determine what foods are available through the school lunch program. Who decides what foods are purchased for use in your household?

Food Preferences: Their Hidden Meanings

The reason a person chooses one food over another may not be clear to an observer. Why? Individual preferences are influenced by a combination of feelings, sensory reactions, cultural beliefs, and social values.

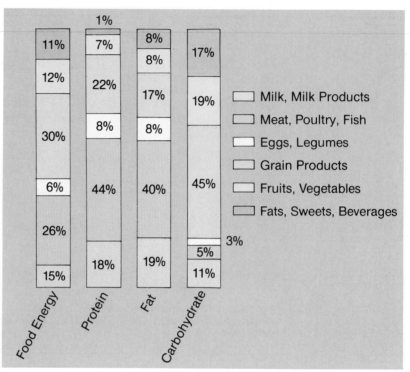

Illustration 12.3.
Sources of Energy and
Energy Nutrients in
Low-Income House-
holds. Adapted from
United States Depart-
ment of Agriculture,
*Survey of Food Con-
sumption in Low-Income
Households 1977-78*
(preliminary data in 48
conterminous states
November 1977 to
March 1978) (Washing-
ton, D.C.: United States
Government Printing
Office, 1978).

Culture Shapes Habits. Cultural heritage plays a role in
what a person views as edible. A group of people living in a certain
geographic area develop a set of habits which become customs that
influence ways of thinking and acting. These customs are transmitted
generation to generation. This set of customs is referred to as a
culture. A society is composed of people with a similar culture, such
as a tribe, ethnic group, or nation. Within a nation there may be
subcultures with differing food patterns.

Custom determines what a society prizes or prohibits as food.
In France snails are a delicacy. Raw fish is eaten by the Japanese. In
some African tribes, pregnant women are prohibited from eating eggs.
People in the United States would not consider eating cat or dog meat.

Food is also a part of religious custom. Beef is not eaten in
India, where the cow is considered sacred by the Hindu. Jewish
dietary laws prohibit the eating of pork. Until recently, Catholics did
not eat meat on Fridays. The Seventh Day Adventists are vegetarians.

In the United States eating pattern differences evolved based on ethnic background of the population. When people migrated from their homeland to settle in the United States they brought with them their ethnic food patterns. Thus, the eating patterns of a region were influenced by the people settling the area. For example, the German-Dutch heritage influenced the cooking style in Pennsylvania. French tradition shaped the cuisine in Louisiana. A blend of Scandinavian, German, and Polish heritage molded the eating patterns of the Upper Midwest. A Black African pattern evolved in the South. More recently Mexican, Chinese, and Southeast Asian food patterns can be identified in areas where these immigrants settled. Each wave of new immigrants has brought unique foods and methods of preparation. The ethnic eating pattern may become less evident as the new group is assimilated into the American culture. Ethnic foods can also be popularized and become a familiar food to all Americans. The popularity of both Mexican and Chinese foods is an example.

Foods chosen for special occasions are often determined by custom. In the United States, the Thanksgiving meal reflects the bountiful harvest. Turkey, cranberries, squash, and pumpkin or mincemeat pie are a part of this traditional meal. A day at an amusement park means hot dogs, cotton candy, snow cones, and carameled apples. The aroma of hot buttered popcorn fills the lobby of movie theaters. These are but a few examples of how custom influences food habits. What foods do you associate with birthdays, weddings, and holidays?

Food Fulfills Emotional Needs. A baby learns to associate being fed with comfort and love. This association often remains throughout life. Each person develops emotional responses to a variety of foods. Chicken noodle soup is associated with care given during an illness. Homemade chocolate chip cookies bring back memories of visits to Grandma. A picnic just isn't a picnic without potato salad and baked beans. Almost everyone has a "security" food that they like to eat when they are feeling blue. Sweet desserts and snacks are often thought of as rewards. Sharing food with another conveys caring and friendship.

People also develop negative feelings about foods. An adult tells a child to eat all the broccoli or no dessert will be served. The child then resents eating broccoli and as a result dislikes it. A person eats a spicy casserole and becomes ill. He or she may avoid that food in the future, even if it was not related to the illness. Food is withheld as a punishment. The absence of food may then be associated with the lack of caring or loving. Young children refuse food to gain attention.

Food Appeals to Our Senses. How a food looks, smells, feels, and tastes affects individual likes and dislikes. Our sense of taste identifies foods as sweet, salty, sour, or bitter. A child's earliest experiences with new foods form reactions that are hard to change. Young children prefer mildly flavored foods and dislike bitter or sour foods. It has been observed that Mexican children develop a taste for hot peppers. Researchers believe a preference for salt and sugar may also be acquired. The smell and appearance of food may affect selection. Examples are the aroma of fresh baked bread or the strong odor of sauerkraut.

Influence of Family and Friends. Social customs are practiced in family settings. Young children model their food behavior after family members or adult caretakers. Studies show that a father's food preferences have a significant impact on what foods are prepared in the home. In addition, his display of food likes and dislikes influence a child's attitudes toward trying new foods. However, family

Figure 12.5. Certain foods fulfill emotional and social needs.

Figure 12.6. Many people prefer brand-name items over generic items.

composition differs greatly. How might a grandparent, single parent, or a day care teacher influence food practices?

As a child mixes with other children, his or her peers tend to exert a greater influence on food choice. Eating with friends exposes a child to a variety of food practices. These experiences may build positive nutrition attitudes or reinforce poor eating habits. What happens when one grade school student in the cafeteria line expresses dislike for a food on the menu?

Food Builds Relationships. Food provides a vehicle for belonging. Going out for pizza after a football game may mean acceptance by the group. Refusal to eat with someone may be viewed as personal rejection. The giving of food as a gift is a common way of expressing thanks or affection.

Food Means Status. Food choice conveys social status. Foods may be ranked to show their value in any society. In Western countries a tenderloin steak means wealth and prominent social position. Generally, a more expensive food or a food that is difficult to obtain has a higher status. Superior quality also raises the value. Consumers tend to rate a name brand product over a generic item because they believe the brand name to be superior. Technology in food processing may be viewed with status. In developing nations women perceive commercial baby formulas as having more status than breastfeeding. Until recently, refined foods, such as white bread and rice, were valued over unrefined foods. In other words, people use food selection to show others that they are successful.

Food Patterns Change with Values. Personal values are also expressed through food choices. *Values* are a collection of beliefs and feelings about what is good, worthy, and correct. They form the basis of our attitudes and influence our actions. Societal change often alters personal values. The women's movement, space exploration, and computer technology have made an impact on society. These forces produced changes in values and practices related to food production, purchasing, and preparation.

With over 50% of adult women in the work force, family food purchasing and preparation have changed dramatically. Time is critical when a person is juggling school, work, and household tasks. Thus, reliance on convenience foods has replaced cooking from scratch for many families. Processed foods have captured a greater portion of our food dollar in the past decade than before. See Table 12.4. Generally, you pay more for convenience items, but there are exceptions. See Table 12.5.

Food technology and packaging for the space exploration program have expanded the number and types of convenience foods available to the consumer. Have you purchased fluid milk packaged for storage without refrigeration?

Individual activities, such as sports and musical events, often disrupt the family meal routine. As family members lead more independent lives, there is an increase in the number of meals eaten

Figure 12.7. Convenience items are purchased more often now because the number of women in the work force has increased.

Table 12.4   Dollar Shares by Degree of Processing, 1970 and 1980

Category	Share of each $100		Percentage Change
	1970	1980	
Fresh, unprocessed.................................	$ 47.49	$ 45.35	−4.5
Frozen, canned, dried, cured, or refined with little change	16.50	16.74	+1.5
Minor Ingredient, such as sugar added...........	8.51	9.09	+6.8
Mixes and Mixtures, ready-to-heat or ready-to-eat	19.73	20.00	+1.4
Non-alcoholic Beverages, Condiments, Leavenings, and Seasonings....................	7.77	8.82	+13.5
	$100.00	$100.00	

Source: B. Peterkin, "Food Patterns—Where are They Headed?" in United States Department of Agriculture, *Food—From Farm to Table* (Washington, D.C.: United States Printing Office, 1982).

Table 12.5   Cost Comparisons—Complex-Type Convenience Foods

	Relative Cost (percent)
Main Dishes	
Homemade Fried Chicken with Mashed Potatoes and Carrots	100
Frozen, ready-to-heat Fried Chicken Plate Dinner.........................	144
Homemade Lasagna..	100
Frozen Lasagna	144
Vegetables	
Fresh Broccoli with Butter Sauce	100
Frozen Broccoli with Butter Sauce (boil-in-the-bag)	180
Baked Products	
Homemade White Bread..	100
Ready-to-eat White Bread (firm-crumb type).............................	227
Ready-to-eat White Bread (soft-crumb type)	82
Homemade Waffles...	100
Frozen Waffles	268
Homemade Apple Pie...	100
Ready-to-eat Apple Pie	185

Source: "Convenience Foods—What They Cost You," in United States Department of Agriculture, *Food—From Farm to Table* (Washington, D.C.: United States Government Printing Office, 1982).

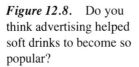

Figure 12.8. Do you think advertising helped soft drinks to become so popular?

outside the home. In the United States, this trend supports a $129.8 billion per year food service industry.

Today individual family members often take more responsibility for their own food preparation. It is not uncommon for both men and women to develop cooking skills. The computerized microwave oven simplifies the meal preparation task. Who knows what the future will bring?

ADVERTISING IS A POWERFUL PERSUADER

Food advertising in mass media is a persuasive influence on food habits. Advertisements are often designed to send more than one message to the viewer. The obvious message is to buy a certain product. A more subtle, or hidden, message may link use of the product with achieving another goal. This *hidden message* appeals to an individual's emotions or values. Frequently, ads will portray products as assuring beauty, success, health, a long life, love and romance, or good times with friends. Identifying the hidden message may help a person determine what prompts his or her food purchase.

Advertisements from many different sources bombard almost everyone. Ninety-eight percent of all American homes have at least one television set. On the average, a high school graduate may have watched 20,000 hours of television, including 350,000 commercials. Over $600 million is spent annually in advertising aimed directly to children. Based on Nielsen ratings, the average child sees more than 20,000 television commercials each year. Studies reveal that more than 70% of the food commercials aimed at children are for heavily sugared products. Young children are encouraged to ask their parents to buy a cereal with a toy in the box. Many times a favorite cartoon character is shown enjoying a candy bar.

Children aren't the only targeted audience for advertising. Parents are told a sugared beverage they enjoyed as a child certainly makes the most sense to give to their children. Young adults are led to believe good times go better with a leading soft drink. Advertising has moved soft drinks into the leading beverage consumed in the United States. See Illustration 12.4.

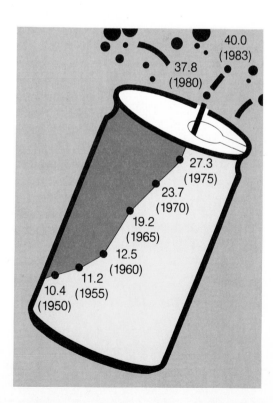

Illustration 12.4. Soft Drink Consumption, Reported in Gallons per Person per Year. Adapted from Food and Drug Administration, "America's Changing Diet," *FDA Consumer* (Washington, D.C.: United States Government Printing Office, October, 1985).

YOUR FOOD, YOUR CHOICE

Obviously, some foods are more nutritious than others. For example, certain snacks and beverages provide high amounts of sugar and fat, with little else of value. Processed foods often contain high amounts of salt. However, no single food choice is necessarily right or wrong, good or bad.

Whether we realize it or not, many factors aside from nutritional value influence our daily food choices. In a world of unevenly distributed resources, energy used in the production and preparation of food may also be a factor to consider. Making a conscious food choice involves trade-offs. Everyone has the opportunity to weigh the alternatives: cost, convenience, social value, taste preference, and fitness and nutritional needs. Rank the factors influencing your food decisions (1 = most important—10 = least important):

Figure 12.9. Making food choices involves decisions about cost, taste preference, and nutrition.

?	Cost
?	Nutrition/health
?	Taste
?	Emotional satisfaction
?	Tradition
?	Convenience
?	Ease of preparation
?	Availability
?	Status of peer acceptance
?	Religious or moral beliefs

Choices made over a lifetime may have health and social consequences; the responsibility for wellness rests with each person. Thus the choice is yours.

And what did *you* eat for lunch?

CHECK YOUR PROGRESS

1. Identify national trends in food consumption.
2. Define food pattern.
3. List the factors which influence a person's access to food. Which of these factors affect your food choice?
4. Describe how individual food preferences develop. Identify your favorite food(s) and explain why you like each food item.
5. Define values. Explain how a person's (or society's) values affect food decisions.
6. Describe techniques advertisers use to persuade consumers to buy their food products.
7. List the foods you most frequently eat during a week. Identify each item as: (a) prepared and consumed at home, (b) totally prepared outside the home but consumed at home, or (c) commercially prepared and eaten outside the home. For those items prepared and consumed at home identify as: (a) prepared from "scratch," (b) convenience items with some commercial preparation involved, or (c) ready-to-eat or heat and serve. How do these choices relate to your lifestyle?

FOOD PATTERNS

Mark had been noticing changes in his sister Sarah's eating habits. Since her marriage to David a year ago, Sarah had been eating three meals a day. Recently Sarah had stopped drinking regular coffee, soft drinks, and wine. Instead, she was consuming more milk and fruit juices. One day Sarah happily announced to her family that she and David were expecting their first baby. Because Sarah had received prenatal nutrition counseling, she has been able to make dietary changes to benefit the developing baby.

Last summer Mei-ling began baby-sitting neighborhood children to earn money. One of her tasks is to feed the children. Tommy, the 2-year-old terror, often plays with his food and refuses to eat. Julie, at 13 months of age, still clings to her bottle of milk. Four-year-old Jason always wants to eat his dessert first. What types and amounts of food do these children need?

Jack's grandfather, Charlie, is 80 years old. His income is limited. He lives alone in a senior citizen apartment complex. At noon a meal is provided for all the residents. Many of the residents have medical needs that require a special diet. In Charlie's case, he has poorly fitting dentures and finds it difficult to chew meat and raw vegetables and fruits. Charlie also takes a blood pressure pill, and the doctor recommended that he limit his salt intake. Nevertheless, Charlie relies heavily on convenience foods such as luncheon meats for the meals he must prepare himself. What suggestions might Jack offer to improve Charlie's nutrition?

Until now our focus has been on nutrition concerns for the young adult. However, each phase of life raises special nutrition challenges. Meeting these challenges as we grow older will help ensure that we will enjoy good health.

Your objectives in this chapter will be to:

■ *Identify the nutrition recommendations for pregnant and breast-feeding women*

■ *Describe current infant feeding guidelines*

■ *Adjust a diet pattern to meet nutritional needs throughout the life cycle*

■ *Plan a vegetarian menu*

NUTRITION DURING PREGNANCY

Your nutrition began with the quality of your mother's diet while she was pregnant. Adequate nutrient and caloric intake during pregnancy is very important to the development of a healthy baby. A woman's need for all nutrients increases during pregnancy, as you can see in Table 13.1. The increased need for nutrients is to support the rapid growth of the developing baby. These nutrients and oxygen are transferred from the mother's blood to the developing child.

Need for Extra Energy

Many physical changes occur in a woman's body to support the developing child. There is an increase in maternal body tissue and

Figure 13.1. A pregnant woman needs a healthy diet with extra nutrients to support the growth of her unborn child.

Table 13.1   Recommended Dietary Allowances for Nonpregnant, Pregnant, and Breast-Feeding Women

Age (yr)	Nonpregnant				Pregnant	Breast-feeding
	11-14	15-18	19-22	23-50		
Weight (lb)	101	120	120	120		120
Height (in)	62	64	64	64		64
Energy (Calories)	2200	2100	2100	2000	+300	+500
Protein (gm)	46	46	44	44	+ 30	+ 20
Fat-Soluble Vitamins						
Vitamin A (RE)[a]	800	800	800	800	+200	+400
Vitamin D (μg)[b]	10	10	7.5	5	+ 5	+ 5
Vitamin E (mg)..............	8	8	8	8	+ 2	+ 3
Water-Soluble Vitamins						
Ascorbic Acid (mg).........	50	60	60	60	+ 20	+ 40
Folacin (μg)	400	400	400	400	+400	+100
Niacin (mg)..................	15	14	14	13	+ 2	+ 5
Riboflavin (mg)	1.3	1.3	1.3	1.2	+ 0.3	+ 0.5
Thiamin (mg)................	1.1	1.1	1.1	1.0	+ 0.4	+ 0.5
Vitamin B_6 (mg)	1.8	2.0	2.0	2.0	+ 0.6	+ 0.5
Vitamin B_{12} (μg)............	3.0	3.0	3.0	3.0	+ 1.0	+ 1.0
Minerals						
Calcium (mg)................	1200	1200	800	800	+400	+400
Phosphorus (mg)	1200	1200	800	800	+400	+400
Iodine (μg)....................	150	150	150	150	+ 25	+ 50
Iron (mg)	18	18	18	18	18+[c]	18+[c]
Magnesium (mg)............	300	300	300	300	+150	+150
Zinc (mg)	15	15	15	15	+ 5	+ 10

Source: Food and Nutrition Board, National Academy of Science, National Research Council, *Recommended Dietary Allowances,* ed. 9 (Washington, D.C.: National Academy Press, 1980).
[a] 1 Retinol Equivalent (RE) = 5 international units (IU).
[b] 1 μg = 40 IU.
[c] The use of a 30 to 60 mg oral iron supplement is recommended.

fluids, including blood volume. In the first week after conception, the fertilized egg is composed of a few rapidly multiplying cells weighing a small fraction of an ounce. A newborn infant weighs 6 to 8 pounds. The total energy cost for all this extra work is estimated at 80,000 Calories.

Pregnant women will vary in the amount and pattern of weight gain during the 40 weeks of pregnancy. However, the normal recommended pattern of weight gain is 3 to 4 pounds during the first *trimester* (first third) and 1 pound per week during the second and third trimesters (last two thirds). See Illustration 13.1. A gradual weight gain is desirable. A sudden gain after the twentieth week of pregnancy may reflect excess fluid retention.

For a woman whose prepregnancy weight is within a normal weight-for-height range, the recommended weight gain is between 24 and 30 pounds. A 16-pound weight gain is recommended for an obese pregnant woman. A woman entering pregnancy underweight should gain at least 30 pounds. The components of this weight gain are distributed between the developing child and the mother. Table 13.2 shows how the weight gain is distributed. Inadequate weight gain during pregnancy may result in a baby with a low birth weight. Infants with a birth weight below 5½ pounds are at greater risk for health problems at birth.

Illustration 13.1. Weight Gain Grid for a Pregnant Teenager. Adapted from United States Department of Health and Human Services, United States Department of Agriculture, and March of Dimes Birth Defects Foundation, "Food for the Teenager During and After Pregnancy." Washington, D.C.: United States Government Printing Office, 1982; United States Department of Health and Human Services Publication No. (HRSA) 82-5106.

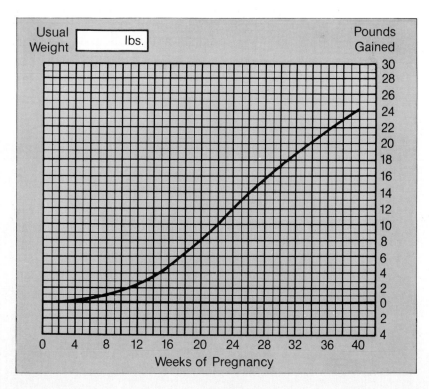

Table 13.2   Components of Average Weight Gain during Pregnancy

Products	Pounds
Infant at Birth	7.5
Placenta	1.5
Amniotic Fluid	2
Uterus	2
Expanded Blood Volume	4.0
Increased Breast Tissue	1.0
Increased Body Fluids	2.0
Maternal Tissue Stores	4.0–8.0
Total:	24–28

Gaining weight means there is a positive energy balance. No weight gain or a weight loss indicates a negative energy balance. Poor appetite, nausea, and vomiting early in pregnancy may increase the risk of ketosis. *Ketosis,* the presence of excess ketones in the blood, occurs when carbohydrate intake is inadequate to meet energy needs. Ketones are produced when fats are burned for energy. High levels of ketones may have a negative effect on the brain development of the *fetus,* the term given to a developing baby from the second month of pregnancy until birth.

Table 13.3   Daily Food Guide for Pregnancy and Breast-Feeding

Food	Servings per Day	
	Pregnancy	Breast-Feeding
Whole Grain or Enriched Breads and Cereals	4 or more[a]	5 or more[a]
Dark Green Vegetables	1	1
Vitamin C–rich Fruits or Vegetables	1	1
Other Fruits and Vegetables	2	3
Milk or Milk Products	3 or more[a]	4 or more[a]
Meat and Meat Alternates (1 serving = 2 oz)	3 or more[a]	4
Other Foods	To meet Calorie needs	To meet Calorie needs

[a] Additional servings required for the pregnant and breast-feeding teenager.

Increased Nutrient Needs

The quality of the diet is also important during pregnancy. As you can see in Table 13.3 additional servings are needed from some food groups. Choices within other food groups should be tailored to support the need for extra nutrients.

Protein. Extra protein is required during pregnancy to build new tissue. An additional 30 grams of protein each day is recommended. In food terms, this means adding 3 more ounces of meat, fish, or poultry (21 grams) and another cup of milk (8 grams). Increasing the quantities of vegetables and grains also raises protein intake. See Table 13.4.

Calories. An increase of 300 Calories per day is needed during the last 6 months of the pregnancy to support the growth of the fetus.

Table 13.4   Modified Food Guide for Vegetarian Diets for Adults and Pregnant Women

| | Recommended Number of Servings | | | |
| | Lacto-vegetarian | | Lacto-ovo-vegetarian | |
Food Group	Adult	Pregnant Adult	Adult	Pregnant Adult
Milk	4	5	4	5
Protein				
Eggs (2 = 1 serving)	0	0	0.5	1
Legumes	2	3	2	3
Nuts	1	1	1	1
Fruits and Vegetables				
Vitamin C	3	3	3	3
Vitamin A	1.5	2	1.5	2
Other	3	4	3	3
Whole Grain Products	6	7	5	6
Others	0	1	0	1

Source: Worthington-Roberts, B., and Taylor, L., *A Doctor Discusses Nutrition during Pregnancy and Breast Feeding* (Chicago, Ill.: Budlong Press Co., 1981), p. 62. Reprinted by permission of Budlong Press.

Iron. Extra iron is essential to produce hemoglobin for the mother's and the developing child's red blood cells. The demand for iron is greatest during the last half of pregnancy. The total amount of extra iron required is 700 to 800 milligrams, or an additional 5 to 6 milligrams each day. The average diet provides about 6 milligrams of iron for each 1000 Calories of food. Although iron absorption usually improves during pregnancy, it is unlikely that most women can meet this increased need by diet alone. Thus an oral supplement of 30 to 60 milligrams of iron per day is recommended. This iron may be provided as part of a prenatal vitamin/mineral supplement or as a separate tablet.

Folacin. Folacin is another nutrient essential for red blood cell production and tissue growth. The need for folacin doubles during pregnancy. Green, leafy vegetables, legumes, nuts, and whole grain

Figure 13.2. Green leafy vegetables, legumes, nuts, and whole grains are good sources of folacin.

products are good sources of folacin. Because processing and cooking destroys folacin, raw or slightly cooked vegetables and whole grain and cereal food items are recommended. For added insurance, most prenatal vitamins contain 1 milligram of folacin.

Calcium. Adequate calcium is important for the development of the unborn child's bone structure. Research continues to define the exact amount required during pregnancy.

Calcium absorption is affected by many factors; refer back to Chapter 4 to review the factors that influence calcium absorption. Although calcium absorption appears to improve during pregnancy, the consumption of an additional 400 milligrams of calcium is currently recommended. If intake is inadequate, calcium will be drawn out of the mother's bones to meet the developing child's needs. A calcium supplement is advisable for women who do not consume any milk or milk products. Many prenatal vitamin/mineral supplements contain 100 to 300 milligrams of calcium per tablet. However, supplements should not be relied on to replace a balanced diet.

Potential Problems

Pregnancy involves many body changes.

Initial Complaints. Some women experience *nausea* (upset stomach) and vomiting during the early part of the pregnancy. Although most common in the morning, these problems may occur any time of the day. Irregular eating patterns, an empty stomach, odors, and tiredness may contribute to the onset of nausea. Nausea is often relieved by eating dry crackers or toast before rising; consuming fluids between meals; eating small, low-fat meals; and avoiding highly spiced foods.

Heartburn. The growing fetus places pressure on the mother's stomach. This pressure may cause food to back up into the esophagus. *Heartburn* (burning chest pain and discomfort) is the result. Small, low-fat meals offer some help. Spicy foods should be avoided. Eating no later than 2 to 3 hours before going to bed and sleeping in an elevated position is also beneficial.

Constipation. The pressure of the fetus on the lower intestinal tract and decreased physical activity may contribute to constipation. Large amounts of supplemental iron may also produce constipation. Drinking plenty of fluids, consuming a high-fiber diet, and increasing physical activity are recommended. Dietary treatment is preferable to use of laxatives to relieve constipation.

Toxemia. This term describes a group of three symptoms that may appear during pregnancy and vary in degree of severity. The symptoms include: (1) increased blood pressure, (2) *edema,* or fluid retention, and (3) *proteinuria,* or presence of protein in the urine. The cause of toxemia is not known, although low income and poor diet are associated with higher rates of toxemia. The disorder is also more common among very young women, women over 30 years old, and women in their first pregnancy. In the past doctors recommended sodium restriction to decrease fluid retention. However, scientists have shown that this practice often worsens the problem. A well-balanced diet is an important part of preventing toxemia.

Anemia. A frequent problem in pregnancy is *anemia* (a reduction in the number of red blood cells, in hemoglobin, or in volume of packed red blood cells). Iron deficiency is the most common type of anemia. Under a microscope, iron-deficient red blood cells appear small and pale. Many women enter pregnancy with low iron stores and consume diets low in iron. Because a pregnant woman's need for iron is high, reserves can quickly be depleted. Iron supplementation is needed to correct the anemia. A well-balanced diet, including foods rich in iron, is important in preventing anemia.

Megaloblastic anemia results from a lack of folacin. In this condition, the red blood cells are larger than normal. Because folacin is essential for cell division and tissue growth, a deficiency is a critical problem during pregnancy. A folacin supplement is required to treat the deficiency.

Substances to Avoid

What a woman consumes while pregnant is shared with her developing baby. Some chemicals she may use are harmful to the unborn child and should be avoided.

Drugs. Taking drugs of any sort is a cause for concern during pregnancy. Drugs include prescribed medicines, over-the-counter aids, such as cold remedies and aspirin, and legal and illegal social

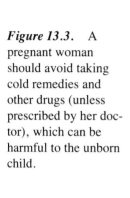

Figure 13.3. A pregnant woman should avoid taking cold remedies and other drugs (unless prescribed by her doctor), which can be harmful to the unborn child.

drugs, such as alcohol, caffeine, nicotine, and marijuana. Drugs may cause physical and mental damage to the unborn child, alter genetic material, or cause the infant to be born with a drug addiction. Effects differ according to the stage of pregnancy and the amount of drug consumed. A pregnant woman should consult her doctor before taking any drugs.

Caffeine. *Caffeine,* a stimulant, is present in coffee, tea, and some soft drinks. Many cold capsules, weight control pills, and pain relief tablets also contain caffeine. Table 13.5 lists several sources of caffeine. Caffeine enters the unborn child's bloodstream at the same level found in the mother's blood. Research suggests a possible relationship between large amounts of caffeine and birth defects. It is recommended that a pregnant woman limit caffeine intake during pregnancy.

Alcohol. Alcoholic beverages are to be avoided during pregnancy. Women who drink alcohol during pregnancy have a greater risk of delivering a baby with physical and brain defects. About 1 in every 750 infants is born with *fetal alcohol syndrome.* These infants exhibit abnormal facial features, inadequate growth, and impaired mental ability.

Table 13.5   Sources of Caffeine

	Milligrams Caffeine	
Item	Average	Range
Coffee (5-oz cup)		
Brewed, drip method	115	60-180
Brewed, percolator	80	40-170
Instant	65	30-120
Decaffeinated, brewed	3	2-5
Decaffeinated, instant	2	1-5
Tea (5-oz cup)		
Brewed, major U.S. brands	40	20-90
Brewed, imported brands	60	25-110
Instant	30	25-50
Iced (12-oz glass)	70	67-76
Chocolate		
Cocoa beverage (5-oz cup)	4	2-20
Chocolate milk beverage (8 oz)	5	2-7
Milk chocolate (1 oz)	6	1-15
Dark chocolate, semi-sweet (1 oz)	20	5-35
Baker's chocolate (1 oz)	26	26
Chocolate-flavored syrup (1 oz)	4	4
Soft drinks		
Sugar-Free Mr. PIBB	58.8	
Mountain Dew	54.0	
Mello Yello	52.8	
TAB	46.8	
Coca-Cola	45.6	
Diet Coke	45.6	
Shasta Cola	44.4	
Shasta Cherry Cola	44.4	
Shasta Diet Cola	44.4	
Mr. PIBB	40.8	
Dr. Pepper	39.6	
Sugar-Free Dr. Pepper	39.6	
Big Red	38.4	
Sugar-Free Big Red	38.4	

Table 13.5 (cont'd)

Item	Milligrams Caffeine	
	Average	**Range**
Soft drinks (cont'd)		
Pepsi-Cola.....................................	38.4	
Aspen	36.0	
Diet Pepsi....................................	36.0	
Pepsi Light	36.0	
RC Cola.......................................	36.0	
Diet Rite	36.0	
Kick	31.2	
Canada Dry Jamaica Cola.................	30.0	
Canada Dry Diet Cola	1.2	
Prescription Drugs		
Cafergot (for migraine headache).........	100	
Fiorinal (for tension headache)...........	40	
Soma Compound (pain relief, muscle relaxant)	32	
Darvon Compound (pain relief)..........	32.4	
Nonprescription Drugs		
Weight-Control Aids		
Codexin		
Dex-A-Diet II............................	200	
Dexatrim, Dexatrim Extra Strength ...	200	
Dietac capsules	200	
Maximum Strength Appedrine	100	
Prolamine.................................	140	
Alertness Tablets		
Nodoz.....................................	100	
Vivarin....................................	200	
Analgesic/Pain Relief		
Anacin, Maximum Strength Anacin...	32	
Excedrin	65	
Midol......................................	32.4	
Vanquish	33	

(Continued)

Table 13.5 (cont'd)

Item	Milligrams Caffeine	
	Average	Range
Nonprescription Drugs (cont'd)		
Diuretics		
Aqua-Ban.............................	100	
Maximum Strength Aqua-Ban Plus ...	200	
Permathene H2 Off	200	
Cold/Allergy Remedies		
Coryban-D capsules	30	
Triaminicin tablets	30	
Dristan Decongestant tablets and		
Dristan A-F Decongestant tablets...	16.2	
Duradyne-Forte..........................	30	

Source: Lecos, C., "The Latest Caffeine Scorecard" (Washington, D.C.: U.S. Government Printing Office, 1984), Department of Health and Human Services Publication No. (FDA) 84-2184.

Smoking. Mothers who smoke tend to have babies with a lower birth weight and an increased chance of fetal death. *Nicotine* acts on hormones that cause blood vessels to get smaller and the heart rate to increase. The result is a decreased oxygen and nutrient supply to the developing child. Smoking raises levels of carbon monoxide in the blood, and as a result the hemoglobin can carry less oxygen.

BABY'S FIRST FOODS

During the first year of life a baby experiences rapid growth— often tripling in weight and doubling in length. A nutritious diet is important to sustain this growth. For the first 4 to 6 months of life, an infant's diet consists solely of human milk or a commercial formula. Both types of feeding will support the growth and development of a baby, because no solid foods are needed at this time. Both methods of infant feeding offer some advantages and disadvantages. During pregnancy a woman needs to consider infant feeding options and

Figure 13.4. During the first year of life a baby grows rapidly and so needs a very nutritious diet.

make an informed choice about which method will best suit her and her infant.

Breast-feeding

Regardless of breast size or shape, most women can nurse their infant successfully. Accurate information on breast-feeding and plenty of emotional support are important factors in achieving success. Breast milk is nutritionally designed for the human infant. *Colostrum,* a yellow fluid produced before breast milk, is rich in proteins that provide the infant with immunity from certain bacteria. This property cannot be duplicated by a formula. The only nutrients that need to be supplemented are vitamin D and fluoride.

Nursing is quick and convenient. No sterilized bottles or refrigeration are needed. Nursing may also be less expensive than formula feeding. All that is required is for the mother to add to her daily diet an extra 500 Calories and 20 grams of protein from a variety of nutrient-dense foods. Refer to Table 13.3. Best of all, nursing establishes a warm, loving bond between mother and baby.

Social customs may limit where a mother can comfortably nurse her infant, which can hamper the convenience of feeding on demand. An infant will normally nurse every two to four hours for 10 to 15 minutes at each breast. Infant weight gain is the best measure of feeding adequacy.

For the working mother, breast feeding requires making arrangements to nurse or *express* (manually empty the breast of milk) and store milk while at work. Because breast milk can be expressed, bottled, and refrigerated, other people can assist in infant feeding when mother is away.

While breast-feeding her baby, a woman should avoid drugs, alcohol, and foods that might be contaminated with chemicals or heavy metals. These substances are transmitted through breast milk and are harmful to the infant. Dieting to lose weight should not be attempted while breast-feeding.

Formulas and Bottle-Feeding

If bottle-feeding is the method of choice, a variety of products are available to meet an infant's individual needs. Commercial formulas are available in three forms: ready-to-feed, concentrate, or powder. Ready-to-feed is the most expensive, while powder is the least expensive. The use of a concentrate or powder requires mixing the formula with water. Private wells should be tested for bacteria and nitrates to be certain water is safe for an infant.

Standard formulas are based on cow's milk. For infants with allergies or digestive problems, special soy-based and predigested

Figure 13.5. Many kinds of formula are available to meet the individual needs of bottle-fed infants.

formulas are available. Nutritionally complete commercial formulas are fortified with vitamins and minerals. Iron may or may not be added. By four months of age an infant will need a dietary source of iron. The use of whole cow's milk is not recommended before one year of age, because its nutrient content is inappropriate for an infant. Low-fat milk and skim milk are not recommended before two years of age. These products are inadequate in caloric density and poor sources of essential fatty acids and fat-soluble vitamins.

Sterilization of the water, bottles, and other equipment used in infant feeding is an important step in formula preparation. Because bacteria may develop in milk any formula left in a bottle after feeding should be discarded.

Love and security are often communicated through food, and this is especially true for infants. A baby should be held while being fed. Remember that continuous oral exposure to fermentable sugars causes dental caries. Thus a bottle of formula should never be used as a pacifier.

Introduction of Solid Foods

In the first month of life, a baby feeds six to eight times a day, consuming a total of 15 to 25 ounces of formula. Between four to six months, most infants consume 28 to 32 ounces of formula per day. At this time infants begin to show a readiness to accept solid foods. Signs of readiness include holding the head erect, sitting without support, making chewing motions, and drawing in the lower lip as the spoon is removed from the mouth.

The first solid food introduced is infant cereal. Rice cereal is introduced first because it is least likely to cause an allergic reaction. Infant cereals are fortified with iron. The cereal should be mixed with formula or breast milk. No sugar is needed. The cereal should be offered from a spoon, not from a bottle or syringe-type feeder. Offering cereal in a bottle requires that the nipple hole be enlarged. A baby may use his or her tongue to slow the flow of the mixture through the larger hole. As a result, improper swallowing motions are learned, motions that interfere with normal tooth development.

Once an infant has mastered taking cereal from a spoon, the goal is to increase the variety of foods eaten. Vegetables and fruits are the next foods to add to an infant's diet. See Illustration 13.2. New foods should be offered one at a time in small quantities. If one food

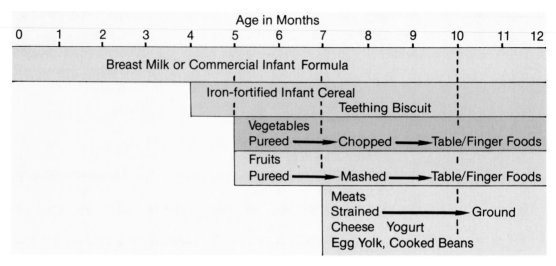

Illustration 13.2.   Introduction of Solid Foods.

is refused, another food should be tried and the rejected food item can be reintroduced later. Baby foods may be home-cooked foods that are pureed before salt, sugar, or fat has been added for the other family members' tastes. Commercially prepared foods may also be purchased. Read the labels carefully to obtain the most food value for your dollar. Baby food desserts and sweetened beverages (soda pop or fruit-flavored drinks) are high in sugar and low in nutrient value. Such products are unnecessary for an infant. If a baby is thirsty between feedings, offer a bottle of sterile water.

Gradual changes in texture from pureed and mashed foods to lumpy and chunky foods are made as teeth develop and the infant masters chewing. Offering finger foods, such as baby crackers and dry cereal, will help an infant develop skills in grasping and bringing food to his or her mouth. As the quantity of solids eaten increases, the amount of formula or breast milk consumed will decrease. However, breast milk or formula should remain the major source of Calories and protein until a baby is consuming a wide variety of table foods.

Between 7 and 10 months of age, an infant is able to handle more table foods and begins to develop self-feeding skills. Now is the time to begin weaning from the bottle or breast to drinking from a cup. At mealtime, small amounts of formula and fruit juice should be offered from a cup. Ground meats are also introduced during this period.

Figure 13.6. At seven to ten months, infants can begin to feed themselves and eat more table foods.

FEEDING THE TODDLER

Achieving a balanced diet is a challenge when feeding a toddler. A child between the ages of one and three years is learning to function as an independent person. Self-feeding skills continue to improve. A toddler's rate of growth slows and his or her interest in eating may decline. Offer a wide variety of foods to expand a child's experience with food. Food likes and dislikes are often vigorously expressed. Don't be too concerned, as preferences do change!

Foods should be offered in a positive, relaxed environment. Conflicts at mealtimes are to be avoided. Food preferences and eating behavior are learned, although taste preference for sweet is believed to be automatic. Adults are role models, and young children are very good at copying what they see.

Calorie Needs

A toddler's Calorie needs increase with activity. Key nutrients to plan for in the child's diet are protein, calcium, vitamin C, and iron. See Table 13.6. Offering nutritious snacks is an important part of a toddler's diet pattern. Snacks help the toddler obtain the quantity and

Table 13.6   Food Guide for Toddlers (1-3 years)

Food	Servings/Day	Average Serving Size
Fruits and Vegetables	4	2-3 Tblsp or ¼-⅓ cup
Vitamin C	1	
Vitamin A	1 (2-3 times/wk)	
Other items	2	
Breads and Cereals	4	
Bread (Enriched or Whole Grain)		½-¾ slices
Crackers		2-3
Cold Cereals		½-¾ cup
Cooked Cereals/Pasta		⅓ cup
Milk and Milk Products	4	
Milk		½-¾ cup
Cheese		1 oz
Yogurt		½-¾ cup
Meat and Meat Alternates	2-3	
Eggs		1
Meat, Fish, Poultry		2-3 Tblsp
Peanut Butter		1 Tblsp
Dried Beans/Peas		4 Tblsp
Fats and Oils	To meet Calorie needs	
Butter, Margarine, Mayonnaise, Vegetable Oils		1 tsp

variety of foods needed for good health. Make snacks count! Limit the consumption of sweets. Some foods are easy for a young child to choke on. Avoid small, round, hard items, such as nuts, raisins, and popcorn. Table 13.7 lists nutritious snacks.

Keep food portions child sized. Offer ½ to ¾ slice of bread or ½ cup of cereal. A fruit and vegetable portion is generally one tablespoon per year of age. A fruit juice serving is ¼ cup. One egg, one ounce of meat or cheese, one tablespoon of peanut butter, or ¼ cup of cooked beans is a protein serving. Four to six ounces of milk is a serving. Commercial toddler foods are convenient, but expensive.

Table 13.7   Nutritious Snacks

Fresh Fruit	Milk and Fruit Shakes
Fruit Juice	Cottage Cheese
Fruit Juice Pops (frozen juice)	Low-fat Yogurt
	Cheese
Apple Sauce, Unsweetened	Peanut Butter
Apple Cider	Bean Dip
Fresh Vegetables	Whole Grain Crackers, Breads, Muffins
Tomato Juice	
Milk	Whole Grain Cereals

Figure 13.7. An active toddler has increased Calorie needs.

CHILDHOOD FOOD PATTERNS

During the preschool years a child begins developing food preparation and serving skills. As eye-hand coordination improves, a child learns to pour beverages, use a knife for spreading, and serve food from a serving bowl. Child-sized eating utensils are helpful in assisting a child to master these skills. At this time a child becomes more aware of food advertising and food selections made by friends. These are powerful forces that influence a child's food choices.

Nutritional Concerns

A child's appetite is often erratic. Food likes and dislikes can change from day to day. Familiar foods are often preferred. Appropriate portion sizes increase with age and activity.

Iron. Many children pass through a stage of not liking meat or cooked vegetables. As a result, their diet may be low in iron. Overconsumption of milk may also contribute to low iron intake for some children. The wider the variety of nutrient-dense foods offered, the less likely deficiencies will occur. See Table 13.8. Iron deficiency

Figure 13.8. Would watermelon be a good nutrient-dense snack?

Table 13.8   Food Guide for Children (4-12 years)

Food	Servings/Day	Average Serving Size		
		4-5 yr	**6-9 yr**	**10-12 yr**
Fruits and Vegetables	4			
Vitamin C	1	¼ cup	¼ cup	¼-½ cup
Vitamin A	1 (2-3 times/wk)	¼ cup	⅓ cup	⅓ cup
Other items	2	¼ cup	½ cup	½ cup
Breads and Cereals	4			
Bread (Enriched or Whole Grain)		¾-1 slice	1 slice	1 slice
Crackers		3-4	4-6	4-6
Cold Cereal		½ cup	1 cup	1 cup
Cooked Cereals/Pasta		½ cup	½ cup	½ cup
Milk and Milk Products	3-4			
Milk		½-¾ cup	¾-1 cup	1 cup
Cheese		1 oz	1½ oz	2 oz
Yogurt		½-¾ cup	¾ cup	1 cup
Meat and Meat Alternates	3			
Eggs		1	1	1
Meat, Fish, Poultry		2 oz	2-3 oz	3 oz
Peanut Butter		1 Tblsp	2 Tblsp	2 Tblsp
Dried Beans/Peas		⅓ cup	½ cup	¾ cup
Fats and Oils	To meet Calorie needs			
Butter, Margarine, Mayonnaise		1 tsp	1 tsp	1 tsp
Vegetable Oils		1 tsp	1 tsp	1 tsp
Bacon		1 slice	1 slice	1 slice

affects about one quarter of all young children. If anemia occurs, an iron supplement is recommended.

Obesity. Overconsumption of food, especially high-Calorie junk food, is a factor in childhood obesity. Lack of activity also contributes to a positive energy balance and weight gain. A child should be permitted to grow into his or her weight as height increases. This can be achieved through limiting high-Calorie foods and increasing physical activity. Changes in family eating patterns and life-style often need to occur to achieve long-term results.

Dental Caries. A pattern of frequent snacking on sugar-containing foods may begin in childhood. Children should avoid frequent use of sweetened drinks, candies, cookies, and cakes. Nutrient-dense snacks, such as fresh fruits, vegetables, whole grain products, and milk products, can be an important part of a child's diet. To prevent tooth decay, brushing and flossing the teeth after meals should be encouraged. A fluoride supplement is recommended if the water supply is not fluoridated.

THE ADULT YEARS

Basal energy needs decline with each decade during the adult years. The energy needs of adults vary greatly depending on daily activities. For example, an adult with an office job requires less Calories than a person engaged in heavy manual labor. Leisure time pursuits also count toward the total Calorie need. Participating in regular aerobic exercise requires more energy than watching television. Adjusting the quantity of food consumed to meet changes in life-style is a nutrition challenge for many adults. Obesity is a major problem for those unable to balance energy intake and output.

A healthful adult diet pattern is designed to meet nutritional needs without excess Calories. Eating a wide variety of nutrient-dense foods is prudent advice. As the body ages during the adult years, chronic diseases begin to surface. Modification of the diet, as suggested in Chapter 6, may decrease the risk of developing a chronic disease.

Women Only

Adult women have special nutritional needs. About 40% of women are low in iron. Blood loss during menstruation increases a woman's need for iron. Methods of *contraception* (pregnancy prevention) also influence a woman's nutrition needs. When an intrauterine device (IUD) is used, bleeding during menstruation is usually heavier and iron needs are greater. Use of the birth control pill causes blood triglycerides and cholesterol levels to be elevated. Additionally, levels of folacin and vitamins B_6, C, and A are decreased. Unwanted weight gain often occurs when women take birth control pills. Eating nutrient-dense foods and avoiding excess fat and Calories are recommended.

For women with a family history of osteoporosis, a diet with an adequate calcium intake is important. If a woman does not drink milk, a calcium carbonate supplement may be needed. For women past their child-bearing years, a calcium intake of 1000 to 1500 milligrams has been suggested to maintain bone mass.

Older Adults

Today over 11% of the American population is over 65 years of age.

Physical Changes. The normal aging process brings about changes in body cells and organ functioning. These physical changes affect food intake and use. For example, gastric acidity decreases and nutrient absorption is impaired. Anemias are common. Intestinal tract motility slows down and constipation is a problem. The basal metabolism and activity level decreases, which may result in excess weight gain. The building of body tissue declines, so wound healing is slower. Body composition changes with age. There is a decline in lean body mass and an increase in body fat. Because bone mass decreases, fractures are more common. Taste and smell sensitivity decrease, which affects appetite. Tooth loss occurs and chewing may be a problem.

An older adult is more likely to have an advanced chronic disease, such as congestive heart failure, cancer, or lung disease. These diseases impair nutritional well-being. Many older adults need to use multiple medications to treat coexisting diseases. Food and drug interactions are known to depress appetite, decrease nutrient absorption, increase nutrient excretion, and alter nutrient needs.

Changes in Life-Style. In addition to physical changes, an older adult goes through profound life-style changes. Retirement and living on a fixed income limits the food budget. The death of a spouse or friend often causes loneliness, depression, and a lack of appetite. Lack of transportation or decline in physical health impairs the ability to procure and prepare food. Furthermore, the elderly tend to have limited nutrition knowledge. Some have little skill or interest in food preparation, so they rely on convenience foods. These foods are often high in fat, sugar, and sodium and low in essential nutrients. Seeking to be healthier, older adults are likely to be persuaded to purchase megadoses of vitamins and minerals.

Alterations in Dietary Patterns. The diet pattern for an elderly person needs to consider both physical and social needs for food. Calorie needs are less for the elderly, which means limiting fat and sugar intake. Most nutrient needs of older adults are similar or perhaps greater than those of younger adults. However, it is difficult to obtain needed nutrients from diets that contain less than 1200 Calories a day. Nutrients that may be needed in greater amounts include protein, calcium, and vitamin D.

Other nutrient needs may be altered by disease. Bleeding ulcers, for example, may cause iron deficiency. Supplemental iron prescribed by a doctor would be needed to correct the anemia. Self-medication with large doses of vitamin or minerals is not wise. In general, a nutrient-dense diet is the basic plan for an older adult. The use of low-fat milk, lean meat and meat alternates, complex carbohydrates, and fruits and vegetables is recommended. Recipes for older adults should feature simple preparation methods and require a minimum of kitchen utensils.

Figure 13.9. Older persons should consider physical changes and life-style changes when planning their diet, because their Calorie needs may now be lower.

Small, frequent meals are usually easier for an older person to eat and digest. Increasing dietary fiber often helps correct constipation. If a person has no teeth or poorly-fitting dentures, a diet consisting of soft foods may be indicated. Special diet modifications are also required for persons with chronic diseases. A dietitian should be consulted to assist in meal planning for special diets.

THE VEGETARIAN ALTERNATIVE

Food patterns described up to this point have included animal products as the major source of dietary proteins. However, *vegetarian,* or meatless diet patterns, have existed for centuries. People choose to follow vegetarian diets for many different reasons. Meatless eating patterns have been prescribed for moral and religious reasons. For example, religious monks avoid meat to comply with vows of a simple life-style. Abstaining from meat may also be considered an act of self-discipline for some religious groups. Hindus believe human souls may be present in animal forms, so an animal must not be killed for food. Economic necessity is another reason for eating a diet without meat. The cost or availability of animal products forced some cultures to develop *foodways,* or eating practices, that excluded meat. The Mexican diet pattern of tortillas and beans is an example.

Additionally, health concerns and the natural foods movement prompted some people to become vegetarians. The vegetarian diet is lower in saturated fat, cholesterol, and Calories and higher in fiber than an average diet that includes meat. The incidence of obesity, heart disease, cancer, osteoporosis, and digestive tract disorders is reportedly less among vegetarians. More recently, issues of global ecology and world food distribution are also being presented as reasons for changing to a meatless diet pattern.

Patterns of Vegetarianism

Vegetarians vary widely in the foods they include and exclude from their eating pattern. Generally, two types of patterns are recognized. A *lacto-ovo vegetarian* pattern includes milk and milk products, eggs, and plant foods. See Table 13.9. A *vegan* diet consists

Table 13.9 Food Guide for Lacto-Ovo Diets

Food Group	Minimum Number of Servings per Day										Standard Serving
	1-3 yr Both Sexes	4-6 yr Both Sexes	7-9 yr Both Sexes	10-12 yr Both Sexes	13-17 yr M	13-17 yr F	18-19 yr M	18-19 yr F	20+ yr M	20+ yr F	
Cereals, whole grains, breads	3	3-4	4	5	7	5	9	5	8	6	1 slice whole-grain or enriched bread, 3/4 cup cooked cereal, 1 oz dry cereal
Legumes, Meat Analogs, Textured Vegetable Protein (TVP)	1/3	1/4	1/2	1/2	3/4	1/2	1 1/2	1	1	3/4	1 cup cooked legume, 2-3 oz meat analog, 20-30 gm TVP
Nuts and Seeds	1/8	1/4	1/2	3/4	1	3/4	2	1	1	1	1 1/2 oz, 3 Tblsp
Milk and Milk Products	2-3	2-3	3	4	4	4	2-3	2-3	1 1/2	1 1/2	1 cup milk[a]
Eggs	1	1	1	1 1/2	1 1/2	1 1/2	1 1/2	1 1/2	1 1/2	1 1/2	1 medium
Fruits, Vegetables	2-3	3-4	4	5	5	5	6	5	6	5	1/2 cup juice, 1 medium piece, 1 cup raw, 1/2 cup cooked
Oils	1/3-1	2/3-1	2/3-1	1	1	1	1	1	1	1	1 Tblsp

Source: Reprinted with permission of Ross Laboratories, Columbus, OH 43216, from *Dietetic Currents*, Vol. 10, No. 1, © 1983 Ross Laboratories.

[a]Common portions of dairy foods and their milk equivalents in calcium: 1-in cube cheddar-type cheese = 1/2 cup milk; 1/2 cup yogurt = 1/2 cup milk; 1/2 cup cottage cheese = 1/4 cup milk; 2 Tblsp cream cheese = 1 Tblsp milk; and 1/2 cup ice cream or ice milk = 1/3 cup milk.

only of plant foods. See Table 13.10. The more restrictive a diet is in excluding foods, the greater the risk for nutrient deficiency. However, vegetarian diets can be nutritionally sound and may even offer added health benefits. Planning is the key to obtaining nutrients—and especially protein—usually provided by the excluded foods.

Planning for Adequate Protein Intake

Planning for adequate quantity and quality of protein is a basic task in managing a vegetarian diet. In Chapter 3 you learned that the human body is unable to make eight of the 22 amino acids that are the building blocks of protein. These eight are considered essential and must be obtained in the diet. A person needs all the essential amino acids in the right proportions to build body proteins. If one amino acid is in short supply, the building process slows down or stops.

Dietary proteins that provide the essential amino acids in amounts needed to support tissue growth are referred to as *complete*

Table 13.10   Food Guide for Adult Vegan Diets

Food Group	Minimum Number of Servings per Day[a]	Estimated Protein Per Serving (gm)[b]
Bread	4	2
Whole grains	3-5	4
Legumes	2	10
Nuts and Seeds	1	5
Fruits	1-4	—
Vegetables	4	2
Oils	1	—

Source: Reprinted with permission of Ross Laboratories, Columbus, OH 43216, from *Dietetic Currents,* Vol. 10, No. 1, © 1983 Ross Laboratories.

[a] A serving = 1 slice whole-grain or enriched bread; 1 cup cooked cereal or whole grains; 1 cup cooked legumes; 3 Tblsp nuts or seeds; ½ cup fruit juice; ½ cup cooked or 1 cup raw vegetables; and 1 Tblsp oil.

[b] Vegan protein balance formula: 60% of protein from grains; 35% of protein from legumes; 5% of protein from leafy, green vegetables. (D. Calloway, Professor of Nutrition, University of California, Berkeley).

Figure 13.10. Milk, eggs, meat, fish, and poultry have complete proteins.

proteins. Complete proteins with a high biological value include milk, eggs, meat, fish, and poultry. Proteins lacking in one or more of the essential amino acids are considered *incomplete*. All plant proteins are deficient in at least one essential amino acid. The essential amino acid present in the lowest amount is known as the *limiting amino acid*. Plants differ in their amino acid composition. Grains are high in methionine, but low in lysine. Nuts and seed are also low in lysine. Legumes (dried beans, peas, and lentils) are high in lysine, but low in methionine and tryptophan.

When a food low in a given essential amino acid is combined with another food high in that limiting amino acid, the proteins are described as *complementary*. Combining complementary proteins is the key to obtaining the required quality of protein in a vegetarian diet. See Illustration 13.3. Complementary food combinations include: (1) grains (wheat, rye, rice, corn) plus legumes (dried beans, peas, lentils); and (2) seeds (sesame, sunflower) and nuts plus legumes. Additionally, milk and milk products enhance the protein quality of grains. Some of these specific food combinations may be familiar to you. See Table 13.11. How many of these combinations have you tried?

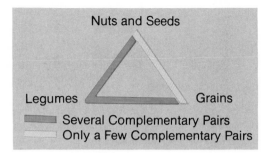

Illustration 13.3. The Complementary Protein Picture.

Processed Alternatives. In addition to the above natural combinations, the food industry has introduced *textured vegetable protein* (dried, processed soybean fibers) and *meat analogs* (plant proteins designed to simulate meat in appearance and taste).

Special Nutrient Concerns with a Vegan Diet

Nutrient problems for a person following the vegan diet include iron, vitamin B_{12}, calcium, vitamin D, and zinc intakes. As described in Chapter 4, meats are an excellent source of iron. Iron in plants is less well absorbed. Consuming foods that contain ascorbic acid while eating plant foods will improve iron absorption. Vitamin B_{12} is present only in foods of animal origin, so following a vegan diet for a long period of time may result in vitamin B_{12} deficiency. Thus a

Table 13.11   Examples of Complementary Protein Pairs
Peanut Butter and Whole Wheat Bread
Hummus (Sesame Seeds and Chick Peas)
Tofu (Soybean Curd) and Rice
Tortilla and Refried Beans
Baked Beans and Boston Brown Bread
Black-Eyed Peas and Rice

vegan diet should be supplemented with vitamin B_{12}. The richest source of calcium is milk. When milk and milk products are not consumed, calcium and vitamin D intakes are likely to be low. The calcium in dark green, leafy vegetables is not readily available because of the presence of phytates and oxalic acid. Additional calcium can be obtained by consuming fortified soy milk or *tofu* (calcium-precipitated soybean curd).

The lacto-ovo vegetarian diet is nutritionally adequate for children and adults. The vegan diet pattern is not recommended for children under 12 years of age unless cautiously supplemented. Fortified soy milks are now available to enhance the diet's quality. Achieving an adequate caloric intake to support growth may be difficult. Active adult vegans may also find it hard to maintain their desirable body weight.

NUTRITION: THE CHALLENGE OF A LIFETIME

As we have learned in this chapter, good nutrition is an essential part of life—even before birth! Understanding how nutrition demands change during the various phases of life will enable you to meet the nutrition challenge and live a healthy, active life.

CHECK YOUR PROGRESS

1. Define the term *fetus*.
2. According to the food guide in Table 13.1, what are the recommendations for increased Calorie and nutrient intake during pregnancy?
3. What is the recommended weight gain during pregnancy for a woman within the normal weight-for-height range? An obese pregnant woman? An underweight pregnant woman?
4. Why is inadequate weight gain a concern?
5. Why is an increased protein intake important during pregnancy?
6. Describe which nutrients are needed in additional amounts to build red blood cells.
7. How much extra calcium is recommended? Why?
8. List the common nutrition-related problems in pregnancy.

9. Identify the substances to avoid consuming during pregnancy. Explain why.
10. Name the two infant feeding options available during the first 4 months of life. What are the advantages and disadvantages of each?
11. If an infant is breast fed, which two nutrients should be supplemented?
12. Define colostrum and describe its value to the infant.
13. What is the recommended food pattern for a breast-feeding woman?
14. What substances or practices should a woman avoid while breast-feeding?
15. How old should an infant be before switching to whole cow's milk? Why are low-fat and skim milk not recommended before 2 years of age?
16. Identify the types of infant formulas available and the forms in which they can be purchased.
17. For what two substances should private wells be tested before being used in formula preparation?
18. When should solid foods be introduced? In what sequence?
19. Why are nutritious snacks an important part of a toddler's diet? What kinds of foods should be avoided?
20. Identify appropriate food portion sizes for a toddler.
21. Describe the major nutrition concerns during childhood.
22. What is the main nutrition challenge for adults? What diet recommendations are most appropriate for this age group?
23. Identify two nutrient concerns for many adult women.
24. Describe the physical, social, and emotional changes that affect an elderly person's nutritional well-being.
25. Identify specific dietary recommendations for older adults.
26. Define *vegetarian*. Why do people choose to be vegetarian?
27. Identify the two broad categories of vegetarians. Describe differences between the two.
28. What, if any, are the nutritional concerns associated with vegetarian diets? What are the positive health benefits of vegetarianism?
29. Why are plant proteins considered incomplete? How can the protein quality of plant foods be improved when consumed as part of a vegetarian diet?
30. Give an example of two complementary protein foods.

IT'S YOUR DECISION

The network evening news televises pictures from an emergency food relief camp that provides aid to thousands of people starving in Africa. The tragic scenes of malnutrition and death make Jason grateful for the tasty dinner he has just finished eating. Nevertheless, questions regarding world hunger remain on his mind. Why are people starving? Isn't there enough food? Can the United States feed the world?

Jenny and Sam live in an inner city housing unit with limited yard space. Neither of them knew anything about gardening until they enrolled in a community garden project. With seeds, hoe, and tender loving care, they produced a bumper crop of vegetables for their family.

Fresh corn-on-the-cob, plump red tomatoes, sweet green peppers, tender green peas, juicy watermelon, and delicate red raspberries decorate the parking lot at the farmers' market. During the growing season, dozens of area fruit and vegetable growers bring their produce to town and sell directly to consumers. Heather and her mother make a weekly visit to the farmers' market to purchase fresh, locally grown products at a considerable cost savings.

Your objectives in this chapter will be to:

- *Describe the types of information gathered to assess individual nutritional status*

- *Identify factors that contribute to world hunger and malnutrition*

- *Describe current approaches to feeding the world's hungry*

- *Explain the ecological concerns related to food resources*

- *Analyze the contributions of alternative foods, farming methods, and consumer practices to the world food system*

- *Apply critical thinking skills in forming a personal stand on food issues*

FOOD AND HEALTH: THE GLOBAL PICTURE

In an era of instant worldwide communications, the comparison of life in the United States with that in the remote villages of Africa, Latin America, and Asia is an everyday part of the news. Many Americans are deeply moved by the graphic details of famine, yet have only a vague understanding of why the problem exists and what, if anything, can be done to solve the problem. Consumers are asked by advocacy groups to boycott products because of the actions of a multinational corporation in a Third World, or developing, nation. As voters and taxpayers, Americans are asked by political leaders to support food assistance and relief efforts to these same nations. For many people the problems seem too complex and remote to become personally involved. However, concerned experts challenge us to see how our individual life-style and food choices impact on world food and health issues.

Identifying Hunger and Malnutrition

Hunger is a term used to describe the physical and emotional response to a lack of food. *Malnutrition,* or poor nourishment, can

Figure 14.1. Why does famine exist?

result from too few or too many Calories and nutrients. The consumption of an inadequate diet results in *undernutrition*. Also, the quality and quantity of the diet may be deficient. Throughout history periodic drought and warfare have produced food shortages that lead to *starvation*, or death from a lack of food. *Famine*, an extreme food shortage, is less likely today as a result of worldwide food relief efforts. Instead, chronic undernutrition is the major problem. In many parts of the world, the presence of bacterial and viral diseases compounds the severity of the nutritional problems.

A person's *nutritional status*, or degree of nutritional health, can be assessed based on physical, biochemical, and dietary information. Physical assessment includes clinical observation of appearance and measurement of height, weight, and skin fold thickness. Analysis of blood and urine samples reveals more subtle changes in nutrient levels in a person's body. Food surveys and diet interviews provide supportive evidence of the adequacy or lack of food.

Over a period of time, a diet inadequate in both Calories and protein will result in a type of malnutrition known as *marasmus*. A skeleton-like appearance is typical in marasmus. Another type of malnutrition, *kwashiorkor*, develops when Calorie intake is adequate but protein intake is deficient. Characteristics of kwashiorkor include dry, brittle, orangish hair and protruding stomach caused by *edema*, or

Figure 14.2. A person's nutritional health can be assessed.

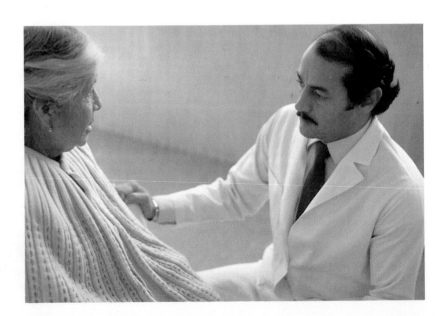

fluid retention. Lack of specific nutrients can also produce deficiency diseases such as those described in Chapter 4. For example, night blindness caused by vitamin A deficiency is still quite common in the rural Philippines.

Most people recognize access to food as a basic human right. However, the United Nations Food and Agriculture Organization (FAO) estimates that 450 million people are severely undernourished. The World Bank and the United States government estimate that 800 million people are too poor to meet their basic needs for food, clothing, and shelter. Other estimates are that one quarter of the world's population is suffering from hunger. Who are the hungry? They are the world's poor, primarily living in the Third World nations. See Table 14.1. Why do hunger and undernutrition exist?

Nutritional well-being is influenced by biological, environmental, economic, political, and social forces. Many people have proposed theories on the causes of world hunger. The view a person holds on the causes of hunger usually affects his or her attitudes and actions toward solutions. Hunger may result when (1) population demands exceed the food produced, (2) access to the food supply is limited, or (3) available food is too costly to purchase. Explore each

Table 14.1   Identify the World's Hungry

Country	Number of Hungry People
India	201 Million
Indonesia	33 Million
Bangladesh	27 Million
Nigeria	14 Million
Brazil	12 Million
Ethiopia	12 Million
Pakistan	12 Million
Philippines	10 Million
Afghanistan (pre-war)	6 Million
Burma	5 Million
Columbia	5 Million
Thailand	5 Million

Source: The United Nations Food and Agriculture Organization.

of these factors to form your own opinions concerning the world food crisis.

Global Food Resources

The United States is often described as the "breadbasket" of the world. As you learned in Chapter 11, the American agricultural system has produced an abundance of food, which is exported throughout the world. Our technology has also been marketed to countries that desire to increase their food production.

The adoption of advanced scientific growing techniques by nations previously lacking self-sufficiency in food production is referred to as the *green revolution*. Dr. Norman E. Borlaug, a farmer and plant pathologist, is recognized as the pioneer of the green revolution. Borlaug's promotion of high-yielding varieties of wheat and rice has caused wheat production to quadruple in Mexico and to more than double in India and Pakistan. This production success also requires the use of insecticides, pesticides, fertilization, irrigation, and modern farming practices. Thousands of acres of previously nonproductive land have been brought into cultivation. The green revolution has permitted many nations in Africa, Asia, the Middle East, and Latin America to increase their grain production dramatically.

Figure 14.3. This dam and irrigation ditch supply water to land that was previously unsuitable to grow crops.

The FAO reports that global food production averages 3,000 Calories per person per day. However, this food energy is not equally distributed between countries or people within countries. Large amount of grain are fed to livestock, and a significant amount is lost to spoilage and pests. According to the FAO, the total Calorie deficit for 86 nations studied in 1981 was estimated to be 311 billion Calories, or equal to the energy provided by 37 million tons of wheat. This amount of wheat is just 2.4% of the 1981 grain harvest, which had a value of $6.6 billion in October of that year.

World Population Growth

An eighteenth century economist, Thomas Malthus, set forth his theory on population and food supply. Malthus stated that the population, when unchecked, increases in a *geometrical ratio* (that is, the ratio between numbers is always the same, such as 2, 4, 8, 16, 32, 64). However, food production increases in an *arithmetical ratio* (the difference between a number and its predecessor is always the same, such as 3, 5, 7, 9, 11). Accepting this theory means that, if left uncontrolled, population demands would eventually exceed the food production capacity of the earth.

Concerns regarding uncontrolled population growth sparked the effort during the 1970s for zero population growth. Although food production has increased and birth rates have declined, the overall world population continues to grow. See Illustration 14.1. The current world population is estimated to be 5 billion, and is projected to reach 6.1 billion by the year 2000. See Illustration 14.2. The immense population in Southeast Asia, even with lower birth rates, presents the greatest challenge for meeting future food needs. See Illustration 14.3. Producing enough food makes possible, but does not guarantee, the elimination of hunger in the world.

Current Approaches to Feeding the World's Hungry

Many experts claim that the current food problem in developing countries is not a global lack of food. As the FAO statistics show, more than enough food is currently produced and stored to provide all people with an adequate diet. Instead, social, political, and economic differences within and between countries are cited as roadblocks to food delivery to those in need. Distribution of income within a

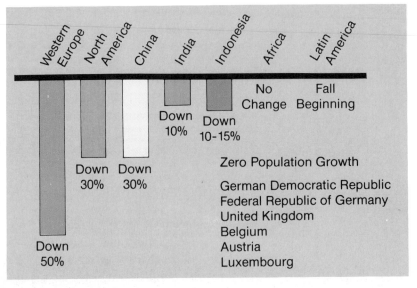

Illustration 14.1.
Growth Rates in
Selected Countries.
(Adapted from *The Mil-
waukee Journal* [Mil-
waukee, Wis.] , July 9,
1978.)

country is viewed by many as an important factor in determining food
consumption. Three ways currently used to increase food supplies to
needy people in less developed nations are food aid, food trade, and
increased local production.

Food Aid. Countries with abundant food supplies (primarily
the United States) provide food aid to nations in need. In 1954 the law

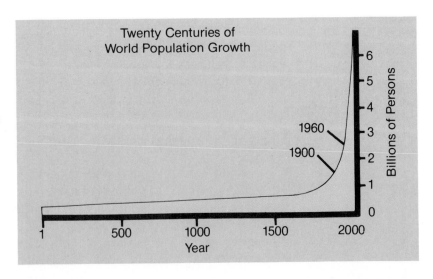

Illustration 14.2.
Growth in the World's
Population. (Data
from the United
States Department of
Agriculture.)

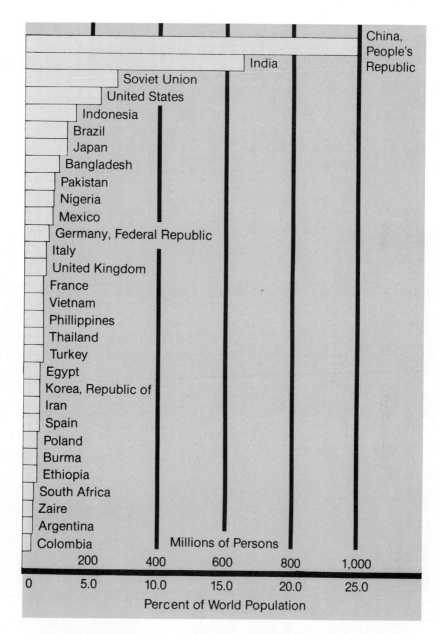

Illustration 14.3.
Population of the World's Thirty Largest Countries as of 1977. (Data from the United States Bureau of the Census.)

number P.L. 480, more commonly known as "Food for Peace," was designed to dispense U.S. farm surplus, create new markets for farm products, and support governments important to U.S. national security. Over the past 25 years the United States has distributed over $30 billion worth of food aid. See Illustration 14.4. Food aid may be

Illustration 14.4. P.L. 480 Shipments in Fiscal Years 1955 to 1985. (Adapted from the United States Department of Agriculture, *U.S. Agriculture in A Global Economy,* 1985 Agricultural Yearbook [Washington, D.C.: United States Government Printing Office, 1985, p. 375].)

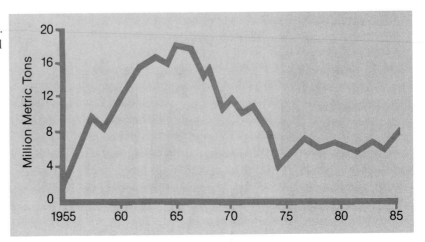

donated or sold to governments at low interest rates. Food aid may be given to meet food emergencies, such as famines in Biafra and Bangladesh. Because internal conflict may be the cause of the famine, neutral agencies such as the Red Cross may distribute the food. Food aid may also be offered to supplement a nation's food supply when shortages occur, or to meet special nutritional needs for mothers and children. Supporters of food aid see this as a way of contributing to a

Figure 14.4. Developing countries must have adequate transportation systems to distribute food trade products to the needy.

nation's economic and agricultural development. However, critics charge that aid has a negative effect when it is used other than for emergency relief. Food aid prices are often lower than the cost to produce the same food locally. As a result, the governments of developing nations may not encourage local food production.

Food Trade. A second method of distributing food is through trade with developing nations. As described in Chapter 11, food exports are an important source of income to American farmers. See Tables 14.2 and 14.3. Trade implies that consumers have the ability to purchase the foods, so trade benefits wealthy consumers in developing nations. Trade is also dependent on transportation and storage of the

Table 14.2   Major Importers and Exporters of Basic Commodities Traded in the World

Wheat	Feed Grains	Soybeans and Products	Beef	Pork
Importers				
U.S.S.R.	Japan	European	United States	United States
China	U.S.S.R.	Community	U.S.S.R.	Japan
Japan	European	Japan	Japan	U.S.S.R.
Egypt	Community	Spain	European	European
Eastern	Mexico	Taiwan	Community	Community
Europe	Taiwan	Mexico	Egypt	Hong Kong
European	South Korea	Eastern Europe	Canada	
Community	Eastern Europe	U.S.S.R.	Saudi Arabia	
Brazil	Saudi Arabia	India		
Exporters				
United States	United States	United States	European	European
Canada	Argentina	Brazil	Community	Community
Australia	Canada	Argentina	Australia	Eastern Europe
France	South Africa	European	Argentina	
Argentina	Thailand	Community	New Zealand	
	Australia		Brazil	
	France		Canada	

Source: E. Marsar Manfredi, "The Importers and the Exporters," United States Department of Agriculture, *U.S. Agriculture in a Global Economy,* 1985 Agricultural Yearbook (Washington, D.C.: United States Government Printing Office, 1985).

Table 14.3   U.S. Agricultural Exports to Southeast Asia, 1981-84

Commodity group	Fiscal Years (in millions of dollars)			
	1981	1982	1983	1984
Animals and Products	62	73	73	75
Grains and Preparations	529	417	466	433
Wheat and Products............	374	339	354	342
Rice	64	7	21	29
Coarse Grains and Products ..	66	48	68	39
Fruits and Preparations	53	57	63	60
Vegetables and Preparations	23	27	29	22
Oilseeds and Products	129	190	195	215
Protein Meal	2	34	27	88
Soybeans	103	139	146	93
Oil and Waxes	29	16	27	35
Tobacco............................	116	176	116	108
Cotton, Ex Linters	209	195	191	235
Other...............................	73	72	66	62
Total............................	1,193	1,207	1,199	1,210

Source: U.S. Bureau of the Census, as cited in C. Nohre, "Agriculture in Asia and the Pacific," United States Department of Agriculture, *U.S. Agriculture in a Global Economy,* 1985 Agricultural Yearbook (Washington, D.C.: United States Government Printing Office, 1985).

food products. Many developing countries do not have the *transportation systems* (roads, railways, and waterways) to move foods quickly and cheaply to the people in need. As a result, tons of grain are often lost to spoilage, pests, or theft. An overall question to be raised is whether it is desirable to create food dependence on international trade or to promote national food self-sufficiency.

Increasing Local Production. Increasing food production within developing nations is the third option for eliminating hunger. See Table 14.4. As described earlier, the green revolution has greatly increased this source of food. Some people argue that the green revolution has substituted fertilizer for land. Environmental problems associated with modern farming may limit long-term increases in food

Table 14.4   Total Grains: Production, Consumption, and Net Exports (in millions of metric tons) for Selected Years

Region	1960/61-1962/63			1969/70-1971/72			1983/84			Rate of Growth of Net Exports
	Production	Consumption	Net Exports[a]	Production	Consumption	Net Exports[a]	Production	Consumption	Net Exports[a]	
										Percent
Developed	316	300	20	403	377	32	459	417	120	8.8
U.S.	168	140	33	209	169	40	206	180	96	5.2
Canada......	24	15	10	35	22	15	48	25	28	5.2
European Community ...	70	91	−22	93	111	−17	124	118	−11	11.9
U.S.S.R. and East Europe ...	180	179	—	237	340	−2	283	318	−34	22.0
Others	54	54	−1	66	75	−6	82	95	−16	16.9
Developing	210	220	−10	285	305	−19	449	510	−67	9.3
East Asia....	20	23	−4	30	38	−9	15	27	−12	6.9
South Asia..	98	99	−2	126	128	−2	256	255	−5	5.0
South and Central America..	42	42	−1	64	61	−3	92	95	−3	6.5
Middle East	30	35	−4	39	49	−9	49	87	−38	9.5
Africa	16	17	−1	21	23	−2	37	47	−9	12.0
World	806	801	—	1,051	1,051	—	1,483	1,545	—	—

Source: United States Department of Agriculture, *World Agricultural Situation,* various issues, as cited in C. Hanrahan, "Feeding the Developing World," United States Department of Agriculture, *U.S. Agriculture in a Global Economy,* 1985 Agricultural Yearbook (Washington, D.C.: United States Government Printing Office, 1985).
[a]Numbers with a minus sign are imports.

production. Other experts question whether the increased production has benefited the people most in need of food.

Local Problems in the Food Supply. Governments of developing nations often fail to address the need for transportation and storage of the increased food supply. Instead, many governments focus financial resources on industrialization and the export of cheaper products in the world market. The farm policies of developing nations often result in land ownership being controlled by a few wealthy people, with the rural poor being displaced. Furthermore, the lack of employment and income opportunities for the poor limits access and ability to purchase the available food. In addition, the food produced locally may be changed from foods needed for a basic diet to cash-generating crops (coffee, sugar, bananas), which can be exported for greater profit. The income generated often goes to the government and the wealthy land owners. An added danger is that unequal patterns of economic growth within a developing nation can result in social unrest.

Ecology of Food Resources

Earth is a planet of *finite,* or limited, geographical area and material resources. In a view from an orbiting spacecraft, Earth

Figure 14.5. Earth seems to be a tranquil paradise when viewed from outer space. We must remember it has limited area and resources.

appears to be a tranquil paradise. The planet's contrasting features of fertile green valleys, snowy mountain peaks, deep blue oceans, and sandy brown deserts are clearly visible. However, hidden from view at this distance are the interactions of humans with their environment.

Earth's environment is composed of a series of interdependent biological systems whose balance is essential to support life. The food chain is part of this fragile network. Biological systems have a limited *carrying capacity,* or ability to support a given number of living things. Systems that are part of our food supply include fisheries, forests, grasslands, and croplands.

As described in Chapter 11, American farmers have had a profound effect on increasing the productivity of croplands. However, some experts warn that overplowing, irrigation, and fertilization have disturbed nature's balance. See Illustration 14.5. Soil erosion and depletion of the ground water are occurring in many areas of the world. Erosion of fertile topsoil threatens future crop production. In addition, billions of tons of soil with fertilizer and pesticide residue are being washed into rivers and lakes. The resulting pollution reduces water quality and endangers fish and wildlife. The increase in world population has also placed a greater demand on fisheries, forests, and grasslands. Again, some experts warn of the damage caused when demand for these resources exceeds the rate of natural renewal. Others who are more optimistic suggest the possibility of a second green revolution brought about by genetic engineering. Research is being conducted on designing plants that will thrive in poor soil without fertilizer.

Illustration 14.5. Irrigated Land in the United States. (Data from the United States Department of Agriculture, *Agricultural Statistics 1980* [Washington, D.C.: United States Government Printing Office, 1980, p. 421], and the United States Department of Commerce, *1978 Census of Agriculture* [Washington, D.C.: United States Government Printing Office, 1981, vol. 1, part 51, p. 9].)

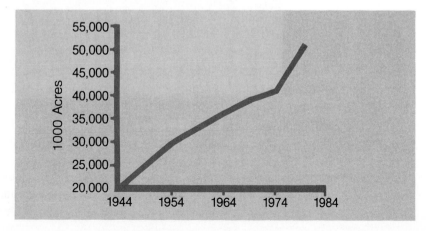

Figure 14.6. Although pesticides and fertilizers can increase crop yields, they can also pollute lakes and rivers and endanger fish and wildlife.

The fact that these resources are commonly held by all people of the earth makes it more difficult to set limits on their use. Who regulates how many fish can be taken from the oceans, or how many animals can graze on an acre of grassland? What impact can overfishing and overgrazing have on future production? Who controls what crops will be produced and to whom they will be marketed?

Protecting and preserving food resources constitute an international challenge, but actions are just as important at the local level as at the national level. Developing respect for food resources is basic to guiding personal decisions about the use and misuse of our food supply.

STRATEGIES FOR MEETING FUTURE FOOD NEEDS

Many ideas surface in a search for solutions to meet future food needs. Suggestions range from revival of food production practices that are centuries old, to creating new foods with twenty-first century scientific methods. *Futurists,* people who analyze and predict social change, say developed nations are moving from an *industrial society* (based on industry) to an *information society* (based on services and information communications). These experts say a global economy is already emerging. Another trend is the movement from a *centralized* (national) structure to *decentralized* (local, state, or regional) control and organization. In this change process, consumers are viewed as becoming more oriented to self-help. One futurist describes this trend as the rise of the *prosumer,* or individual who performs many services and produces products for his or her own use. Against this backdrop of social change, a variety of approaches to meeting future food needs are being proposed.

Agricultural Research

Some experts say the solution to meeting food needs lies in expanding agricultural research. Billions of dollars are being spent by federal and state agencies and private industry on agricultural research. See Table 14.5. Particular emphasis is being given to the process of *genetic engineering.* The process relies on a *gene-splicing* technique that permits scientists to combine genetic material of different plants and thus create new forms of plants. Scientists are working on one application of genetic engineering called *nitrogen fixation.* Bacteria on the roots of legumes (such as soybeans and peanuts) are able to take nitrogen from the air and transform it into nitrates. This process provides fertilizer for the plant to grow. Cereal crops, such as wheat and corn, do not have the ability to collect nitrogen in this way. Scientists are experimenting with transferring the

Table 14.5 Estimates of U.S. Crop Yields and Animal Production Efficiency

Crop	No-New-Technology Environment			Baseline Environment		More-New-Technology Environment	
	1982	1990	2000	1990	2000	1990	2000
Corn (bu per acre)....	115	117	124	119	139	121	150
Cotton (lb per acre) ..	481	502	511	514	554	518	571
Rice (bu per acre)	105	105	109	111	124	115	134
Soybeans (bu per acre)	30	32	35	32	37	33	37
Wheat (bu per acre)..	36	38	41	39	45	40	46
Beef							
Pounds meat per pound feed	0.070	0.071	0.066	0.072	0.072	0.072	0.073
Calves per cow	0.90	0.94	0.96	0.95	1.0	0.95	1.04
Dairy							
Pounds milk per pound feed	0.94	0.94	0.95	0.95	1.03	0.96	1.11
Milk per cow per year (1,000 lb)..	12.3	13.7	15.7	14.0	17.6	14.2	19.3
Poultry							
Pounds meat per pound feed	0.44	0.52	0.53	0.53	0.57	0.53	0.58
Eggs per layer per year	245	255	260	258	275	257	281
Swine							
Pounds meat per pound feed	0.165	0.167	0.17	0.17	0.176	0.17	0.18
Pigs per sow per year	14.4	14.8	15.7	15.2	17.4	15.5	17.8

Source: Office of Technology Assessment, as cited in D. Paarlberg, "Factors Affecting U.S. Production in A.D. 2000," United States Department of Agriculture, *U.S. Agriculture in a Global Economy,* 1985 Agricultural Yearbook (Washington, D.C.: United States Government Printing Office, 1985).

gene for nitrogen fixation in soybeans to wheat and corn. Scientists are also studying ways to splice genes to increase photosynthesis efficiency and thus help plants grow faster. Faster growth would yield greater food production.

Figure 14.7. Scientists are experimenting with transferring the gene from a nitrogen fixation plant to cereal crops.

Alternate Food Production Methods

Growing plants in substances other than soil is a production alternative. *Hydroponics* is the technique of growing crops indoors in nutrient-rich water instead of soil. Plants such as lettuce, cucumbers, and tomatoes are being grown year round in large hydroponic greenhouses. However, one drawback is that the technique is expensive and energy intensive.

Attention is also being given to providing energy-efficient sources of protein. One method is *aquaculture,* the cultivation of fish in an enclosed tank, pond, lake, or reservoir. A species of fish is stocked in the enclosed water area and given supplemental feed. Water temperature, oxygen, nutrients, light, and pests are all controlled by the farmer. The crop of fish is harvested when large enough to market. The world leader in fish farming is China. Catfish and trout are being farmed in the United States.

Developing New Food Sources

Although the idea seems strange to many people, cultivating *algae* (seaweed) and harvesting insects are two approaches being

Figure 14.8. Bean sprouts are inexpensive and nutritious.

considered to increase available protein. Both substances are abundant and offer high-quality protein, but cultural biases make their general acceptance unlikely. However, several alternate foods are gaining popularity. Eating *sprouts,* or seeds harvested a few days after sprouting, is an inexpensive way to increase the nutritional value of a diet. Another food gaining in acceptance is *tofu,* a cheese-like substance made from soybeans.

Developing Regional Food Systems

The United States is often described according to a *region,* or area, such as the southwest, northeast, and midwest. These regions are markedly different in geography, population, economic base, and food resources. The centralized food system described in Chapter 11 provides a similar mix of food products to each region all year round. Transportation and marketing costs contribute significantly to food prices in this system. The process is also highly dependent on petroleum energy. A regionally based food production and distribution network has been proposed as a more responsible approach to managing food resources. The suggestion is recognized by many as having merit. However, achieving a nutritionally balanced and culturally acceptable diet pattern in each region presents a great challenge. To begin with, states would need to diversify food production and use more varied approaches to raising crops, livestock, fish, and poultry. *Intrastate* (within a state) food processing would need to be developed, and more local markets would need to be created.

Consumer demand for high-quality fruits and vegetables has already shown how to increase local markets. Today, more roadside stands sell farm produce directly to the consumer. See Table 14.6. In addition, the number of pick-your-own farms has increased. Many urban areas have a weekly *farmers' market,* or an organized sale of produce by local growers.

During the 1970s food cooperatives reemerged as an alternative to the supermarket. The *cooperative concept,* with member ownership and control of the business, began in the late 1800s. Original cooperatives usually sold products at prevailing prices, but offered members a yearly rebate based on the percent of annual purchases. Most new-style cooperatives have replaced rebates with direct savings to consumers by selling as close to wholesale cost as operating costs permit. Cooperatives generally stay small and responsive to their members.

Gardening and Home Food Preservation

In the late 1970s nearly 31 million Americans reported growing some of their own food. Many others indicated they would grow their own food if they had a place to do so. Home gardening continues to increase in popularity. For those without yard space, *community gardening,* or growing food on public land, is an option. The return on investment is usually very good. One study showed a $19 cost for seeds, gardening supplies, and the like yielded an average of $325 worth of produce. One drawback is that gardening is time consuming.

Many people are also returning to home canning, freezing, and drying of food. This trend offers consumers an alternative to paying for commercial processing and packaging costs. However, there is an investment in equipment and time required. Also, home food preservation requires learning skills to produce safe, high-quality products. Developing these skills allows consumers to regulate what goes into their processed foods.

Table 14.6   Total Gross Sales for Roadside Markets

State	Sales
New York	$ 90,000,000
Pennsylvania	68,550,500
New Jersey	65,000,000
Ohio	35,000,000
Massachusetts	30,375,000
North Carolina	27,700,000
Illinois	25,000,000
California	22,000,000
Maryland	17,200,000
New Hampshire	13,500,000
Arizona	11,500,000
Maine	6,000,000
Tennessee	6,000,000
Virginia	6,000,000
Delaware	5,000,000
Oregon	5,000,000
Vermont	4,550,000
Oklahoma	4,000,000
Missouri	3,800,000
Kentucky	2,700,000
Alabama	2,170,000
West Virginia	1,287,000
Georgia	1,250,000
Utah	640,000
Alaska	500,000
Texas	246,016
Nevada	150,000
Montana	120,000
Nebraska	100,000
North Dakota	24,000
Wyoming	5,000
Total: 31 states	$455,367,516

Source: *The Cornucopia Project Newsletter,* Vol. 2, No. 1, Cornucopia Project of the Regenerative Agriculture Association (RAA), 222 Main St., Emmaus, PA 18049.

Figure 14.9. Home gardening continues to increase in popularity.

Developing a Prudent Diet Pattern

Consumer preferences are reflected in food purchases. The food system is generally responsive to the consumer's demands. As described in Chapter 12, American eating patterns are changing. As consumers modify their diets to decrease fat, cholesterol, sugar, and salt and to increase complex carbohydrates and fiber, the demand for various types of foods changes. The emerging prudent diet pattern focuses on obtaining more Calories in the diet from grains, fruits, and vegetables and fewer from fats and meat.

Some people promote a vegetarian diet pattern as being more healthful as well as more ecologically responsible.

Research conducted by Dr. David Pimentel at Cornell University indicates that animal foods require a much greater input of water and petroleum energy than do plants for an equal amount of protein produced. About 3,000 to 15,000 gallons of water are needed to produce one pound of protein from beef, but only 1,065 gallons are needed to produce a pound of protein from soybeans. Plants also require much lower amounts of fossil fuels than do animals to yield one Calorie of protein. It is estimated that for feedlot beef 78 Calories of fossil fuel are expended to yield 1 Calorie of protein. Similarly, for each Calorie of protein obtained, 36 Calories are expended for milk,

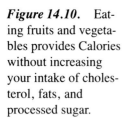

Figure 14.10. Eating fruits and vegetables provides Calories without increasing your intake of cholesterol, fats, and processed sugar.

22 for broiler chickens, 13 for eggs, 10 for range-fed beef, 3.6 for corn, 3.4 for wheat, and 2 for soybeans.

FORMING YOUR OWN DECISIONS ON FOOD ISSUES

World food issues are complex, and proposed solutions require careful analysis. A person's viewpoint on the causes of world hunger serves as the platform for judging solutions. What global approaches or personal actions are beneficial in ensuring an adequate food supply for everyone?

Food issues can be debated on several levels: technical, ecological, economic, political, social, and moral. For example, an agricultural expert may say, "technically speaking," that modern farming methods make it possible to feed 6 billion people. The assertion should be judged on the evidence presented.

A debate of proposed options requires accepting or rejecting the claim being made. Rational reasoning of the issue means taking a step-by-step look at the merits of the claim. To judge the merits of any claim, identify the facts presented. Do the facts support the claim? What kind of evidence is provided to show that the facts are sound and relevant? To what degree and under what conditions is the claim being made valid? Finally, are there any exceptions to the claim?

The same approach can be used to debate food issues on a moral level. Considerations to be made in ethical decisions include assessing actions or results as: (1) acceptable or unacceptable; or (2) preferable. Many of the food issues have moral overtones. A proposed social solution to control world population may be to allow famine to take its natural course. For many people this option is morally unacceptable. Others might argue that the preferable option is to share food resources equally. A rebuttal to this suggestion might be that resources held in common result in greedy overproduction without consideration of the carrying capacity of the earth. Moral considerations place overriding effects or priority ranking on the solutions proposed at technical, political, economic, and ecological levels.

As a person sharing the finite resources of the planet Earth, you are a participant in the search for answers to the food issues that face the world today. Eating for health is a goal for all people. Your food choices *do* make a difference!

CHECK YOUR PROGRESS

1. Define malnutrition and undernutrition.
2. List the three types of information collected to assess nutritional status.
3. Describe the differences between marasmus and kwashiorkor.
4. Identify several nations in which a large portion of the population is undernourished.
5. List three major factors that can contribute to hunger and malnutrition.
6. Describe what is meant by the green revolution. What impact has it had on world food production?
7. Experts currently report that global food production averages 3,000 Calories per person per day. Thus, even with adequate production, why are some people hungry?
8. Birth rates are generally declining, so why is population growth a concern?
9. Under what program does the United States distribute food to needy nations? Explain the concerns raised about this distribution.

10. What drawbacks does food trade with developing nations have in meeting the needs of the hungry?
11. Identify the problems associated with increasing food production within developing nations.
12. Define carrying capacity. What ecological problems are associated with modern farming methods?
13. Describe some of the social and economic changes predicted by futurists.
14. How might genetic engineering increase food production?
15. Describe the production methods of hydroponics and aquaculture.
16. Identify several items that are not eaten by the general population, but are nutritious and could be consumed.
17. Describe the advantages and disadvantages of a regional food distribution system.
18. Describe several alternatives to purchasing food at a supermarket.
19. What would happen to the demand for highly processed foods, particularly meats, snacks, and dessert items, if more people followed a prudent diet?
20. Describe the thought process through which rational stands on food issues can be developed.

APPENDIX A

NUTRITIVE VALUE OF THE EDIBLE
PARTS OF FOODS*

*Source: U.S. Department of Agriculture, "Nutritive Value of Foods," Home and Garden Bulletin No. 72 (Washington, D.C.: U.S. Government Printing Office, 1981).

(Dashes (—) denote lack of reliable data for a constituent believed to be present in measurable amount)

NUTRIENTS IN INDICATED QUANTITY

Item No. (A)	Foods, approximate measures, units, and weight (edible part unless footnotes indicate otherwise) (B)		Grams	Water (C) Per cent	Food energy (D) Calories	Pro-tein (E) Grams	Fat (F) Grams	Fatty Acids Satu-rated (total) (G) Grams	Unsaturated Oleic (H) Grams	Lino-leic (I) Grams	Carbo-hydrate (J) Grams	Calcium (K) Milligrams	Phos-phorus (L) Milligrams	Iron (M) Milligrams	Potas-sium (N) Milligrams	Vitamin A value (O) International units	Thiamin (P) Milligrams	Ribo-flavin (Q) Milligrams	Niacin (R) Milligrams	Ascorbic acid (S) Milligrams
	DAIRY PRODUCTS (CHEESE, CREAM, IMITATION CREAM, MILK; RELATED PRODUCTS)																			
	Butter. See Fats, oils; related products, items 103-108.																			
	Cheese:																			
	Natural:																			
1	Blue	1 oz	28	42	100	6	8	5.3	1.9	0.2	1	150	110	0.1	73	200	0.01	0.11	0.3	0
2	Camembert (3 wedges per 4-oz container)	1 wedge	38	52	115	8	9	5.8	2.2	.2	Trace	147	132	.1	71	350	.01	.19	.2	0
	Cheddar:																			
3	Cut pieces	1 oz	28	37	115	7	9	6.1	2.1	.2	Trace	204	145	.2	28	300	.01	.11	Trace	0
4		1 cu in	17.2	37	70	4	6	3.7	1.3	.1	Trace	124	88	.1	17	180	Trace	.06	Trace	0
5	Shredded	1 cup	113	37	455	28	37	24.2	8.5	.7	1	815	579	.8	111	1,200	.03	.42	.1	0
	Cottage (curd not pressed down):																			
	Creamed (cottage cheese, 4% fat):																			
6	Large curd	1 cup	225	79	235	28	10	6.4	2.4	.2	6	135	297	.3	190	370	.05	.37	.3	Trace
7	Small curd	1 cup	210	79	220	26	9	6.0	2.2	.2	6	126	277	.3	177	340	.04	.34	.3	Trace
8	Low fat (2%)	1 cup	226	79	205	31	4	2.8	1.0	.1	8	155	340	.4	217	160	.05	.42	.3	Trace
9	Low fat (1%)	1 cup	226	82	165	28	2	1.5	.5	.1	6	138	302	.3	193	80	.05	.37	.3	Trace
10	Uncreamed (cottage cheese dry curd, less than 1/2% fat)	1 cup	145	80	125	25	1	.4	.1	Trace	3	46	151	.3	47	40	.04	.21	.2	0
11	Cream	1 oz	28	54	100	2	10	6.2	2.4	.2	1	23	30	.3	34	400	Trace	.06	Trace	0
	Mozzarella, made with—																			
12	Whole milk	1 oz	28	48	90	6	7	4.4	1.7	.2	1	163	117	.1	21	260	Trace	.08	Trace	0
13	Part skim milk	1 oz	28	49	80	8	5	3.1	1.2	.1	1	207	149	.1	27	180	.01	.10	Trace	0
	Parmesan, grated:																			
14	Cup, not pressed down	1 cup	100	18	455	42	30	19.1	7.7	.3	4	1,376	807	1.0	107	700	.05	.39	.3	0
15	Tablespoon	1 tbsp	5	18	25	2	2	1.0	.4	Trace	Trace	69	40	Trace	5	40	Trace	.02	Trace	0
16	Ounce	1 oz	28	18	130	12	9	5.4	2.2	.1	1	390	229	.3	30	200	.01	.11	.1	0
17	Provolone	1 oz	28	41	100	7	8	4.8	1.7	.1	1	214	141	.1	39	230	.01	.09	Trace	0
	Ricotta, made with—																			
18	Whole milk	1 cup	246	72	430	28	32	20.4	7.1	.7	7	509	389	.9	257	1,210	.03	.48	.3	0
19	Part skim milk	1 cup	246	74	340	28	19	12.1	4.7	.5	13	669	449	1.1	308	1,060	.05	.46	.2	0
20	Romano	1 oz	28	31	110	9	8	—	—	—	1	302	215	—	—	160	—	.11	—	0
21	Swiss	1 oz	28	37	105	8	8	5.0	1.7	.2	1	272	171	Trace	31	240	.01	.10	Trace	0
	Pasteurized process cheese:																			
22	American	1 oz	28	39	105	6	9	5.6	2.1	.2	Trace	174	211	.1	46	340	.01	.10	Trace	0
23	Swiss	1 oz	28	42	95	7	7	4.5	1.7	.1	1	219	216	.2	61	230	Trace	.08	Trace	0
24	Pasteurized process cheese food, American	1 oz	28	43	95	6	7	4.4	1.7	.1	2	163	130	.2	79	260	.01	.13	Trace	0
25	Pasteurized process cheese spread, American	1 oz	28	48	80	5	6	3.8	1.5	.1	2	159	202	.1	69	220	.01	.12	Trace	0
	Cream, sweet:																			
26	Half-and-half (cream and milk)	1 cup	242	81	315	7	28	17.3	7.0	.6	10	254	230	.2	314	260	.08	.36	.2	2
27		1 tbsp	15	81	20	Trace	2	1.1	.4	Trace	1	16	14	Trace	19	20	.01	.02	Trace	Trace
28	Light, coffee, or table	1 cup	240	74	470	6	46	28.8	11.7	1.0	9	231	192	.1	292	1,730	.08	.36	.1	2
29		1 tbsp	15	74	30	Trace	3	1.8	.7	.1	1	14	12	Trace	18	110	Trace	.02	Trace	Trace

(A)	(B)	(C)	(D)	(E)	(F)	(G)	(H)	(I)	(J)	(K)	(L)	(M)	(N)	(O)	(P)	(Q)	(R)	(S)
	Whipping, unwhipped (volume about double when whipped):																	
30	Light — 1 cup — 239	64	700	5	74	46.2	18.3	1.5	7	166	146	0.1	231	2,690	0.06	0.30	0.1	1
31	1 tbsp — 15	64	45	Trace	5	2.9	1.1	.1	Trace	10	9	Trace	15	170	Trace	.02	Trace	Trace
32	Heavy — 1 cup — 238	58	820	5	88	54.8	22.2	2.0	7	154	149	.1	179	3,500	.05	.26	.1	1
33	1 tbsp — 15	58	80	Trace	6	3.4	1.4	.1	Trace	10	9	Trace	11	220	Trace	.02	Trace	Trace
34	Whipped topping, (pressurized) — 1 cup — 60	61	155	2	13	8.3	3.4	.3	7	61	54	Trace	88	550	.02	.04	Trace	0
35	1 tbsp — 3	61	10	Trace	1	.4	.2	Trace	Trace	3	3	Trace	4	30	Trace	Trace	Trace	0
36	Cream, sour — 1 cup — 230	71	495	7	48	30.0	12.1	1.1	10	268	195	.1	331	1,820	.08	.34	.2	2
37	1 tbsp — 12	71	25	Trace	3	1.6	.6	.1	1	14	10	Trace	17	90	Trace	.02	Trace	Trace
	Cream products, imitation (made with vegetable fat): Sweet: Creamers:																	
38	Liquid (frozen) — 1 cup — 245	77	335	2	24	22.8	.3	Trace	28	23	157	.1	467	[2]220	0	0	0	0
39	1 tbsp — 15	77	20	Trace	1	1.4	Trace	0	2	1	10	Trace	29	[2]10	0	0	0	0
40	Powdered — 1 cup — 94	2	515	5	33	30.6	.9	Trace	52	21	397	Trace	763	[1]190	0	.16	0	0
41	1 tsp — 2	2	10	Trace	1	.7	Trace	0	1	Trace	8	Trace	16	[1]Trace	0	Trace	0	0
	Whipped topping:																	
42	Frozen — 1 cup — 75	50	240	1	19	16.3	1.0	.2	17	5	6	.1	14	[1]650	0	0	0	0
43	1 tbsp — 4	50	15	Trace	1	.9	.1	Trace	1	Trace	Trace	Trace	Trace	[1]30	0	0	0	0
44	Powdered, made with whole milk. — 1 cup — 80	67	150	3	10	8.5	.6	.1	13	72	69	Trace	121	[2]290	.02	.09	Trace	1
45	1 tbsp — 4	67	10	Trace	Trace	.4	Trace	Trace	1	4	3	Trace	6	[2]10	Trace	Trace	Trace	Trace
46	Pressurized — 1 cup — 70	60	185	1	16	13.2	1.4	.2	11	4	13	Trace	13	[1]330	0	0	0	0
47	1 tbsp — 4	60	10	Trace	1	.8	.1	Trace	Trace	Trace	1	Trace	1	[1]20	0	0	0	0
48	Sour dressing (imitation sour cream) made with nonfat dry milk. — 1 cup — 235	75	415	8	39	31.2	4.4	1.1	11	266	205	.1	380	[1]120	.09	.38	.2	2
49	1 tbsp — 12	75	20	Trace	2	1.6	.2	.1	1	14	10	Trace	19	[1]Trace	.01	.02	Trace	Trace
	Ice cream. See Milk desserts, frozen (items 75–80).																	
	Ice milk. See Milk desserts, frozen (items 81–83).																	
	Milk: Fluid:																	
50	Whole (3.3% fat) — 1 cup — 244	88	150	8	8	5.1	2.1	.2	11	291	228	.1	370	[2]310	.09	.40	.2	2
	Lowfat (2%):																	
51	No milk solids added — 1 cup — 244	89	120	8	5	2.9	1.2	.1	12	297	232	.1	377	500	.10	.40	.2	2
52	Milk solids added: Label claim less than 10 g of protein per cup. — 1 cup — 245	89	125	9	5	2.9	1.2	.1	12	313	245	.1	397	500	.10	.42	.2	2
53	Label claim 10 or more grams of protein per cup (protein fortified). — 1 cup — 246	88	135	10	5	3.0	1.2	.1	14	352	276	.1	447	500	.11	.48	.2	3
	Lowfat (1%):																	
54	No milk solids added — 1 cup — 244	90	100	8	3	1.6	.7	.1	12	300	235	.1	381	500	.10	.41	.2	2
55	Milk solids added: Label claim less than 10 g of protein per cup. — 1 cup — 245	90	105	9	2	1.5	.6	.1	12	313	245	.1	397	500	.10	.42	.2	2
56	Label claim 10 or more grams of protein per cup (protein forti-fied). — 1 cup — 246	89	120	10	3	1.8	.7	.1	14	349	273	.1	444	500	.11	.47	.2	3
	Nonfat (skim):																	
57	No milk solids added — 1 cup — 245	91	85	8	Trace	.3	.1	Trace	12	302	247	.1	406	500	.09	.34	.2	2

[1] Vitamin A value is largely from beta-carotene used for coloring. Riboflavin value for items 40–41 apply to products with added riboflavin.

[2] Applies to product without added vitamin A. With added vitamin A, value is 500 International Units (I.U.).

(Dashes (—) denote lack of reliable data for a constituent believed to be present in measurable amount)

Item No. (A)	Foods, approximate measures, units, and weight (edible part unless footnotes indicate otherwise) (B)		(Grams)	Water (C) Percent	Food energy (D) Calories	Protein (E) Grams	Fat (F) Grams	Fatty Acids Saturated (total) (G) Grams	Unsaturated Oleic (H) Grams	Linoleic (I) Grams	Carbohydrate (J) Grams	Calcium (K) Milligrams	Phosphorus (L) Milligrams	Iron (M) Milligrams	Potassium (N) Milligrams	Vitamin A value (O) International units	Thiamin (P) Milligrams	Riboflavin (Q) Milligrams	Niacin (R) Milligrams	Ascorbic acid (S) Milligrams
	DAIRY PRODUCTS (CHEESE, CREAM, IMITATION CREAM, MILK; RELATED PRODUCTS)—Con.																			
	Milk—Continued																			
	Fluid—Continued																			
	Nonfat (skim)—Continued																			
	Milk solids added:																			
58	Label claim less than 10 g of protein per cup.	1 cup	245	90	90	9	1	0.4	0.1	Trace	12	316	255	0.1	418	500	0.10	0.43	0.2	2
59	Label claim 10 or more grams of protein per cup (protein fortified).	1 cup	246	89	100	10	1	.4	.1	Trace	14	352	275	.1	446	500	.11	.48	.2	3
	Buttermilk:																			
60	Buttermilk	1 cup	245	90	100	8	2	1.3	.5	Trace	12	285	219	.1	371	[3]80	.08	.38	.1	2
	Canned:																			
	Evaporated, unsweetened:																			
61	Whole milk	1 cup	252	74	340	17	19	11.6	5.3	0.4	25	657	510	.5	764	[3]610	.12	.80	.5	5
62	Skim milk	1 cup	255	79	200	19	1	.3	.1	Trace	29	738	497	.7	845	[4]1,000	.11	.79	.4	3
63	Sweetened, condensed	1 cup	306	27	980	24	27	16.8	6.7	.7	166	868	775	.6	1,136	[3]1,000	.28	1.27	.6	8
	Dried:																			
64	Buttermilk	1 cup	120	3	465	41	7	4.3	1.7	.2	59	1,421	1,119	.4	1,910	[3]260	.47	1.90	1.1	7
	Nonfat instant:																			
65	Envelope, net wt., 3.2 oz[5]	1 envelope	91	4	325	32	Trace	.4	.1	Trace	47	1,120	896	.3	1,552	[6]2,160	.38	1.59	.8	5
66	Cup[7]	1 cup	68	4	245	24	Trace	.3	.1	Trace	35	837	670	.2	1,160	[6]1,610	.28	1.19	.6	4
	Milk beverages:																			
	Chocolate milk (commercial):																			
67	Regular	1 cup	250	82	210	8	8	5.3	2.2	.2	26	280	251	.6	417	[3]300	.09	.41	.3	2
68	Lowfat (2%)	1 cup	250	84	180	8	5	3.1	1.3	.1	26	284	254	.6	422	500	.10	.42	.3	2
69	Lowfat (1%)	1 cup	250	85	160	8	3	1.5	.7	.1	26	287	257	.6	426	500	.10	.40	.2	2
70	Eggnog (commercial)	1 cup	254	74	340	10	19	11.3	5.0	.6	34	330	278	.5	420	890	.09	.48	.3	4
	Malted milk, home-prepared with 1 cup of whole milk and 2 to 3 heaping tsp of malted milk powder (about 3/4 oz):																			
71	Chocolate	1 cup of milk plus 3/4 oz of powder.	265	81	235	9	9	5.5	—	—	29	304	265	.5	500	330	.14	.43	.7	2
72	Natural	1 cup of milk plus 3/4 oz of powder.	265	81	235	11	10	6.0	—	—	27	347	307	.3	529	380	.20	.54	1.3	2
	Shakes, thick:[8]																			
73	Chocolate, container, net wt., 10.6 oz.	1 container	300	72	355	9	8	5.0	2.0	.2	63	396	378	.9	672	260	.14	.67	.4	0
74	Vanilla, container, net wt., 11 oz.	1 container	313	74	350	12	9	5.9	2.4	.2	56	457	361	.3	572	360	.09	.61	.5	0
	Milk desserts, frozen:																			
	Ice cream:																			
	Regular (about 11% fat):																			
75	Hardened	1/2 gal	1,064	61	2,155	38	115	71.3	28.8	2.6	254	1,406	1,075	1.0	2,052	4,340	.42	2.63	1.1	6
76		1 cup	133	61	270	5	14	8.9	3.6	.3	32	176	134	.1	257	540	.05	.33	.1	1
77		3-fl oz container	50	61	100	2	5	3.4	1.4	.1	12	66	51	Trace	96	200	.02	.12	.1	Trace
78	Soft serve (frozen custard)	1 cup	173	60	375	7	23	13.5	5.9	.6	38	236	199	.4	338	790	.08	.45	.2	1
79	Rich (about 16% fat), hardened	1/2 gal	1,188	59	2,805	33	190	118.3	47.8	4.3	256	1,213	927	.8	1,771	7,200	.36	2.27	.9	5
80		1 cup	148	59	350	4	24	14.7	6.0	.5	32	151	115	.1	221	900	.04	.28	.1	1
	Ice milk:																			
81	Hardened (about 4.3% fat)	1/2 gal	1,048	69	1,470	41	45	28.1	11.3	1.0	232	1,409	1,035	1.5	2,117	1,710	.61	2.78	.9	6
82		1 cup	131	69	185	5	6	3.5	1.4	.1	29	176	129	.1	265	210	.08	.35	.1	1

(A)	(B)	(C)	(D)	(E)	(F)	(G)	(H)	(I)	(J)	(K)	(L)	(M)	(N)	(O)	(P)	(Q)	(R)	(S)
83	Soft serve (about 2.6% fat) 1 cup	70	225	8	5	2.9	1.2	0.7	38	274	202	0.3	412	180	0.12	0.54	0.2	1
84	Sherbet (about 2% fat) 1/2 gal	66	2,160	17	31	19.0	7.7	.7	469	827	594	2.5	1,585	1,480	.26	.71	1.0	31
85	1 cup	66	270	2	4	2.4	1.0	.1	59	103	74	.3	198	190	.03	.09	.1	4
86	Milk desserts, other: Custard, baked 1 cup	77	305	14	15	6.8	5.4	.7	29	297	310	1.1	387	930	.11	.50	.3	1
	Puddings: From home recipe: Starch base:																	
87	Chocolate 1 cup	66	385	8	12	7.6	3.3	.3	67	250	255	1.3	445	390	.05	.36	.3	2
88	Vanilla (blancmange) 1 cup	76	285	9	10	6.2	2.5	.2	41	298	232	Trace	352	410	.08	.41	.3	2
89	Tapioca cream 1 cup	72	220	8	8	4.1	2.5	.5	28	173	180	.7	223	480	.07	.30	.2	2
	From mix (chocolate) and milk:																	
90	Regular (cooked) 1 cup	70	320	9	8	4.3	2.6	.2	59	265	247	.8	354	340	.05	.39	.3	2
91	Instant 1 cup	69	325	8	7	3.6	2.2	.3	63	374	237	1.3	335	340	.08	.39	.3	2
	Yogurt: With added milk solids: Made with lowfat milk:																	
92	Fruit-flavored 1 container, net wt., 8 oz	75	230	10	3	1.8	.6	.1	42	343	269	.2	439	[10]120	.08	.40	.2	1
93	Plain 1 container, net wt., 8 oz	85	145	12	4	2.3	.8	.1	16	415	326	.2	531	[10]150	.10	.49	.3	2
94	Made with nonfat milk 1 container, net wt., 8 oz	85	125	13	Trace	.3	.3	Trace	17	452	355	.2	579	[10]20	.11	.53	.3	2
	Without added milk solids:																	
95	Made with whole milk 1 container, net wt., 8 oz	88	140	8	7	4.8	1.7	.1	11	274	215	.1	351	280	.07	.32	.2	1

EGGS

(A)	(B)	(C)	(D)	(E)	(F)	(G)	(H)	(I)	(J)	(K)	(L)	(M)	(N)	(O)	(P)	(Q)	(R)	(S)
	Eggs, large (24 oz per dozen): Raw:																		
96	Whole, without shell 1 egg	75	80	6	6	1.7	2.0	.6	1	28	90	1.0	65	260	.04	.15	Trace	0
97	White 1 white	88	15	3	Trace	0	0	0	Trace	4	4	Trace	45	0	Trace	.09	Trace	0
98	Yolk 1 yolk	49	65	3	6	1.7	2.1	.6	Trace	26	86	.9	15	310	.04	.07	Trace	0
	Cooked:																		
99	Fried in butter 1 egg	72	85	5	6	2.4	2.2	.6	1	26	80	.9	58	290	.03	.13	Trace	0
100	Hard-cooked, shell removed 1 egg	75	80	6	6	1.7	2.0	.6	1	28	90	1.0	65	260	.04	.14	Trace	0
101	Poached 1 egg	74	80	6	6	1.7	2.0	.6	1	28	90	1.0	65	260	.04	.13	Trace	0
102	Scrambled (milk added) in butter. Also omelet. 1 egg	76	95	6	7	2.8	2.3	.6	1	47	97	.9	85	310	.04	.16	Trace	0

FATS, OILS; RELATED PRODUCTS

(A)	(B)	(C)	(D)	(E)	(F)	(G)	(H)	(I)	(J)	(K)	(L)	(M)	(N)	(O)	(P)	(Q)	(R)	(S)
	Butter: Regular (1 brick or 4 sticks per lb):																		
103	Stick (1/2 cup) 1 stick	16	815	1	92	57.3	23.1	2.1	Trace	27	26	.2	29	[11]3,470	.01	.04	Trace	0
104	Tablespoon (about 1/8 stick) 1 tbsp	16	100	Trace	12	7.2	2.9	.3	Trace	3	3	Trace	4	[11]430	Trace	Trace	Trace	0
105	Pat (1 in square, 1/3 in high; 90 per lb) 1 pat	16	35	Trace	4	2.5	1.0	.1	Trace	1	1	Trace	1	[11]150	Trace	Trace	Trace	0
	Whipped (6 sticks or two 8-oz containers per lb):																		
106	Stick (1/2 cup) 1 stick	16	540	1	61	38.2	15.4	1.4	Trace	18	17	.1	20	[11]2,310	Trace	.03	Trace	0
107	Tablespoon (about 1/8 stick) 1 tbsp	16	65	Trace	8	4.7	1.9	.2	Trace	2	2	Trace	2	[11]290	Trace	Trace	Trace	0
108	Pat (1 1/4 in square, 1/3 in high; 120 per lb) 1 pat	16	25	Trace	3	1.9	.8	.1	Trace	1	1	Trace	1	[11]120	0	Trace	Trace	0

[3] Applies to product without vitamin A added.
[4] Applies to product with added vitamin A. Without added vitamin A, value is 20 International Units (I.J.).
[5] Yields 1 qt of fluid milk when reconstituted according to package directions.
[6] Applies to product with added vitamin A.
[7] Weight applies to product with label claim of 1 1/3 cups equal 3.2 oz.
[8] Applies to products made from thick shake mixes and that do not contain added ice cream. Products made from milk shake mixes are higher in fat and usually contain added ice cream.
[9] Content of fat, vitamin A, and carbohydrate varies. Consult the label when precise values are needed for special diets.
[10] Applies to product made with milk containing no added vitamin A.
[11] Based on year-round average.

(Dashes (—) denote lack of reliable data for a constituent believed to be present in measurable amount)

NUTRIENTS IN INDICATED QUANTITY

Item No. (A)	Foods, approximate measures, units, and weight (edible part unless footnotes indicate otherwise) (B)	Weight Grams	Water Percent (C)	Food energy Calories (D)	Protein Grams (E)	Fat Grams (F)	Fatty Acids Saturated (total) Grams (G)	Unsaturated Oleic Grams (H)	Unsaturated Linoleic Grams (I)	Carbohydrate Grams (J)	Calcium Milligrams (K)	Phosphorus Milligrams (L)	Iron Milligrams (M)	Potassium Milligrams (N)	Vitamin A value International units (O)	Thiamin Milligrams (P)	Riboflavin Milligrams (Q)	Niacin Milligrams (R)	Ascorbic acid Milligrams (S)
	FATS, OILS; RELATED PRODUCTS—Con.																		
109	Fats, cooking (vegetable shortenings). — 1 cup	200	0	1,770	0	200	48.8	88.2	48.4	0	0	0	0	0	—	0	0	0	0
110	1 tbsp	13	0	110	0	13	3.2	5.7	3.1	0	0	0	0	0	—	0	0	0	0
111	Lard — 1 cup	205	0	1,850	0	205	81.0	83.8	20.5	0	0	0	0	0	0	0	0	0	0
112	1 tbsp	13	0	115	0	13	5.1	5.3	1.3	0	0	0	0	0	0	0	0	0	0
	Margarine: Regular (1 brick or 4 sticks per lb):																		
113	Stick (1/2 cup) — 1 stick	113	16	815	1	92	16.7	42.9	24.9	Trace	27	26	.2	29	[1,2]3,750	.01	.04	Trace	0
114	Tablespoon (about 1/8 stick) — 1 tbsp	14	16	100	Trace	12	2.1	5.3	3.1	Trace	3	3	Trace	4	[1,2]470	Trace	Trace	Trace	0
115	Pat (1 in square, 1/3 in high; 90 per lb) — 1 pat	5	16	35	Trace	4	.7	1.9	1.1	Trace	1	1	Trace	1	[1,2]170	Trace	Trace	Trace	0
116	Soft, two 8-oz containers per lb — 1 container	227	16	1,635	1	184	32.5	71.5	65.4	Trace	53	52	.4	59	[1,2]7,500	.01	.08	.1	0
117	1 tbsp	14	16	100	Trace	12	2.0	4.5	4.1	Trace	3	3	Trace	4	[1,2]470	Trace	Trace	Trace	0
	Whipped (6 sticks per lb):																		
118	Stick (1/2 cup) — 1 stick	76	16	545	Trace	61	11.2	28.7	16.7	Trace	18	17	.2	20	[1,2]2,500	Trace	.03	Trace	0
119	Tablespoon (about 1/8 stick) — 1 tbsp	9	16	70	Trace	8	1.4	3.6	2.1	Trace	2	2	Trace	2	[1,2]310	Trace	Trace	Trace	0
	Oils, salad or cooking: Corn:																		
120	1 cup	218	0	1,925	0	218	27.7	53.6	125.1	0	0	0	0	0	—	0	0	0	0
121	1 tbsp	14	0	120	0	14	1.7	3.3	7.8	0	0	0	0	0	—	0	0	0	0
	Olive:																		
122	1 cup	216	0	1,910	0	216	30.7	154.4	17.7	0	0	0	0	0	—	0	0	0	0
123	1 tbsp	14	0	120	0	14	1.9	9.7	1.1	0	0	0	0	0	—	0	0	0	0
	Peanut:																		
124	1 cup	216	0	1,910	0	216	37.4	98.5	67.0	0	0	0	0	0	—	0	0	0	0
125	1 tbsp	14	0	120	0	14	2.3	6.2	4.2	0	0	0	0	0	—	0	0	0	0
	Safflower:																		
126	1 cup	218	0	1,925	0	218	20.5	25.9	159.8	0	0	0	0	0	—	0	0	0	0
127	1 tbsp	14	0	120	0	14	1.3	1.6	10.0	0	0	0	0	0	—	0	0	0	0
	Soybean oil, hydrogenated (partially hardened).																		
128	1 cup	218	0	1,925	0	218	31.8	93.1	75.6	0	0	0	0	0	—	0	0	0	0
129	1 tbsp	14	0	120	0	14	2.0	5.8	4.7	0	0	0	0	0	—	0	0	0	0
130	Soybean-cottonseed oil blend, hydrogenated. — 1 cup	218	0	1,925	0	218	38.2	63.0	99.6	0	0	0	0	0	—	0	0	0	0
131	1 tbsp	14	0	120	0	14	2.4	3.9	6.2	0	0	0	0	0	—	0	0	0	0
	Salad dressings: Commercial: Blue cheese:																		
132	Regular — 1 tbsp	15	32	75	1	8	1.6	1.7	3.8	1	12	11	Trace	6	30	Trace	.02	Trace	Trace
133	Low calorie (5 Cal per tsp) — 1 tbsp	16	84	10	Trace	1	.5	.3	Trace	1	10	8	Trace	5	30	Trace	.01	Trace	Trace
	French:																		
134	Regular — 1 tbsp	16	39	65	Trace	6	1.1	1.3	3.2	3	2	2	.1	13	—	—	—	—	—
135	Low calorie (5 Cal per tsp) — 1 tbsp	16	77	15	Trace	Trace	.1	.1	.4	2	2	2	.1	13	—	—	—	—	—
	Italian:																		
136	Regular — 1 tbsp	15	28	85	Trace	9	1.6	1.9	4.7	1	2	1	Trace	2	Trace	Trace	Trace	Trace	—
137	Low calorie (2 Cal per tsp) — 1 tbsp	15	90	10	Trace	1	.1	.1	.4	Trace	2	1	Trace	2	Trace	Trace	Trace	Trace	—
138	Mayonnaise — 1 tbsp	14	15	100	Trace	11	2.0	2.4	5.6	Trace	3	4	.1	5	40	Trace	.01	Trace	—
	Mayonnaise type:																		
139	Regular — 1 tbsp	15	41	65	Trace	6	1.1	1.4	3.2	2	2	4	Trace	1	30	Trace	Trace	Trace	Trace
140	Low calorie (8 Cal per tsp) — 1 tbsp	16	81	20	Trace	2	.4	1.0	1.0	2	3	3	Trace	1	40	Trace	Trace	Trace	Trace
141	Tartar sauce, regular — 1 tbsp	14	34	75	Trace	8	1.5	1.8	4.1	1	3	4	Trace	11	30	Trace	Trace	Trace	Trace
	Thousand Island:																		
142	Regular — 1 tbsp	16	32	80	Trace	8	1.4	1.7	4.0	2	2	3	.1	18	50	Trace	Trace	Trace	Trace
143	Low calorie (10 Cal per tsp) — 1 tbsp	15	68	25	Trace	2	.4	.4	1.0	2	2	3	.1	17	50	Trace	Trace	Trace	Trace
	From home recipe:																		
144	Cooked type[11] — 1 tbsp	16	68	25	1	2	.5	.6	.3	2	14	15	.1	19	80	.01	.03	Trace	Trace

FISH, SHELLFISH, MEAT, POULTRY; RELATED PRODUCTS

Columns: (A) Item No. — (B) Food, measure, weight (g) — (C) Water (%) — (D) Food energy — (E) Protein — (F) Fat — (G) Saturated — (H) Oleic — (I) Linoleic — (J) Carbohydrate — (K) Calcium — (L) Phosphorus — (M) Iron — (N) Potassium — (O) Vitamin A — (P) Thiamin — (Q) Riboflavin — (R) Niacin — (S) Ascorbic acid

(A)	(B)	(C)	(D)	(E)	(F)	(G)	(H)	(I)	(J)	(K)	(L)	(M)	(N)	(O)	(P)	(Q)	(R)	(S)
	Fish and shellfish:																	
145	Bluefish, baked with butter or margarine — 3 oz — 85	68	135	22	4	--	--	--	0	25	244	0.6	--	40	0.09	0.08	1.6	--
	Clams:																	
146	Raw, meat only — 3 oz — 85	82	65	11	1	--	--	--	2	59	138	5.2	154	90	.08	.15	1.1	8
147	Canned, solids and liquid — 3 oz — 85	86	45	7	1	--	Trace	Trace	2	47	116	3.5	119	--	.01	.09	.9	--
148	Crabmeat (white or king), canned, not pressed down — 1 cup — 135	77	135	24	3	0.2	0.4	0.1	1	61	246	1.1	149	--	.11	.11	2.6	--
149	Fish sticks, breaded, cooked, frozen (stick, 4 by 1 by 1/2 in) — 1 fish stick or 1 oz — 28	66	50	5	3	--	--	--	2	3	47	.1	--	0	.01	.02	.5	--
150	Haddock, breaded, fried[14] — 3 oz — 85	66	140	17	5	1.4	2.2	1.2	5	34	210	1.0	296	--	.03	.06	2.7	--
151	Ocean perch, breaded, fried[14] — 1 fillet — 85	59	195	16	11	2.7	4.4	2.3	6	28	192	1.1	242	--	.10	.10	1.6	2
152	Oysters, raw, meat only (13-19 medium Selects) — 1 cup — 240	85	160	20	4	1.3	1.7	.1	8	226	343	13.2	290	740	.34	.43	6.0	2
153	Salmon, pink, canned, solids and liquid — 3 oz — 85	71	120	17	5	.9	.8	.1	0	[15]167	243	.7	307	60	.03	.16	6.8	--
154	Sardines, Atlantic, canned in oil, drained solids — 3 oz — 85	62	175	20	9	3.0	2.5	.5	0	372	424	2.5	502	190	.02	.17	4.6	--
155	Scallops, frozen, breaded, fried, reheated — 6 scallops — 90	60	175	16	8	--	--	--	9	--	--	--	--	--	--	--	--	--
156	Shad, baked with butter or margarine, bacon — 3 oz — 85	64	170	20	10	--	--	--	0	20	266	.5	320	30	.11	.22	7.3	--
	Shrimp:																	
157	Canned meat — 3 oz — 85	70	100	21	1	.1	Trace	Trace	1	98	224	2.6	104	50	.01	.03	1.5	--
158	French fried[16] — 3 oz — 85	57	190	17	9	2.3	3.7	2.0	9	61	162	1.7	195	--	.03	.07	2.3	--
159	Tuna, canned in oil, drained solids — 3 oz — 85	61	170	24	7	1.7	1.7	.7	0	7	199	1.6	--	70	.04	.10	10.1	--
160	Tuna salad[17] — 1 cup — 205	70	350	30	22	4.3	6.3	6.7	7	41	291	2.7	--	590	.08	.23	10.3	2
	Meat and meat products:																	
161	Bacon, (20 slices per lb, raw), broiled or fried, crisp — 2 slices — 15	8	85	4	8	2.5	3.7	.7	Trace	2	34	.5	35	0	.08	.05	.8	--
	Beef,[18] cooked: Cuts braised, simmered or pot roasted:																	
162	Lean and fat (piece, 2 1/2 by 2 1/2 by 3/4 in) — 3 oz — 85	53	245	23	16	6.8	6.5	.4	0	10	114	2.9	184	30	.04	.18	3.6	--
163	Lean only from item 162 — 2.5 oz — 72	62	140	22	5	2.1	1.8	.2	0	10	108	2.7	176	10	.04	.17	3.3	--
	Ground beef, broiled:																	
164	Lean with 10% fat — 3 oz or patty 3 by 5/8 in — 85	60	185	23	10	4.0	3.9	.3	0	10	196	3.0	261	20	.08	.20	5.1	--
165	Lean with 21% fat — 2.9 oz or patty 3 by 5/8 in — 82	54	235	20	17	7.0	6.7	.4	0	9	159	2.6	221	30	.07	.17	4.4	--
	Roast, oven cooked, no liquid added: Relatively fat, such as rib:																	
166	Lean and fat (2 pieces, 4 1/8 by 2 1/4 by 1/4 in) — 3 oz — 85	40	375	17	33	14.0	13.6	.8	0	8	158	2.2	189	70	.05	.13	3.1	--
167	Relatively lean, such as heel of round: Lean only from item 166 — 1.8 oz — 51	57	125	14	7	3.0	2.5	.3	0	6	131	1.8	161	10	.04	.11	2.6	--
168	Lean and fat (2 pieces, 4 1/8 by 2 1/4 by 1/4 in) — 3 oz — 85	62	165	25	7	2.8	2.7	.2	0	11	208	3.2	279	10	.06	.19	4.5	--

[12] Based on average vitamin A content of fortified margarine. Federal specifications for fortified margarine require a minimum of 15,000 International Units (I.U.) of vitamin A per pound.
[13] Fatty acid values apply to product made with regular-type margarine.
[14] Dipped in egg, milk or water, and breadcrumbs; fried in vegetable shortening.
[15] If bones are discarded, value for calcium will be greatly reduced.
[16] Dipped in egg, breadcrumbs, and flour or batter.
[17] Prepared with tuna, celery, salad dressing (mayonnaise type), pickle, onion, and egg.
[18] Outer layer of fat on the cut was removed to within approximately 1/2 in of the lean. Deposits of fat within the cut were not removed.

(Dashes (—) denote lack of reliable data for a constituent believed to be present in measurable amount)

FISH, SHELLFISH, MEAT, POULTRY; RELATED PRODUCTS—Con.

Item No. (A)	Foods, approximate measures, units, and weight (edible part unless footnotes indicate otherwise) (B)	(weight) Grams	Water (C) Percent	Food energy (D) Calories	Protein (E) Grams	Fat (F) Grams	Saturated (total) (G) Grams	Oleic (H) Grams	Linoleic (I) Grams	Carbohydrate (J) Grams	Calcium (K) Milligrams	Phosphorus (L) Milligrams	Iron (M) Milligrams	Potassium (N) Milligrams	Vitamin A value (O) International units	Thiamin (P) Milligrams	Riboflavin (Q) Milligrams	Niacin (R) Milligrams	Ascorbic acid (S) Milligrams
	Meat and meat products—Continued																		
	Beef,[1] cooked—Continued																		
	Roast, oven cooked, no liquid added—Continued																		
	Relatively lean such as heel of round—Continued																		
169	Lean only from item 168--- 2.8 oz	78	65	125	24	3	1.2	1.0	0.1	0	10	199	3.0	268	Trace	0.06	0.18	4.3	—
	Steak:																		
	Relatively fat—sirloin, broiled:																		
170	Lean and fat (piece, 2 1/2 by 2 1/2 by 3/4 in). 3 oz	85	44	330	20	27	11.3	11.1	.6	0	9	162	2.5	220	50	.05	.15	4.0	—
171	Lean only from item 170--- 2.0 oz	56	59	115	18	4	1.8	1.6	.2	0	7	146	2.2	202	10	.05	.14	3.6	—
	Relatively lean—round, braised:																		
172	Lean and fat (piece, 4 1/8 by 2 1/4 by 1/2 in). 3 oz	85	55	220	24	13	5.5	5.2	.4	0	10	213	3.0	272	20	.07	.19	4.8	—
173	Lean only from item 172--- 2.4 oz	68	61	130	21	4	1.7	1.5	.2	0	9	182	2.5	238	10	.05	.16	4.1	—
	Beef, canned:																		
174	Corned beef--- 3 oz	85	59	185	22	10	4.9	4.5	.2	0	17	90	3.7	440	—	.01	.20	2.9	—
175	Corned beef hash--- 1 cup	220	67	400	19	25	11.9	10.9	.5	24	29	147	4.4	—	—	.02	.20	4.6	—
176	Beef, dried, chipped--- 2 1/2-oz jar	71	48	145	24	4	2.1	2.0	.1	0	14	287	3.6	142	—	.05	.23	2.7	0
177	Beef and vegetable stew--- 1 cup	245	82	220	16	11	4.9	4.5	.2	15	29	184	2.9	613	2,400	.15	.17	4.7	17
178	Beef potpie (home recipe), baked[19] (piece, 1/3 of 9-in diam. pie). 1 piece	210	55	515	21	30	7.9	12.8	6.7	39	29	149	3.8	334	1,720	.30	.30	5.5	6
179	Chili con carne with beans, canned. 1 cup	255	72	340	19	16	7.5	6.8	.3	31	82	321	4.3	594	150	.08	.18	3.3	—
180	Chop suey with beef and pork (home recipe). 1 cup	250	75	300	26	17	8.5	6.2	.7	13	60	248	4.8	425	600	.28	.38	5.0	33
181	Heart, beef, lean, braised--- 3 oz	85	61	160	27	5	1.5	1.1	.6	1	5	154	5.0	197	20	.21	1.04	6.5	1
	Lamb, cooked:																		
	Chop, rib (cut 3 per lb with bone), broiled:																		
182	Lean and fat--- 3.1 oz	89	43	360	18	32	14.8	12.1	1.2	0	8	139	1.0	200	—	.11	.19	4.1	—
183	Lean only from item 182--- 2 oz	57	60	120	16	6	2.5	2.1	.2	0	6	121	1.1	174	—	.09	.15	3.4	—
	Leg, roasted:																		
184	Lean and fat (2 pieces, 4 1/8 by 2 1/4 by 1/4 in). 3 oz	85	54	235	22	16	7.3	6.0	.6	0	9	177	1.4	241	—	.13	.23	4.7	—
185	Lean only from item 184--- 2.5 oz	71	62	130	20	5	2.1	1.8	.2	0	9	169	1.4	227	—	.12	.21	4.4	—
	Shoulder, roasted:																		
186	Lean and fat (3 pieces, 2 1/2 by 2 1/2 by 1/4 in). 3 oz	85	50	285	18	23	10.8	8.8	.9	0	9	146	1.0	206	—	.11	.20	4.0	—
187	Lean only from item 186--- 2.3 oz	64	61	130	17	6	3.6	2.3	.2	0	8	140	1.0	193	—	.10	.18	3.7	—
188	Liver, beef, fried[20] (slice, 6 1/2 by 2 3/8 by 3/8 in). 3 oz	85	56	195	22	9	2.5	3.5	.9	5	9	405	7.5	323	[21]45,390	.22	3.56	14.0	23
	Pork, cured, cooked:																		
189	Ham, light cure, lean and fat, roasted (2 pieces, 4 1/8 by 2 1/4 by 1/4 in).[22] 3 oz	85	54	245	18	19	6.8	7.9	1.7	0	8	146	2.2	199	0	.40	.15	3.1	—
	Luncheon meat:																		
190	Boiled ham, slice (8 per 8-oz pkg.). 1 oz	28	59	65	5	5	1.7	2.0	.4	0	3	47	.8	—	0	.12	.04	.7	—
191	Canned, spiced or unspiced: Slice, approx. 3 by 2 by 1/2 in. 1 slice	60	55	175	9	15	5.4	6.7	1.0	1	5	65	1.3	133	0	.19	.13	1.8	—

(A)	(B)	(C)	(D)	(E)	(F)	(G)	(H)	(I)	(J)	(K)	(L)	(M)	(N)	(O)	(P)	(Q)	(R)	(S)
	Pork, fresh,[18] cooked:																	
	Chop, loin (cut 3 per lb with bone), broiled:																	
192	Lean and fat------- 2.7 oz---	78	305	19	25	8.9	10.4	2.2	0	9	209	2.7	216	0	0.75	0.22	4.5	—
193	Lean only from item 192---- 2 oz---	56	150	17	9	3.1	3.6	.8	0	7	181	2.2	192	0	.63	.18	3.8	—
	Roast, oven cooked, no liquid added:																	
194	Lean and fat (piece, 2 1/2 by 2 1/2 by 3/4 in). 3 oz---	85	310	21	24	8.7	10.2	2.2	0	9	218	2.7	233	0	.78	.22	4.8	—
195	Lean only from item 194---- 2.4 oz---	68	175	20	10	3.5	4.1	.8	0	9	211	2.6	224	0	.73	.21	4.4	—
	Shoulder cut, simmered:																	
196	Lean and fat (3 pieces, 2 1/2 by 2 1/2 by 1/4 in). 3 oz---	85	320	20	26	9.3	10.9	2.3	0	9	118	2.6	158	0	.46	.21	4.1	—
197	Lean only from item 196---- 2.2 oz---	63	135	18	6	2.2	2.6	.6	0	8	111	2.3	146	0	.42	.19	3.7	—
	Sausages (see also Luncheon meat (items 190-191)):																	
198	Bologna, slice (8 per 8-oz pkg.). 1 slice---	28	85	3	8	3.0	3.4	.5	Trace	2	36	.5	65	—	.05	.06	.7	—
199	Braunschweiger, slice (6 per 6-oz pkg.). 1 slice---	28	90	4	8	2.6	3.4	.8	1	3	69	1.7	—	1,850	.05	.41	2.3	—
200	Brown and serve (10-11 per 8-oz pkg.), browned. 1 link---	17	70	3	6	2.3	2.8	.7	Trace	—	—	—	—	—	—	—	—	—
201	Deviled ham, canned------- 1 tbsp---	13	45	2	4	1.5	1.8	.4	0	1	12	.3	—	0	.02	.01	.2	—
202	Frankfurter (8 per 1-lb pkg.), cooked (reheated). 1 frankfurter---	56	170	7	15	5.6	6.5	1.2	1	3	57	.8	—	—	.08	.11	1.4	—
203	Meat, potted (beef, chicken, turkey), canned. 1 tbsp---	13	30	2	2	—	—	—	0	—	—	—	—	—	Trace	.03	.2	—
204	Pork link (16 per 1-lb pkg.), cooked. 1 link---	13	60	2	6	2.1	2.4	.5	Trace	1	21	.3	35	0	.10	.04	.5	—
	Salami:																	
205	Dry type, slice (12 per 4-oz pkg.). 1 slice---	10	45	2	4	1.6	1.6	.1	Trace	1	28	.4	—	—	.04	.03	.5	—
206	Cooked type, slice (8 per 8-oz pkg.). 1 slice---	28	90	5	7	3.1	3.0	.2	Trace	3	57	.7	—	—	.07	.07	1.2	—
207	Vienna sausage (7 per 4-oz can). 1 sausage---	16	40	2	3	1.2	1.4	.2	Trace	1	24	.3	—	—	.01	.02	.4	—
	Veal, medium fat, cooked, bone removed:																	
208	Cutlet (4 1/8 by 2 1/4 by 1/2 in), braised or broiled. 3 oz---	85	185	23	9	4.0	3.4	.4	0	9	196	2.7	258	0	.06	.21	4.6	—
209	Rib (2 pieces, 4 1/8 by 2 1/4 by 1/4 in), roasted. 3 oz---	85	230	23	14	6.1	5.1	.6	0	10	211	2.9	259	0	.11	.26	6.6	—
	Poultry and poultry products:																	
	Chicken, cooked:																	
210	Breast, fried,[23] bones removed, 1/2 breast (3.3 oz with bones). 2.8 oz---	79	160	26	5	1.4	1.8	1.1	1	9	218	1.3	—	70	.04	.17	11.6	—
211	Drumstick, fried,[23] bones removed (2 oz with bones). 1.3 oz---	38	90	12	4	1.1	1.3	.9	Trace	6	89	.9	—	50	.03	.15	2.7	—
212	Half broiler, broiled, bones removed (10.4 oz with bones). 6.2 oz---	176	240	42	7	2.2	2.5	1.3	0	16	355	3.0	483	160	.09	.34	15.5	—
213	Chicken, canned, boneless---- 3 oz---	85	170	18	10	3.2	3.8	2.0	0	18	210	1.3	117	200	.03	.11	3.7	3
214	Chicken a la king, cooked (home recipe). 1 cup---	245	470	27	34	2.7	14.3	3.3	12	127	358	2.5	404	1,130	.10	.42	5.4	12
215	Chicken and noodles, cooked (home recipe). 1 cup---	240	365	22	18	5.9	7.1	3.5	26	26	247	2.2	149	430	.05	.17	4.3	Trace

18 Outer layer of fat on the cut was removed to within approximately 1/2 in of the lean. Deposits of fat within the cut were not removed.
19 Crust made with vegetable shortening and enriched flour.
20 Regular-type margarine used.
21 Value varies widely.
22 About one-fourth of the outer layer of fat on the cut was removed. Deposits of fat within the cut were not removed.
23 Vegetable shortening used.

(Dashes (—) denote lack of reliable data for a constituent believed to be present in measurable amount)

Item No. (A)	Foods, approximate measures, units, and weight (edible part unless footnotes indicate otherwise) (B)		Water (C) Per cent	Food energy (D) Cal- ories	Pro- tein (E) Grams	Fat (F) Grams	Fatty Acids Satu- rated (total) (G) Grams	Unsaturated Oleic (H) Grams	Unsaturated Lino- leic (I) Grams	Carbo- hydrate (J) Grams	Calcium (K) Milli- grams	Phos- phorus (L) Milli- grams	Iron (M) Milli- grams	Potas- sium (N) Milli- grams	Vitamin A value (O) Inter- national units	Thiamin (P) Milli- grams	Ribo- flavin (Q) Milli- grams	Niacin (R) Milli- grams	Ascorbic acid (S) Milli- grams
		Grams																	
	FISH, SHELLFISH, MEAT, POULTRY; RELATED PRODUCTS—Con.																		
	Poultry and poultry products—Continued																		
	Chicken chow mein:																		
216	Canned	1 cup	250	89	95	7	Trace	—	—	—	18	45	35	1.3	418	150	0.05	0.10	1.0	13
217	From home recipe	1 cup	250	78	255	31	10	2.4	3.4	3.1	10	58	293	2.5	473	280	.08	.23	4.3	10
218	Chicken potpie (home recipe), baked, 1/3 piece (1/3 or 9-in diam. pie).	1 piece	232	57	545	23	31	11.3	10.9	5.6	42	70	232	3.0	343	3,090	.34	.31	5.5	5
	Turkey, roasted, flesh without skin:																			
219	Dark meat, piece, 2 1/2 by 1 5/8 by 1/4 in.	4 pieces	85	61	175	26	7	2.1	1.5	1.5	0	—	—	2.0	338	—	.03	.20	3.6	—
220	Light meat, piece, 4 by 2 by 1/4 in.	2 pieces	85	62	150	28	3	.9	.6	.7	0	—	—	1.0	349	—	.04	.12	9.4	—
	Light and dark meat:																			
221	Chopped or diced	1 cup	140	61	265	44	9	2.5	1.7	1.8	0	11	351	2.5	514	—	.07	.25	10.8	—
222	Pieces (1 slice white meat, 4 by 2 by 1/4 in with 2 slices dark meat, 2 1/2 by 1 5/8 by 1/4 in).	3 pieces	85	61	160	27	5	1.5	1.0	1.1	0	7	213	1.5	312	—	.04	.15	6.5	—
	FRUITS AND FRUIT PRODUCTS																			
	Apples, raw, unpeeled, without cores:																			
223	2 3/4-in diam. (about 3 per lb with cores).	1 apple	138	84	80	Trace	1	—	—	—	20	10	14	.4	152	120	.04	.03	.1	6
224	3 1/4 in diam. (about 2 per lb with cores).	1 apple	212	84	125	Trace	1	—	—	—	31	15	21	.6	233	190	.06	.04	.2	8
225	Applejuice, bottled or canned [24]	1 cup	248	88	120	Trace	Trace	—	—	—	30	15	22	1.5	250	—	.02	.05	.2	[25]2
	Applesauce, canned:																			
226	Sweetened	1 cup	255	76	230	1	Trace	—	—	—	61	10	13	1.3	166	100	.05	.03	.1	[25]3
227	Unsweetened	1 cup	244	89	100	Trace	Trace	—	—	—	26	10	12	1.2	190	100	.05	.02	.1	[25]2
	Apricots:																			
228	Raw, without pits (about 12 per lb with pits).	3 apricots	107	85	55	1	Trace	—	—	—	14	18	25	.5	301	2,890	.03	.04	.6	11
229	Canned in heavy syrup (halves and syrup).	1 cup	258	77	220	2	Trace	—	—	—	57	28	39	.8	604	4,490	.05	.05	1.0	10
	Dried:																			
230	Uncooked (28 large or 37 medium halves per cup).	1 cup	130	25	340	7	1	—	—	—	86	87	140	7.2	1,273	14,170	.01	.21	4.3	16
231	Cooked, unsweetened, fruit and liquid.	1 cup	250	76	215	4	1	—	—	—	54	55	88	4.5	795	7,500	.01	.13	2.5	8
232	Apricot nectar, canned	1 cup	251	85	145	1	Trace	—	—	—	37	23	30	.5	379	2,380	.03	.03	.5	[25]36
	Avocados, raw, whole, without skins and seeds:																			
233	California, mid- and late-winter (with skin and seed, 3 1/8-in diam.; wt., 10 oz).	1 avocado	216	74	370	5	37	5.5	22.0	3.7	13	22	91	1.3	1,303	630	.24	.43	3.5	30
234	Florida, late summer and fall (with skin and seed, 3 5/8-in diam.; wt., 1 lb).	1 avocado	304	78	390	4	33	6.7	15.7	5.3	27	30	128	1.8	1,836	880	.33	.61	4.9	43
235	Banana without peel (about 2.6 per lb with peel).	1 banana	119	76	100	1	Trace	—	—	—	26	10	31	.8	440	230	.06	.07	.8	12
236	Banana flakes	1 tbsp	6	3	20	Trace	Trace	—	—	—	5	2	6	.2	92	50	.01	.01	.2	Trace

Item	Food, approximate measure, and weight	Grams	Water (%)	Food energy (cal)	Protein (g)	Fat (g)	Saturated (g)	Oleic (g)	Linoleic (g)	Carbohydrate (g)	Calcium (mg)	Phosphorus (mg)	Iron (mg)	Potassium (mg)	Vitamin A (IU)	Thiamin (mg)	Riboflavin (mg)	Niacin (mg)	Ascorbic acid (mg)
237	Blackberries, raw — 1 cup	144	85	85	2	1	—	—	—	19	46	27	1.3	245	290	.04	.06	0.6	30
238	Blueberries, raw — 1 cup	145	83	90	1	1	—	—	—	22	22	19	1.5	117	150	.04	.09	.7	20
	Cantaloup. See Muskmelons (item 271).																		
	Cherries:																		
239	Sour (tart), red, pitted, canned, water pack — 1 cup	244	88	105	2	Trace	—	—	—	26	37	32	.7	317	1,660	.07	.05	.5	12
240	Sweet, raw, without pits and stems — 10 cherries	68	80	45	1	Trace	—	—	—	12	15	13	.3	129	70	.03	.04	.3	7
241	Cranberry juice cocktail, bottled, sweetened — 1 cup	253	83	165	Trace	Trace	—	—	—	42	13	8	.8	25	Trace	.03	.03	.1	[27]81
242	Cranberry sauce, sweetened, canned, strained — 1 cup	277	62	405	Trace	1	—	—	—	104	17	11	.6	83	60	.03	.03	.1	6
	Dates:																		
243	Whole, without pits — 10 dates	80	23	220	2	Trace	—	—	—	58	47	50	2.4	518	40	.07	.08	1.8	0
244	Chopped — 1 cup	178	23	490	4	1	—	—	—	130	105	112	5.3	1,153	90	.16	.18	3.9	0
245	Fruit cocktail, canned, in heavy syrup — 1 cup	255	80	195	1	Trace	—	—	—	50	23	31	1.0	411	360	.05	.03	1.0	5
	Grapefruit: Raw, medium, 3 3/4-in diam. (about 1 lb 1 oz):																		
246	Pink or red — 1/2 grapefruit with peel[28]	241	89	50	1	Trace	—	—	—	13	20	20	.5	166	540	.05	.02	.2	44
247	White — 1/2 grapefruit with peel[28]	241	89	45	1	Trace	—	—	—	12	19	19	.5	159	10	.05	.02	.2	44
248	Canned, sections with syrup — 1 cup	254	81	180	2	Trace	—	—	—	45	33	36	.8	343	30	.08	.05	.5	76
	Grapefruit juice:																		
249	Raw, pink, red, or white — 1 cup	246	90	95	1	Trace	—	—	—	23	22	37	.5	399	([29])	.10	.05	.5	93
	Canned, white:																		
250	Unsweetened — 1 cup	247	89	100	1	Trace	—	—	—	24	20	35	1.0	400	20	.07	.05	.5	84
251	Sweetened — 1 cup	250	86	135	1	Trace	—	—	—	32	20	35	1.0	405	30	.08	.05	.5	78
	Frozen, concentrate, unsweetened:																		
252	Undiluted, 6-fl oz can — 1 can	207	62	300	4	1	—	—	—	72	70	124	.8	1,250	60	.29	.12	1.4	286
253	Diluted with 3 parts water by volume — 1 cup	247	89	100	1	Trace	—	—	—	24	25	42	.2	420	20	.10	.04	.5	96
254	Dehydrated crystals, prepared with water (1 lb yields about 1 gal) — 1 cup	247	90	100	1	Trace	—	—	—	24	22	40	.2	412	20	.10	.05	.5	91
	Grapes, European type (adherent skin), raw:																		
255	Thompson Seedless — 10 grapes	50	81	35	Trace	Trace	—	—	—	9	6	10	.2	87	50	.03	.02	.2	2
256	Tokay and Emperor, seeded types — 10 grapes[30]	60	81	40	Trace	Trace	—	—	—	10	7	11	.2	99	60	.03	.02	.2	2
	Grapejuice:																		
257	Canned or bottled — 1 cup	253	83	165	1	Trace	—	—	—	42	28	30	.8	293	—	.10	.05	.5	[25]Trace
	Frozen concentrate, sweetened:																		
258	Undiluted, 6-fl oz can — 1 can	216	53	395	1	Trace	—	—	—	100	22	32	.9	255	40	.13	.22	1.5	[31]32
259	Diluted with 3 parts water by volume — 1 cup	250	86	135	1	Trace	—	—	—	33	8	10	.3	85	10	.05	.08	.5	[31]10
260	Grape drink, canned — 1 cup	250	86	135	Trace	Trace	—	—	—	35	8	10	.3	88	10	[32].03	[32].03	.3	([32])
261	Lemon, raw, size 165, without peel and seeds (about 4 per lb with peels and seeds) — 1 lemon	74	90	20	1	Trace	—	—	—	6	19	12	.4	102	10	.03	.01	.1	39
	Lemon juice:																		
262	Raw — 1 cup	244	91	60	1	Trace	—	—	—	20	17	24	.5	344	50	.07	.02	.2	112
263	Canned, or bottled, unsweetened — 1 cup	244	92	55	1	Trace	—	—	—	19	17	24	.5	344	50	.07	.02	.2	102
264	Frozen, single strength, unsweetened, 6-fl oz can — 1 can	183	92	40	1	Trace	—	—	—	13	13	16	.5	258	40	.05	.02	.2	81
	Lemonade concentrate, frozen:																		
265	Undiluted, 6-fl oz can — 1 can	219	49	425	Trace	Trace	—	—	—	112	9	13	.4	153	40	.05	.06	.7	66
266	Diluted with 4 1/3 parts water by volume — 1 cup	248	89	105	Trace	Trace	—	—	—	28	2	3	.1	40	10	.01	.02	.2	17

[19] Crust made with vegetable shortening and enriched flour.

[24] Also applies to pasteurized apple cider.

[25] Applies to product without added ascorbic acid. For value of product with added ascorbic acid, refer to label.

[26] Based on product with label claim of 45% of U.S. RDA in 6 fl oz.

[27] Based on product with label claim of 100% of U.S. RDA in 6 fl oz.

[28] Weight includes peel and membranes between sections. Without these parts, the weight of the edible portion is 123 g for item 246 and 118 g for item 247.

[29] For white-fleshed varieties, value is about 20 International Units (I.U.) per cup; for red-fleshed varieties, 1,080 I.U.

[30] Weight includes seeds. Without seeds, weight of the edible portion is 57 g.

[31] For products without added ascorbic acid. With added ascorbic acid, based on claim that 6 fl oz of reconstituted juice contain 45% or 50% of the U.S. RDA, value in milligrams is 108 or 120 for a 6-fl oz can (item 258), 36 or 40 for 1 cup of diluted juice (item 259).

[32] For products with added thiamin and riboflavin but without added ascorbic acid, values in milligrams would be 0.60 for thiamin, 0.80 for riboflavin, and trace for ascorbic acid. For products with only ascorbic acid added, value varies with the brand. Consult the label.

(Dashes (—) denote lack of reliable data for a constituent believed to be present in measurable amount)

Item No. (A)	Foods, approximate measures, units, and weight (edible part unless footnotes indicate otherwise) (B)	(grams)	Water (C) Percent	Food energy (D) Calories	Protein (E) Grams	Fat (F) Grams	Fatty Acids Saturated (total) (G) Grams	Unsaturated Oleic (H) Grams	Unsaturated Linoleic (I) Grams	Carbohydrate (J) Grams	Calcium (K) Milligrams	Phosphorus (L) Milligrams	Iron (M) Milligrams	Potassium (N) Milligrams	Vitamin A value (O) International units	Thiamin (P) Milligrams	Riboflavin (Q) Milligrams	Niacin (R) Milligrams	Ascorbic acid (S) Milligrams
	FRUITS AND FRUIT PRODUCTS—Con.																		
	Limeade concentrate, frozen:																		
267	Undiluted, 6-fl oz can	218	50	410	Trace	Trace	—	—	—	108	11	13	0.2	129	Trace	0.02	0.02	0.2	26
268	Diluted with 4 1/3 parts water by volume.	247	89	100	Trace	Trace	—	—	—	27	3	3	Trace	32	Trace	Trace	Trace	Trace	6
	Limejuice:																		
269	Raw	246	90	65	1	Trace	—	—	—	22	22	27	.5	256	20	.05	.02	.2	79
270	Canned, unsweetened	246	90	65	1	Trace	—	—	—	22	22	27	.5	256	20	.05	.02	.2	52
	Muskmelons, raw, with rind, without seed cavity:																		
271	Cantaloup, orange-fleshed (with rind and seed cavity, 5-in diam., 2 1/3 lb).	477	91	80	2	Trace	—	—	—	20	38	44	1.1	682	9,240	.11	.08	1.6	90
272	Honeydew (with rind and seed cavity, 6 1/2-in diam., 5 1/4 lb).	226	91	50	1	Trace	—	—	—	11	21	24	.6	374	60	.06	.04	.9	34
	Oranges, all commercial varieties, raw:																		
273	Whole, 2 5/8-in diam., without peel and seeds (about 2 1/2 per lb with peel and seeds).	131	86	65	1	Trace	—	—	—	16	54	26	.5	263	260	.13	.05	.5	66
274	Sections without membranes	180	86	90	2	Trace	—	—	—	22	74	36	.7	360	360	.18	.07	.7	90
	Orange juice:																		
275	Raw, all varieties	248	88	110	2	Trace	—	—	—	26	27	42	.5	496	500	.22	.07	1.0	124
276	Canned, unsweetened	249	87	120	2	Trace	—	—	—	28	25	45	1.0	496	500	.17	.05	.7	100
	Frozen concentrate:																		
277	Undiluted, 6-fl oz can	213	55	360	5	Trace	—	—	—	87	75	126	.9	1,500	1,620	.68	.11	2.8	360
278	Diluted with 3 parts water by volume.	249	87	120	2	Trace	—	—	—	29	25	42	.2	503	540	.23	.03	.9	120
279	Dehydrated crystals, prepared with water (1 lb yields about 1 gal).	248	88	115	1	Trace	—	—	—	27	25	40	.5	518	500	.20	.07	1.0	109
	Orange and grapefruit juice:																		
	Frozen concentrate:																		
280	Undiluted, 6-fl oz can	210	59	330	4	1	—	—	—	78	61	99	.8	1,308	800	.48	.06	2.3	302
281	Diluted with 3 parts water by volume.	248	88	110	1	Trace	—	—	—	26	20	32	.2	439	270	.15	.02	.7	102
282	Papayas, raw, 1/2-in cubes	140	89	55	1	Trace	—	—	—	14	28	22	.4	328	2,450	.06	.06	.4	78
	Peaches:																		
	Raw:																		
283	Whole, 2 1/2-in diam., peeled, pitted (about 4 per lb with peels and pits).	100	89	40	1	Trace	—	—	—	10	9	19	.5	202	[34]1,330	.02	.05	1.0	7
284	Sliced	170	89	65	1	Trace	—	—	—	16	15	32	.9	343	[34]2,260	.03	.09	1.7	12
	Canned, yellow-fleshed, solids and liquid (halves or slices):																		
285	Sirup pack	256	79	200	1	Trace	—	—	—	51	10	31	.8	333	1,100	.03	.05	1.5	8
286	Water pack	244	91	75	1	Trace	—	—	—	20	10	32	.7	334	1,100	.02	.07	1.5	7
	Dried:																		
287	Uncooked	160	25	420	5	1	—	—	—	109	77	187	9.6	1,520	6,240	.02	.30	8.5	29
288	Cooked, unsweetened, halves and juice.	250	77	205	3	1	—	—	—	54	38	93	4.8	743	3,050	.01	.15	3.8	5

(A)	(B)	(C)	(D)	(E)	(F)	(G)	(H)	(I)	(J)	(K)	(L)	(M)	(N)	(O)	(P)	(Q)	(R)	(S)
	Frozen, sliced, sweetened:																	
289	10-oz container----	1 container----	284	77	250	1	Trace	---	---	---	64	11	37	1.4	352	1,850	0.03	0.11	2.0	[35]116
290	Cup----------------	1 cup----------	250	77	220	1	Trace	---	---	---	57	10	33	1.3	310	1,630	.03	.10	1.8	[35]103
	Pears:																		
	Raw, with skin, cored:																		
291	Bartlett, 2 1/2-in diam. (about 2 1/2 per lb with cores and stems).	1 pear----	164	83	100	1	1	---	---	---	25	13	18	.5	213	30	.03	.07	.2	7
292	Bosc, 2 1/2-in diam. (about 3 per lb with cores and stems).	1 pear----	141	83	85	1	1	---	---	---	22	11	16	.4	83	30	.03	.06	.1	6
293	D'Anjou, 3-in diam. (about 2 per lb with cores and stems).	1 pear----	200	83	120	1	1	---	---	---	31	16	22	.6	260	40	.04	.08	.2	8
294	Canned, solids and liquid, sirup pack, heavy (halves or slices).	1 cup----	255	80	195	1	1	---	---	---	50	13	18	.5	214	10	.03	.05	.3	3
	Pineapple:																		
295	Raw, diced----	1 cup----	155	85	80	1	Trace	---	---	---	21	26	12	.8	226	110	.14	.05	.3	26
	Canned, heavy sirup pack, solids and liquid:																		
296	Crushed, chunks, tidbits----	1 cup----	255	80	190	1	Trace	---	---	---	49	28	13	.8	245	130	.20	.05	.5	18
	Slices and liquid:																		
297	Large----	1 slice; 2 1/4 tbsp liquid.	105	80	80	Trace	Trace	---	---	---	20	12	5	.3	101	50	.08	.02	.2	7
298	Medium----	1 slice; 1 1/4 tbsp liquid.	58	80	45	Trace	Trace	---	---	---	11	6	3	.2	56	30	.05	.01	.1	4
299	Pineapple juice, unsweetened, canned.	1 cup----	250	86	140	1	Trace	---	---	---	34	38	23	.8	373	130	.13	.05	.5	[2]80
	Plums:																		
	Raw, without pits:																		
300	Japanese and hybrid (2 1/8-in diam., about 6 1/2 per lb with pits).	1 plum----	66	87	30	Trace	Trace	---	---	---	8	8	12	.3	112	160	.02	.02	.3	4
301	Prune-type (1 1/2-in diam., about 15 per lb with pits).	1 plum----	28	79	20	Trace	Trace	---	---	---	6	3	5	.1	48	80	.01	.01	.1	1
	Canned, heavy sirup pack (Italian prunes), with pits and liquid:																		
302	Cup[36]----	1 cup[36]----	272	77	215	1	Trace	---	---	---	56	23	26	2.3	367	3,130	.05	.05	1.0	5
303	Portion----	3 plums; 2 3/4 tbsp liquid.[36]	140	77	110	1	Trace	---	---	---	29	12	13	1.2	189	1,610	.03	.03	.5	3
	Prunes, dried, "softenized," with pits:																		
304	Uncooked----	4 extra large or 5 large prunes.[36]	49	28	110	1	Trace	---	---	---	29	22	34	1.7	298	690	.04	.07	.7	1
305	Cooked, unsweetened, all sizes, fruit and liquid.	1 cup[36]----	250	66	255	2	1	---	---	---	67	51	79	3.8	695	1,590	.07	.15	1.5	2
306	Prune juice, canned or bottled----	1 cup----	256	80	195	1	Trace	---	---	---	49	36	51	1.8	602	—	.03	.03	1.0	5
	Raisins, seedless:																		
307	Cup, not pressed down----		145	18	420	4	Trace	---	---	---	112	90	146	5.1	1,106	30	.16	.12	.7	1
308	Packet, 1/2 oz (1 1/2 tbsp)----		14	18	40	Trace	Trace	---	---	---	11	9	14	.5	107	Trace	.02	.01	.1	Trace
	Raspberries, red:																		
309	Raw, capped, whole----	1 cup----	123	84	70	1	1	---	---	---	17	27	27	1.1	207	160	.04	.11	1.1	31
310	Frozen, sweetened, 10-oz container----	1 container----	284	74	280	2	1	---	---	---	70	37	48	1.7	284	200	.06	.17	1.7	60
	Rhubarb, cooked, added sugar:																		
311	From raw----	1 cup----	270	63	380	1	Trace	---	---	---	97	211	41	1.6	548	220	.05	.14	.8	16
312	From frozen, sweetened----	1 cup----	270	63	385	1	1	---	---	---	98	211	32	1.9	475	190	.05	.11	.5	16

[27] Based on product with label claim of 100% of U.S. RDA in 6 fl oz.

[34] Weight includes rind. Without rind, the weight of the edible portion is 272 g for item 271 and 149 g for item 272.

[33] Represents yellow-fleshed varieties. For white-fleshed varieties, value is 50 International Units (I.U.) for 1 peach, 90 I.U. for 1 cup of slices.

[35] Value represents products with added ascorbic acid. For products without added ascorbic acid, value in milligrams is 116 for a 10-oz container, 103 for 1 cup.

[36] Weight includes pits. After removal of the pits, the weight of the edible portion is 258 g for item 302, 133 g for item 303, 43 g for item 304, and 213 g for item 305.

(Dashes (—) denote lack of reliable data for a constituent believed to be present in measurable amount)

Item No. (A)	Foods, approximate measures, units, and weight (edible part unless footnotes indicate otherwise) (B)	Grams	Water (C) Percent	Food energy (D) Calories	Protein (E) Grams	Fat (F) Grams	Fatty Acids Saturated (total) (G) Grams	Unsaturated Oleic (H) Grams	Unsaturated Linoleic (I) Grams	Carbohydrate (J) Grams	Calcium (K) Milligrams	Phosphorus (L) Milligrams	Iron (M) Milligrams	Potassium (N) Milligrams	Vitamin A value (O) International units	Thiamin (P) Milligrams	Riboflavin (Q) Milligrams	Niacin (R) Milligrams	Ascorbic acid (S) Milligrams
	FRUITS AND FRUIT PRODUCTS—Con.																		
	Strawberries:																		
313	Raw, whole berries, capped	149	90	55	1	1	—	—	—	13	31	31	1.5	244	90	0.04	0.10	0.9	88
	Frozen, sweetened:																		
314	Sliced, 10-oz container	284	71	310	1	1	—	—	—	79	40	48	2.0	318	90	.06	.17	1.4	151
315	Whole, 1-lb container (about 1 3/4 cups)	454	76	415	2	1	—	—	—	107	59	73	2.7	472	140	.09	.27	2.3	249
316	Tangerine, raw, 2 3/8-in diam., size 176, without peel (about 4 per lb with peels and seeds)	86	87	40	1	Trace	—	—	—	10	34	15	.3	108	360	.05	.02	.1	27
317	Tangerine juice, canned, sweetened	249	87	125	1	Trace	—	—	—	30	44	35	.5	440	1,040	.15	.05	.2	54
318	Watermelon, raw, 4 by 8 in wedge with rind and seeds (1/16 of 32 2/3-lb melon, 10 by 16 in) [37]	926	93	110	2	1	—	—	—	27	30	43	2.1	426	2,510	.13	.13	.9	30
	GRAIN PRODUCTS																		
	Bagel, 3-in diam.:																		
319	Egg	55	32	165	6	2	0.5	0.9	0.8	28	9	43	1.2	41	30	.14	.10	1.2	0
320	Water	55	29	165	6	1	.2	.4	.6	30	8	41	1.2	42	0	.15	.11	1.4	0
321	Barley, pearled, light, uncooked	200	11	700	16	2	.3	.2	.8	158	32	378	4.0	320	0	.24	.10	6.2	0
	Biscuits, baking powder, 2-in diam. (enriched flour, vegetable shortening):																		
322	From home recipe	28	27	105	2	5	1.2	2.0	1.2	13	34	49	.4	33	Trace	.08	.08	.7	Trace
323	From mix	28	29	90	2	3	.6	1.1	.7	15	19	65	.6	32	Trace	.09	.08	.8	Trace
324	Breadcrumbs (enriched):[38] Dry, grated	100	7	390	13	5	1.0	1.6	1.4	73	122	141	3.6	152	Trace	.35	.35	4.8	Trace
	Soft. See White bread (items 349-350).																		
	Breads:																		
325	Boston brown bread, canned, slice 3 1/4 by 1/2 in.[38]	45	45	95	2	1	.1	.2	.2	21	41	72	.9	131	[39]0	.06	.04	.7	0
	Cracked-wheat bread (3/4 enriched wheat flour, 1/4 cracked wheat):[38]																		
326	Loaf, 1 lb	454	35	1,195	39	10	2.2	3.0	3.9	236	399	581	9.5	608	Trace	1.52	1.13	14.4	Trace
327	Slice (18 per loaf)	25	35	65	2	1	.1	.2	.2	13	22	32	.5	34	Trace	.08	.06	.8	Trace
	French or Vienna bread, enriched:[38]																		
328	Loaf, 1 lb	454	31	1,315	41	14	3.2	4.7	4.6	251	195	386	10.0	408	Trace	1.80	1.10	15.0	Trace
	Slice:																		
329	French (5 by 2 1/2 by 1 in)	35	31	100	3	1	.2	.4	.4	19	15	30	.8	32	Trace	.14	.08	1.2	Trace
330	Vienna (4 3/4 by 4 by 1/2 in)	25	31	75	2	1	.2	.3	.3	14	11	21	.6	23	Trace	.10	.06	.8	Trace
	Italian bread, enriched:																		
331	Loaf, 1 lb	454	32	1,250	41	4	.6	.3	1.5	256	77	349	10.0	336	0	1.80	1.10	15.0	0
332	Slice, 4 1/2 by 3 1/4 by 3/4 in.	30	32	85	3	Trace	Trace	Trace	.1	17	5	23	.7	22	0	.12	.07	1.0	0
	Raisin bread, enriched:[38]																		
333	Loaf, 1 lb	454	35	1,190	30	13	3.0	4.7	3.9	243	322	395	10.0	1,057	Trace	1.70	1.07	10.7	Trace
334	Slice (18 per loaf)	25	35	65	2	1	.2	.3	.2	13	18	22	.6	58	Trace	.09	.06	.6	Trace

(A)	(B)	(grams)	(C)	(D)	(E)	(F)	(G)	(H)	(I)	(J)	(K)	(L)	(M)	(N)	(O)	(P)	(Q)	(R)	(S)
	Rye Bread:																		
	American, light (2/3 enriched wheat flour, 1/3 rye flour):																		
335	Loaf, 1 lb — 1 loaf	454	36	1,100	41	5	0.7	0.5	2.2	236	340	667	9.1	658	0	1.35	0.98	12.9	0
336	Slice (4 3/4 by 3 3/4 by 7/16 in) — 1 slice	25	36	60	2	Trace	Trace	Trace	.1	13	19	37	.5	36	0	.07	.05	.7	0
	Pumpernickel (2/3 rye flour, 1/3 enriched wheat flour):																		
337	Loaf, 1 lb — 1 loaf	454	34	1,115	41	5	.7	.5	2.4	241	381	1,039	11.8	2,059	0	1.30	.93	8.5	0
338	Slice (5 by 4 by 3/8 in) — 1 slice	32	34	80	3	Trace	.1	Trace	.2	17	27	73	.8	145	0	.09	.07	.6	0
	White bread, enriched:[38]																		
	Soft-crumb type:																		
339	Loaf, 1 lb — 1 loaf	454	36	1,225	39	15	3.4	5.3	4.6	229	381	440	11.3	476	Trace	1.80	1.10	15.0	Trace
340	Slice (18 per loaf) — 1 slice	25	36	70	2	1	.2	.3	.3	13	21	24	.6	26	Trace	.10	.06	.8	Trace
341	Slice, toasted — 1 slice	22	25	70	2	1	.2	.3	.3	13	21	24	.6	26	Trace	.08	.06	.8	Trace
342	Slice (22 per loaf) — 1 slice	20	36	55	2	1	.2	.2	.2	10	17	19	.5	21	Trace	.08	.05	.7	Trace
343	Slice, toasted — 1 slice	17	25	55	2	1	.2	.2	.2	10	17	19	.5	21	Trace	.06	.05	.7	Trace
344	Loaf, 1 1/2 lb — 1 loaf	680	36	1,835	59	22	5.2	7.9	6.9	343	571	660	17.0	714	Trace	2.70	1.65	22.5	Trace
345	Slice (24 per loaf) — 1 slice	28	36	75	2	1	.2	.3	.3	14	24	27	.7	29	Trace	.11	.07	.9	Trace
346	Slice, toasted — 1 slice	24	25	75	2	1	.2	.3	.3	14	24	27	.7	29	Trace	.09	.07	.9	Trace
347	Slice (28 per loaf) — 1 slice	24	36	65	2	1	.2	.3	.3	12	20	23	.6	25	Trace	.10	.06	.8	Trace
348	Slice, toasted — 1 slice	21	25	65	2	1	.2	.3	.3	12	20	23	.6	25	Trace	.08	.06	.8	Trace
349	Cubes — 1 cup	30	36	80	3	1	.2	.3	.3	15	25	29	.8	32	Trace	.12	.07	1.0	Trace
350	Crumbs — 1 cup	45	36	120	4	1	.3	.5	.5	23	38	44	1.1	47	Trace	.18	.11	1.5	Trace
	Firm-crumb type:																		
351	Loaf, 1 lb — 1 loaf	454	35	1,245	41	17	3.9	5.9	5.2	228	435	463	11.3	549	Trace	1.80	1.10	15.0	Trace
352	Slice (20 per loaf) — 1 slice	23	35	65	2	1	.2	.3	.3	12	22	23	.6	28	Trace	.09	.06	.8	Trace
353	Slice, toasted — 1 slice	20	24	65	2	1	.2	.3	.3	12	22	23	.6	28	Trace	.07	.06	.7	Trace
354	Loaf, 2 lb — 1 loaf	907	35	2,495	82	34	7.7	11.8	10.4	455	871	925	22.7	1,097	Trace	3.60	2.20	30.0	Trace
355	Slice (34 per loaf) — 1 slice	27	35	75	2	1	.2	.3	.3	14	26	28	.7	33	Trace	.11	.06	.9	Trace
356	Slice, toasted — 1 slice	23	24	75	2	1	.2	.3	.3	14	26	28	.7	33	Trace	.09	.06	.9	Trace
	Whole-wheat bread:																		
	Soft-crumb type:[38]																		
357	Loaf, 1 lb — 1 loaf	454	36	1,095	41	12	2.2	2.9	4.2	224	381	1,152	13.6	1,161	Trace	1.37	.45	12.7	Trace
358	Slice (16 per loaf) — 1 slice	28	36	65	3	1	.1	.2	.2	14	24	71	.8	72	Trace	.09	.03	.8	Trace
359	Slice, toasted — 1 slice	24	24	65	3	1	.1	.2	.2	14	24	71	.8	72	Trace	.07	.03	.8	Trace
	Firm-crumb type:[38]																		
360	Loaf, 1 lb — 1 loaf	454	36	1,100	48	14	2.5	3.3	4.9	216	449	1,034	13.6	1,238	Trace	1.17	.54	12.7	Trace
361	Slice (18 per loaf) — 1 slice	25	36	60	3	1	.1	.2	.2	12	25	57	.8	68	Trace	.06	.03	.7	Trace
362	Slice, toasted — 1 slice	21	24	60	3	1	.1	.2	.3	12	25	57	.8	68	Trace	.05	.03	.7	Trace
	Breakfast cereals:																		
	Hot type, cooked:																		
	Corn (hominy) grits, degermed:																		
363	Enriched — 1 cup	245	87	125	3	Trace	Trace	Trace	.1	27	2	25	.7	27	[40]Trace	.10	.07	1.0	0
364	Unenriched — 1 cup	245	87	125	3	Trace	Trace	Trace	.1	27	2	25	.2	27	[40]Trace	.05	.02	.5	0
365	Farina, quick-cooking, enriched — 1 cup	245	89	105	3	Trace	Trace	Trace	.1	22	147	[41]113	[42]	25	0	.12	.07	1.0	0
366	Oatmeal or rolled oats — 1 cup	240	87	130	5	2	.4	.8	.9	23	22	137	1.4	146	0	.19	.05	.2	0
367	Wheat, rolled — 1 cup	240	80	180	5	1	—	—	—	41	19	182	1.7	202	0	.17	.07	2.2	0
368	Wheat, whole-meal — 1 cup	245	88	110	4	1	—	—	—	23	17	127	1.2	118	0	.15	.05	1.5	0
	Ready-to-eat:																		
369	Bran flakes (40% bran), added sugar, salt, iron, vitamins — 1 cup	35	3	105	4	1	—	—	—	28	19	125	5.6	137	1,540	.46	.52	6.2	0
370	Bran flakes with raisins, added sugar, salt, iron, vitamins — 1 cup	50	7	145	4	1	—	—	—	40	28	146	7.9	154	[43]2,200	[44]	[44]	[44]	0

[37]Weight includes rind and seeds. Without rind and seeds, weight of the edible portion is 426 g.

[38]Made with vegetable shortening.

[39]Applies to product made with white cornmeal. With yellow cornmeal, value is 30 International Units (I.U.).

[40]Applies to white varieties. For yellow varieties, value is 150 International Units (I.U.).

[41]Applies to products that do not contain di-sodium phosphate. If di-sodium phosphate is an ingredient, value is 162 mg.

[42]Value may range from less than 1 mg to about 8 mg depending on the brand. Consult the label.

[43]Applies to product with added nutrient. Without added nutrient, value is trace.

[44]Value varies with the brand. Consult the label.

(Dashes (—) denote lack of reliable data for a constituent believed to be present in measurable amount)

							Fatty Acids													
								Unsaturated												
Item No.	Foods, approximate measures, units, and weight (edible part unless footnotes indicate otherwise)		Water	Food energy	Protein	Fat	Saturated (total)	Oleic	Linoleic	Carbohydrate	Calcium	Phosphorus	Iron	Potassium	Vitamin A value	Thiamin	Riboflavin	Niacin	Ascorbic acid
(A)	(B)	Grams	Per cent (C)	Calories (D)	Grams (E)	Grams (F)	Grams (G)	Grams (H)	Grams (I)	Grams (J)	Milligrams (K)	Milligrams (L)	Milligrams (M)	Milligrams (N)	International units (O)	Milligrams (P)	Milligrams (Q)	Milligrams (R)	Milligrams (S)
	GRAIN PRODUCTS—Con.																		
	Breakfast cereals—Continued																		
	Ready-to-eat—Continued																		
	Corn flakes:																		
371	Plain, added sugar, salt, iron, vitamins. 1 cup	25	4	95	2	Trace	—	—	—	21	(**)	9	(**)	30	(**)	(**)	(**)	(**)	[4][5]13
372	Sugar-coated, added salt, iron, vitamins. 1 cup	40	2	155	2	Trace	—	—	—	37	1	10	(**)	27	1,760	.53	.50	7.1	[4][5]21
373	Corn, oat flour, puffed, added sugar, salt, iron, vitamins. 1 cup	20	4	80	2	1	—	—	—	16	4	18	5.7	—	880	.26	.30	3.5	11
374	Corn, shredded, added sugar, salt, iron, thiamin, niacin. 1 cup	25	3	95	2	Trace	—	—	—	22	1	10	.6	—	0	.33	.05	4.4	13
375	Oats, puffed, added sugar, salt, minerals, vitamins. 1 cup	25	3	100	3	1	—	—	—	19	44	102	4.0	—	1,100	.33	.38	4.4	13
	Rice, puffed:																		
376	Plain, added iron, thiamin, niacin. 1 cup	15	4	60	1	Trace	—	—	—	13	3	14	.3	15	0	.07	.01	.7	0
377	Presweetened, added salt, iron, vitamins. 1 cup	28	3	115	1	0	—	—	—	26	3	14	(**)	43	[4][5]1,240	(**)	(**)	(**)	[4][5]15
378	Wheat flakes, added sugar, salt, iron, vitamins. 1 cup	30	4	105	3	Trace	—	—	—	24	12	83	4.8	81	1,320	.40	.45	5.3	16
	Wheat, puffed:																		
379	Plain, added iron, thiamin, niacin. 1 cup	15	3	55	2	Trace	—	—	—	12	4	48	.6	51	0	.08	.03	1.2	0
380	Presweetened, added salt, iron, vitamins. 1 cup	38	3	140	3	Trace	—	—	—	33	7	52	(**)	63	1,680	.50	.57	6.7	[4]20
381	Wheat, shredded, plain. 1 oblong biscuit or 1/2 cup spoon-size biscuits.	25	7	90	2	1	—	—	—	20	11	97	.9	87	0	.06	.03	1.1	0
382	Wheat germ, without salt and sugar, toasted. 1 tbsp.	6	4	25	2	1	—	—	—	3	3	70	.5	57	10	.11	.05	.3	1
383	Buckwheat flour, light, sifted. 1 cup	98	12	340	6	1	0.2	0.4	0.4	78	11	86	1.0	314	0	.08	.04	.4	0
384	Bulgur, canned, seasoned. 1 cup	135	56	245	8	4	—	—	—	44	27	263	1.9	151	0	.08	.05	4.1	0
	Cake icings. See Sugars and Sweets (items 532-536).																		
	Cakes made from cake mixes with enriched flour:[46]																		
	Angelfood:																		
385	Whole cake (9 3/4-in diam. tube cake). 1 cake	635	34	1,645	36	1	—	—	—	377	603	756	2.5	381	0	.37	.95	3.6	0
386	Piece, 1/12 of cake. 1 piece	53	34	135	3	Trace	—	—	—	32	50	63	.2	32	0	.03	.08	.3	0
	Coffeecake:																		
387	Whole cake (7 3/4 by 5 5/8 by 1 1/4 in). 1 cake	430	30	1,385	27	41	11.7	16.3	8.8	225	262	748	6.9	469	690	.82	.91	7.7	1
388	Piece, 1/6 of cake. 1 piece	72	30	230	5	7	2.0	2.7	1.5	38	44	125	1.2	78	120	.14	.15	1.3	Trace
	Cupcakes, made with egg, milk, 2 1/2-in diam.:																		
389	Without icing. 1 cupcake	25	26	90	1	3	.8	1.2	.7	14	40	59	.3	21	40	.05	.05	.4	Trace
390	With chocolate icing. 1 cupcake	36	22	130	2	5	2.0	1.6	.6	21	47	71	.4	42	60	.05	.06	.4	Trace
	Devil's food with chocolate icing:																		
391	Whole, 2 layer cake (8- or 9-in diam.). 1 cake	1,107	24	3,755	49	136	50.0	44.9	17.0	645	653	1,162	16.6	1,439	1,660	1.06	1.65	10.1	1
392	Piece, 1/16 of cake. 1 piece	69	24	235	3	8	3.1	2.8	1.1	40	41	72	1.0	90	100	.07	.10	.6	Trace
393	Cupcake, 2 1/2-in diam. 1 cupcake	35	24	120	2	4	1.6	1.4	.5	20	21	37	.5	46	50	.03	.05	.3	Trace

(A)	(B)	(C)	(D)	(E)	(F)	(G)	(H)	(I)	(J)	(K)	(L)	(M)	(N)	(O)	(P)	(Q)	(R)	(S)
	Gingerbread:																	
394	Whole cake (8-in square)——— 1 cake	570	1,575	18	39	9.7	16.6	10.0	291	513	570	8.6	1,562	Trace	0.84	1.00	7.4	Trace
395	Piece, 1/9 of cake——— 1 piece	63	175	2	4	1.1	1.8	1.1	32	57	63	.9	173	Trace	.09	.11	.8	.8
	White, 2 layer with chocolate icing:																	
396	Whole cake (8- or 9-in diam.)— 1 cake	1,140	4,000	44	122	48.2	46.4	20.0	716	1,129	2,041	11.4	1,322	680	1.50	1.77	12.5	2
397	Piece, 1/16 of cake——— 1 piece	71	250	3	8	3.0	2.9	1.2	45	70	127	.7	82	40	.09	.11	.8	Trace
	Yellow, 2 layer with chocolate icing:																	
398	Whole cake (8- or 9-in diam.)— 1 cake	1,108	3,735	45	125	47.8	47.8	20.3	638	1,008	2,017	12.2	1,208	1,550	1.24	1.67	10.6	2
399	Piece, 1/16 of cake——— 1 piece	69	235	3	8	3.0	3.0	1.3	40	63	126	.8	75	100	.08	.10	.7	Trace
	Cakes made from home recipes using enriched flour:[46][47]																	
	Boston cream pie with custard filling:																	
400	Whole cake (8-in diam.)——— 1 cake	825	2,490	41	78	23.0	30.1	15.2	412	553	833	8.2	[47]734	1,730	1.04	1.27	9.6	2
401	Piece, 1/12 of cake——— 1 piece	69	210	3	6	1.9	2.5	1.3	34	46	70	.7	[47]861	140	.09	.11	.8	Trace
	Fruitcake, dark:																	
402	Loaf, 1-lb (7 1/2 by 2 by 1 1/2 in)— 1 loaf	454	1,720	22	69	14.4	33.5	14.8	271	327	513	11.8	2,250	540	.72	.73	4.9	2
403	Slice, 1/30 of loaf——— 1 slice	15	55	1	2	.5	1.1	.5	9	11	17	.4	74	20	.02	.02	.2	Trace
	Plain, sheet cake:																	
	Without icing:																	
404	Whole cake (9-in square)——— 1 cake	777	2,830	35	108	29.5	44.4	23.9	434	497	793	8.5	[48]614	1,320	1.21	1.40	10.2	2
405	Piece, 1/9 of cake——— 1 piece	86	315	4	12	3.3	4.9	2.6	48	55	88	.9	[48]68	150	.13	.15	1.1	Trace
	With uncooked white icing:																	
406	Whole cake (9-in square)——— 1 cake	1,096	4,020	37	129	42.2	49.5	24.4	694	548	822	8.2	[48]669	2,190	1.22	1.47	10.2	2
407	Piece, 1/9 of cake——— 1 piece	121	445	4	14	4.7	5.5	2.7	77	61	91	.8	[48]74	240	.14	.16	1.1	Trace
	Pound:[49]																	
408	Loaf, 8 1/2 by 3 1/2 by 3 1/4 in.— 1 loaf	565	2,725	31	170	42.9	73.1	39.6	273	107	418	7.9	345	1,410	.90	.99	7.3	0
409	Slice, 1/17 of loaf——— 1 slice	33	160	2	10	2.5	4.3	2.3	16	6	24	.5	20	80	.05	.06	.4	0
	Spongecake:																	
410	Whole cake (9 3/4-in diam. tube cake)— 1 cake	790	2,345	60	45	13.1	15.8	5.7	427	237	885	13.4	687	3,560	1.10	1.64	7.4	Trace
411	Piece, 1/12 of cake——— 1 piece	66	195	5	4	1.1	1.3	.5	36	20	74	1.1	57	300	.09	.14	.6	Trace
	Cookies made with enriched flour:[50][51]																	
	Brownies with nuts:																	
	Home-prepared, 1 3/4 by 1 3/4 by 7/8 in:																	
412	From home recipe——— 1 brownie	20	95	1	6	1.5	3.0	1.2	10	8	30	.4	38	40	.04	.03	.2	Trace
413	From commercial recipe——— 1 brownie	20	85	1	4	.9	1.4	1.3	13	9	27	.4	34	20	.03	.02	.2	Trace
414	Frozen, with chocolate icing,[52] 1 1/2 by 1 3/4 by 7/8 in.— 1 brownie	25	105	1	5	2.0	2.2	.7	15	10	31	.4	44	50	.03	.03	.2	Trace
	Chocolate chip:																	
415	Commercial, 2 1/4-in diam., 3/8 in thick.— 4 cookies	42	200	2	9	2.8	2.9	2.2	29	16	48	1.0	56	50	.10	.17	.9	Trace
416	From home recipe, 2 1/3-in diam.— 4 cookies	40	205	2	12	3.5	4.5	2.9	24	14	40	.8	47	40	.06	.06	.5	Trace
417	Fig bars, square (1 5/8 by 1 5/8 by 3/8 in) or rectangular (1 1/2 by 1 3/4 by 1/2 in).— 4 cookies	56	200	2	3	.8	1.2	.7	42	44	34	1.0	111	60	.04	.14	.9	Trace
418	Gingersnaps, 2-in diam., 1/4 in thick.— 4 cookies	28	90	2	2	.7	1.0	.6	22	20	13	.7	129	20	.08	.06	.7	0
419	Macaroons, 2 3/4-in diam., 1/4 in thick.— 2 cookies	38	180	2	9	—	—	—	25	10	32	.3	176	0	.02	.06	.2	0
420	Oatmeal with raisins, 2 5/8-in diam., 1/4 in thick.— 4 cookies	52	235	3	8	2.0	3.3	2.0	38	11	53	1.4	192	30	.15	.10	1.0	Trace

[44]Value varies with the brand. Consult the label.
[45]Applies to product with added nutrient. Without added nutrient, value is trace.
[46]Excepting angelfood cake, cakes were made from mixes containing vegetable shortening; icings, with butter.
[47]Excepting spongecake, vegetable shortening used for cake portion; butter, for icing. If butter or margarine used for cake portion, vitamin A values would be higher.
[48]Applies to product made with a sodium aluminum-sulfate type baking powder. With a low-sodium type baking powder containing potassium, value would be about twice the amount shown.
[49]Equal weights of flour, sugar, eggs, and vegetable shortening.
[50]Products are commercial unless otherwise specified.
[51]Made with enriched flour and vegetable shortening except for macaroons which do not contain flour or shortening.
[52]Icing made with butter.

(Dashes (—) denote lack of reliable data for a constituent believed to be present in measurable amount)

							NUTRIENTS IN INDICATED QUANTITY											
						Fatty Acids												
Item No.	Foods, approximate measures, units, and weight (edible part unless footnotes indicate otherwise)	Water	Food energy	Pro-tein	Fat	Satu-rated (total)	Unsaturated Oleic	Lino-leic	Carbo-hydrate	Calcium	Phos-phorus	Iron	Potas-sium	Vitamin A value	Thiamin	Ribo-flavin	Niacin	Ascorbic acid
(A)	(B)	(C)	(D)	(E)	(F)	(G)	(H)	(I)	(J)	(K)	(L)	(M)	(N)	(O)	(P)	(Q)	(R)	(S)
		Per-cent	Cal-ories	Grams	Grams	Grams	Grams	Grams	Grams	Milli-grams	Milli-grams	Milli-grams	Milli-grams	Inter-national units	Milli-grams	Milli-grams	Milli-grams	Milli-grams
	GRAIN PRODUCTS—Con.																	
	Cookies made with enriched flour[50][51]—Continued																	
421	Plain, prepared from commercial chilled dough, 2 1/2-in diam., 1/4 in thick. 4 cookies	5	240	2	12	3.0	5.2	2.9	31	17	35	0.6	23	30	0.10	0.08	0.9	0
422	Sandwich type (chocolate or vanilla), 1 3/4-in diam., 3/8 in thick. 4 cookies	2	200	2	9	2.2	3.9	2.2	28	10	96	.7	15	0	.06	.10	.7	0
423	Vanilla wafers, 1 3/4-in diam., 1/4 in thick. 10 cookies	3	185	2	6	—	—	—	30	16	25	.6	29	50	.10	.09	.8	0
	Cornmeal:																	
424	Whole-ground, unbolted, dry form. 1 cup	12	435	11	5	.5	1.0	2.5	90	24	312	2.9	346	[53]3620	.46	.13	2.4	0
425	Bolted (nearly whole-grain), dry form. 1 cup	12	440	11	4	.5	.9	2.1	91	21	272	2.2	303	[53]3590	.37	.10	2.3	0
	Degermed, enriched:																	
426	Dry form 1 cup	12	500	11	2	.2	.4	.9	108	8	137	4.0	166	[53]610	.61	.36	4.8	0
427	Cooked 1 cup	88	120	3	Trace	Trace	.1	.2	26	2	34	1.0	38	[53]140	.14	.10	1.2	0
	Degermed, unenriched:																	
428	Dry form 1 cup	12	500	11	2	.2	.4	.9	108	8	137	1.5	166	[53]610	.19	.07	1.4	0
429	Cooked 1 cup	88	120	3	Trace	Trace	.1	.2	26	2	34	.5	38	[53]140	.05	.02	.2	0
	Crackers:[38]																	
430	Graham, plain, 2 1/2-in square 2 crackers	6	55	1	1	.3	.5	.3	10	6	21	.5	55	0	.02	.08	.5	0
431	Rye wafers, whole-grain, 1 7/8 by 3 1/2 in. 2 wafers	6	45	2	Trace	—	—	—	10	7	50	.5	78	0	.04	.03	.2	0
432	Saltines, made with enriched flour. 4 crackers or 1 packet	4	50	1	1	.3	.5	.4	8	2	10	.5	13	0	.05	.05	.4	0
	Danish pastry (enriched flour), plain without fruit or nuts:[54]																	
433	Packaged ring, 12 oz 1 ring	22	1,435	25	80	24.3	31.7	16.5	155	170	371	6.1	381	1,050	.97	1.01	8.6	Trace
434	Round piece, about 4 1/4-in diam. by 1 in. 1 pastry	22	275	5	15	4.7	6.1	3.2	30	33	71	1.2	73	200	.18	.19	1.7	Trace
435	Ounce 1 oz	22	120	2	7	2.0	2.7	1.4	13	14	31	.5	32	90	.08	.08	.7	Trace
	Doughnuts, made with enriched flour:[38]																	
436	Cake type, plain, 2 1/2-in diam., 1 in high. 1 doughnut	24	100	1	5	1.2	2.0	1.1	13	10	48	.4	23	20	.05	.05	.4	Trace
437	Yeast-leavened, glazed, 3 3/4-in diam., 1 1/4 in high. 1 doughnut	26	205	3	11	3.3	5.8	3.3	22	16	33	.6	34	25	.10	.10	.8	0
	Macaroni, enriched, cooked (cut lengths, elbows, shells):																	
	Firm stage (hot):																	
438	1 cup	64	190	7	1	—	—	—	39	14	85	1.4	103	0	.23	.13	1.8	0
	Tender stage:																	
439	Cold macaroni 1 cup	73	115	4	Trace	—	—	—	24	8	53	.9	64	0	.15	.08	1.2	0
440	Hot macaroni 1 cup	73	155	5	1	—	—	—	32	11	70	1.3	85	.0	.20	.11	1.5	0
	Macaroni (enriched) and cheese:																	
441	Canned[55] 1 cup	80	230	9	10	4.2	3.1	1.4	26	199	182	1.0	139	260	.12	.24	1.0	Trace
442	From home recipe (served hot)[56] 1 cup	58	430	17	22	8.9	8.8	2.9	40	362	322	1.8	240	860	.20	.40	1.8	Trace
	Muffins made with enriched flour:[38]																	
	From home recipe:																	
443	Blueberry, 2 3/8-in diam., 1 1/2 in high. 1 muffin	39	110	3	4	1.1	1.4	.7	17	34	53	.6	46	90	.09	.10	.7	Trace
444	Bran 1 muffin	35	105	3	4	1.2	1.4	.8	17	57	162	1.5	172	90	.07	.10	1.7	Trace
445	Corn (enriched degermed corn-meal and flour), 2 3/8-in diam., 1 1/2 in high. 1 muffin	33	125	3	4	1.2	1.6	.9	19	42	68	.7	54	[57]120	.10	.10	.7	Trace

Weight column (Grams): 421: 48; 422: 40; 423: 40; 424: 122; 425: 122; 426: 138; 427: 240; 428: 138; 429: 240; 430: 14; 431: 13; 432: 11; 433: 340; 434: 65; 435: 28; 436: 25; 437: 50; 438: 130; 439: 105; 440: 140; 441: 240; 442: 200; 443: 40; 444: 40; 445: 40.

(A)	(B)	(C)	(D)	(E)	(F)	(G)	(H)	(I)	(J)	(K)	(L)	(M)	(N)	(O)	(P)	(Q)	(R)	(S)
446	Plain, 3-in diam., 1 1/2 in high. — 1 muffin — 40	38	120	3	4	1.0	1.7	1.0	17	42	60	0.6	50	40	0.09	0.12	0.9	Trace
	From mix, egg, milk:																	
447	Corn, 2 3/8-in diam., 1 1/2 in high.[58] — 1 muffin — 40	30	130	3	4	1.2	1.7	.9	20	96	152	.6	44	[57]100	.08	.09	.7	Trace
448	Noodles (egg noodles), enriched, cooked. — 1 cup — 160	71	200	7	2	—	—	—	37	16	94	1.4	70	110	.22	.13	1.9	0
449	Noodles, chow mein, canned. — 1 cup — 45	1	220	6	11	—	—	—	26	—	—	—	—	—	—	—	—	—
	Pancakes, (4-in diam.).[38]																	
450	Buckwheat, made from mix (with buckwheat and enriched flours), egg and milk added. — 1 cake — 27	58	55	2	2	.8	.9	.4	6	59	91	.4	66	60	.04	.05	.2	Trace
	Plain:																	
451	Made from home recipe using enriched flour. — 1 cake — 27	50	60	2	2	.5	.8	.5	9	27	38	.4	33	30	.06	.07	.5	Trace
452	Made from mix with enriched flour, egg and milk added. — 1 cake — 27	51	60	2	2	.7	.7	.3	9	58	70	.3	42	70	.04	.06	.2	Trace
	Pies, piecrust made with enriched flour, vegetable shortening (9-in diam.):																	
	Apple:																	
453	Whole — 1 pie — 945	48	2,420	21	105	27.0	44.5	25.2	360	76	208	6.6	756	280	1.06	.79	9.3	9
454	Sector, 1/7 of pie — 1 sector — 135	48	345	3	15	3.9	6.4	3.6	51	11	30	.9	108	40	.15	.11	1.3	2
	Banana cream:																	
455	Whole — 1 pie — 910	54	2,010	41	85	26.7	33.2	16.2	279	601	746	7.3	1,847	2,280	.77	1.51	7.0	9
456	Sector, 1/7 of pie — 1 sector — 130	54	285	6	12	3.8	4.7	2.3	40	86	107	1.0	264	330	.11	.22	1.0	1
	Blueberry:																	
457	Whole — 1 pie — 945	51	2,285	23	102	24.8	43.7	25.1	330	104	217	9.5	614	280	1.03	.80	10.0	28
458	Sector, 1/7 of pie — 1 sector — 135	51	325	3	15	3.5	6.2	3.6	47	15	31	1.4	88	40	.15	.11	1.4	4
	Cherry:																	
459	Whole — 1 pie — 945	47	2,465	25	107	28.2	45.0	25.3	363	132	236	6.6	992	4,160	1.09	.84	9.8	Trace
460	Sector, 1/7 of pie — 1 sector — 135	47	350	4	15	4.0	6.4	3.6	52	19	34	.9	142	590	.16	.12	1.4	Trace
	Custard:																	
461	Whole — 1 pie — 910	58	1,985	56	101	33.9	38.5	17.5	213	874	1,028	8.2	1,247	2,090	.79	1.92	5.6	0
462	Sector, 1/7 of pie — 1 sector — 130	58	285	8	14	4.8	5.5	2.5	30	125	147	1.2	178	300	.11	.27	.8	0
	Lemon meringue:																	
463	Whole — 1 pie — 840	47	2,140	31	86	26.1	33.8	16.4	317	118	412	6.7	420	1,430	.61	.84	5.2	25
464	Sector, 1/7 of pie — 1 sector — 120	47	305	4	12	3.7	4.8	2.3	45	17	59	1.0	60	200	.09	.12	.7	4
	Mince:																	
465	Whole — 1 pie — 945	43	2,560	24	109	28.0	45.9	25.2	389	265	359	13.3	1,682	20	.96	.86	9.8	9
466	Sector, 1/7 of pie — 1 sector — 135	43	365	3	16	4.0	6.6	3.6	56	38	51	1.9	240	Trace	.14	.12	1.4	1
	Peach:																	
467	Whole — 1 pie — 945	48	2,410	24	101	24.8	43.7	25.1	361	95	274	8.5	1,408	6,900	1.04	.97	14.0	28
468	Sector, 1/7 of pie — 1 sector — 135	48	345	4	14	3.5	6.2	3.6	52	14	39	1.2	201	990	.15	.14	2.0	4
	Pecan:																	
469	Whole — 1 pie — 825	20	3,450	42	189	27.8	101.0	44.2	423	388	850	25.6	1,015	1,320	1.80	.95	6.9	Trace
470	Sector, 1/7 of pie — 1 sector — 118	20	495	6	27	4.0	14.4	6.3	61	55	122	3.7	145	190	.26	.14	1.0	Trace
	Pumpkin:																	
471	Whole — 1 pie — 910	59	1,920	36	102	37.4	37.5	16.6	223	464	628	7.3	1,456	22,480	.78	1.27	7.0	Trace
472	Sector, 1/7 of pie — 1 sector — 130	59	275	5	15	5.4	5.4	2.4	32	66	90	1.0	208	3,210	.11	.18	1.0	Trace
473	Piecrust (home recipe) made with enriched flour and vegetable shortening, baked. — 1 pie shell, 9-in diam. — 180	15	900	11	60	14.8	26.1	14.9	79	25	90	3.1	89	0	.47	.40	5.0	0
474	Piecrust mix with enriched flour and vegetable shortening, 10-oz pkg. prepared and baked. — Piecrust for 2-crust pie, 9-in diam. — 320	19	1,485	20	93	22.7	39.7	23.4	141	131	272	6.1	179	0	1.07	.79	9.9	0

except for macaroons which do not contain flour or shortening.

[38] Made with vegetable shortening.
[50] Products are commercial unless otherwise specified.
[51] Made with enriched flour and vegetable shortening except where specified.
[53] Applies to yellow varieties; white varieties contain only a trace.
[54] Contains vegetable shortening and butter.
[55] Made with corn oil.
[56] Made with regular margarine.
[57] Applies to product made with yellow cornmeal.
[58] Made with enriched degermed cornmeal and enriched flour.

(Dashes (—) denote lack of reliable data for a constituent believed to be present in measurable amount)

NUTRIENTS IN INDICATED QUANTITY

Item No. (A)	Foods, approximate measures, units, and weight (edible part unless footnotes indicate otherwise) (B)	Grams	Water (C) Per cent	Food energy (D) Calories	Protein (E) Grams	Fat (F) Grams	Fatty Acids Saturated (total) (G) Grams	Unsaturated Oleic (H) Grams	Linoleic (I) Grams	Carbohydrate (J) Grams	Calcium (K) Milligrams	Phosphorus (L) Milligrams	Iron (M) Milligrams	Potassium (N) Milligrams	Vitamin A value (O) International units	Thiamin (P) Milligrams	Riboflavin (Q) Milligrams	Niacin (R) Milligrams	Ascorbic acid (S) Milligrams
	GRAIN PRODUCTS—Con.																		
475	Pizza (cheese) baked, 4 3/4-in sector; 1/8 of 12-in diam. pie.[19] — 1 sector	60	45	145	6	4	1.7	1.5	0.6	22	86	89	1.1	67	230	0.16	0.18	1.6	4
	Popcorn, popped:																		
476	Plain, large kernel — 1 cup	6	4	25	1	Trace	Trace	.1	.2	5	1	17	.2	—	—	—	.01	.1	0
477	With oil (coconut) and salt added, large kernel — 1 cup	9	3	40	1	2	1.5	.2	.2	5	1	19	.2	—	—	—	.01	.2	0
478	Sugar-coated — 1 cup	35	4	135	2	1	.5	.2	.4	30	2	47	.5	—	—	—	.02	.4	0
	Pretzels, made with enriched flour:																		
479	Dutch, twisted, 2 3/4 by 2 5/8 in. — 1 pretzel	16	5	60	2	1	—	—	—	12	4	21	.2	21	0	.05	.04	.7	0
480	Thin, twisted, 3 1/4 by 2 1/4 by 1/4 in. — 10 pretzels	60	5	235	6	3	—	—	—	46	13	79	.9	78	0	.20	.15	2.5	0
481	Stick, 2 1/4 in long — 10 pretzels	3	5	10	Trace	Trace				2	1	4	Trace	4	0	.01	.01	.1	0
	Rice, white, enriched: Long grain:																		
482	Instant, ready-to-serve, hot — 1 cup	165	73	180	4	Trace	Trace	Trace	Trace	40	5	31	1.3	—	0	.21	(59)	1.7	0
	Raw:																		
483	— 1 cup	185	12	670	12	1	.2	.2	.2	149	44	174	5.4	170	0	.81	.06	6.5	0
484	Cooked, served hot — 1 cup	205	73	225	4	Trace	.1	.1	.1	50	21	57	1.8	57	0	.23	.02	2.1	0
	Parboiled:																		
485	Raw — 1 cup	185	10	685	14	1	.2	.1	.1	150	111	370	5.4	278	0	.81	.07	6.5	0
486	Cooked, served hot — 1 cup	175	73	185	4	Trace	.1	.1	.1	41	33	100	1.4	75	0	.19	.02	2.1	0
	Rolls, enriched:[38] Commercial:																		
487	Brown-and-serve (12 per 12-oz pkg.), browned. — 1 roll	26	27	85	2	2	.4	.7	.5	14	20	23	.5	25	Trace	.10	.06	.9	Trace
488	Cloverleaf or pan, 2 1/2-in diam., 2 in high. — 1 roll	28	31	85	2	2	.4	.6	.4	15	21	24	.5	27	Trace	.11	.07	.9	Trace
489	Frankfurter and hamburger (8 per 11 1/2-oz pkg.) — 1 roll	40	31	120	3	2	.5	.8	.6	21	30	34	.8	38	Trace	.16	.10	1.3	Trace
490	Hard, 3 3/4-in diam., 2 in high. — 1 roll	50	25	155	5	2	.4	.6	.5	30	24	46	1.2	49	Trace	.20	.12	1.7	Trace
491	Hoagie or submarine, 11 1/2 by 3 by 2 1/2 in. — 1 roll	135	31	390	12	4	.9	1.4	1.4	75	58	115	3.0	122	Trace	.54	.32	4.5	Trace
	From home recipe:																		
492	Cloverleaf, 2 1/2-in diam., 2 in high. — 1 roll	35	26	120	3	3	.8	1.1	.7	20	16	36	.7	41	30	.12	.12	1.2	Trace
	Spaghetti, enriched, cooked:																		
493	Firm stage, "al dente," served hot. — 1 cup	130	64	190	7	1				39	14	85	1.4	103	0	.23	.13	1.8	0
494	Tender stage, served hot — 1 cup	140	73	155	5	1				32	11	70	1.3	85	0	.20	.11	1.5	0
	Spaghetti (enriched) in tomato sauce with cheese:																		
495	From home recipe — 1 cup	250	77	260	9	9	2.0	5.4	.7	37	80	135	2.3	408	1,080	.25	.18	2.3	13
496	Canned — 1 cup	250	80	190	6	2	.5	.3	.4	39	40	88	2.8	303	930	.35	.28	4.5	10
	Spaghetti (enriched) with meat balls and tomato sauce:																		
497	From home recipe — 1 cup	248	70	330	19	12	3.3	6.3	.9	39	124	236	3.7	665	1,590	.25	.30	4.0	22
498	Canned — 1 cup	250	78	260	12	10	2.2	3.3	3.9	29	53	113	3.3	245	1,000	.15	.18	2.3	5
499	Toaster pastries — 1 pastry	50	12	200	3	6				36	[60]54	[60]67	1.9	[60]74	500	.16	.17	2.1	([60])
	Waffles, made with enriched flour, 7-in diam.:[38]																		
500	From home recipe — 1 waffle	75	41	210	7	7	2.3	2.8	1.4	28	85	130	1.3	109	250	.17	.23	1.4	Trace
501	From mix, egg and milk added — 1 waffle	75	42	205	7	8	2.8	2.9	1.2	27	179	257	1.0	146	170	.14	.22	.9	Trace

(A)	(B)	(C)	(D)	(E)	(F)	(G)	(H)	(I)	(J)	(K)	(L)	(M)	(N)	(O)	(P)	(Q)	(R)	(S)
	Wheat flours:																	
	All-purpose or family flour, enriched:																	
502	Sifted, spooned — 1 cup	12	420	12	1	0.2	0.1	0.5	88	18	100	3.3	109	0	0.74	0.46	6.1	0
503	Unsifted, spooned — 1 cup	12	455	13	1	.2	.1	.5	95	20	109	3.6	119	0	.80	.50	6.6	0
504	Cake or pastry flour, enriched, sifted, spooned. 1 cup	12	350	7	1	.1	.1	.3	76	16	70	2.8	91	0	.61	.38	5.1	0
505	Self-rising, enriched, unsifted, spooned. 1 cup	12	440	12	1	.2	.1	.5	93	331	583	3.6	—	0	.80	.50	6.6	0
506	Whole-wheat, from hard wheats, stirred. 1 cup	12	400	16	2	.4	.2	1.0	85	49	446	4.0	444	0	.66	.14	5.2	0
	LEGUMES (DRY), NUTS, SEEDS; RELATED PRODUCTS																	
	Almonds, shelled:																	
507	Chopped (about 130 almonds) 1 cup	5	775	24	70	5.6	47.7	12.8	25	304	655	6.1	1,005	0	.31	1.20	4.6	Trace
508	Slivered, not pressed down (about 115 almonds). 1 cup	5	690	21	62	5.0	42.2	11.3	22	269	580	5.4	889	0	.28	1.06	4.0	Trace
	Beans, dry:																	
	Common varieties as Great Northern, navy, and others:																	
	Cooked, drained:																	
509	Great Northern 1 cup	69	210	14	1	—	—	—	38	90	266	4.9	749	0	.25	.13	1.3	0
510	Pea (navy) 1 cup	69	225	15	1	—	—	—	40	95	281	5.1	790	0	.27	.13	1.3	0
	Canned, solids and liquid:																	
	White with—																	
511	Frankfurters (sliced) 1 cup	71	365	19	18	2.4	2.8	.6	32	94	303	4.8	668	330	.18	.15	3.3	Trace
512	Pork and tomato sauce 1 cup	71	310	16	7	4.3	5.0	1.1	48	138	235	4.6	536	330	.20	.08	1.5	5
513	Pork and sweet sauce 1 cup	66	385	16	12	—	—	—	54	161	291	5.9	673	10	.15	.10	1.3	—
514	Red kidney 1 cup	76	230	15	1	—	—	—	42	74	278	4.6	1,163	10	.13	.10	1.5	—
515	Lima, cooked, drained 1 cup	64	260	16	1	—	—	—	49	55	293	5.9	573	30	.25	.11	1.3	—
516	Blackeye peas, dry, cooked (with residual cooking liquid). 1 cup	80	190	13	1	—	—	—	35	43	238	3.3	573	30	.40	.10	1.0	—
517	Brazil nuts, shelled (6-8 large kernels). 1 oz	5	185	4	19	4.8	6.2	7.1	3	53	196	1.0	203	Trace	.27	.03	.5	—
518	Cashew nuts, roasted in oil 1 cup	5	785	24	64	12.9	36.8	10.2	41	53	522	5.3	650	140	.60	.35	2.5	—
	Coconut meat, fresh:																	
519	Piece, about 2 by 2 by 1/2 in 1 piece	51	155	2	16	14.0	.9	.3	4	6	43	.8	115	0	.02	.01	.2	1
520	Shredded or grated, not pressed down. 1 cup	51	275	3	28	24.8	1.6	.5	8	10	76	1.4	205	0	.04	.02	.4	2
521	Filberts (hazelnuts), chopped (about 80 kernels). 1 cup	6	730	14	72	5.1	55.2	7.3	19	240	388	3.9	810	—	.53	—	1.0	Trace
522	Lentils, whole, cooked 1 cup	72	210	16	Trace	13.7	33.0	20.7	39	50	238	4.2	498	40	.14	.12	1.2	0
523	Peanuts, roasted in oil, salted (whole, halves, chopped). 1 cup	2	840	37	72	—	—	—	27	107	577	3.0	971	—	.46	.19	24.8	0
524	Peanut butter 1 tbsp	2	95	4	8	1.5	3.7	2.3	3	9	61	.3	100	0	.02	.02	2.4	0
525	Peas, split, dry, cooked 1 cup	70	230	16	1	7.2	50.5	20.0	42	22	178	3.4	592	80	.30	.18	1.8	—
526	Pecans, chopped or pieces (about 120 large halves). 1 cup	3	810	11	84	11.8	23.5	27.5	17	86	341	2.8	712	150	1.01	.15	1.1	2
527	Pumpkin and squash kernels, dry, hulled. 1 cup	4	775	41	65	11.8	13.7	43.2	21	71	1,602	15.7	1,386	100	.34	.27	3.4	—
528	Sunflower seeds, dry, hulled 1 cup	5	810	35	69	8.2	13.7	43.2	29	174	1,214	10.3	1,334	70	2.84	.33	7.8	—
	Walnuts:																	
	Black:																	
529	Chopped or broken kernels 1 cup	3	785	26	74	6.3	13.3	45.7	19	Trace	713	7.5	575	380	.28	.14	.9	—
530	Ground (finely) 1 cup	3	500	16	47	4.0	8.5	29.2	12	Trace	456	4.8	368	240	.18	.09	.6	—
531	Persian or English, chopped (about 60 halves). 1 cup	4	780	18	77	8.4	11.8	42.2	19	119	456	3.7	540	40	.40	.16	1.1	2

[19] Crust made with vegetable shortening and enriched flour. Consult the label.
[39] Made with vegetable shortening.
[59] Product may or may not be enriched with riboflavin. Consult the label.
[60] Value varies with the brand. Consult the label.

(Dashes (—) denote lack of reliable data for a constituent believed to be present in measurable amount)

NUTRIENTS IN INDICATED QUANTITY

Item No. (A)	Foods, approximate measures, units, and weight (edible part unless footnotes indicate otherwise) (B)	Grams	Water (C)	Food energy (D)	Protein (E)	Fat (F)	Fatty Acids Saturated (total) (G)	Unsaturated Oleic (H)	Linoleic (I)	Carbohydrate (J)	Calcium (K)	Phosphorus (L)	Iron (M)	Potassium (N)	Vitamin A value (O)	Thiamin (P)	Riboflavin (Q)	Niacin (R)	Ascorbic acid (S)
		Grams	Percent	Calories	Grams	Grams	Grams	Grams	Grams	Grams	Milligrams	Milligrams	Milligrams	Milligrams	International units	Milligrams	Milligrams	Milligrams	Milligrams
	SUGARS AND SWEETS																		
	Cake icings:																		
	Boiled, white:																		
532	Plain— 1 cup	94	18	295	1	0	0	0		75	2	2	Trace	17	0	Trace	0.03	Trace	0
533	With coconut— 1 cup	166	15	605	3	13	11.0	.9	Trace	124	10	50	Trace	277	0	0.02	.07	0.3	0
	Uncooked:																		
534	Chocolate made with milk and butter. 1 cup	275	14	1,035	9	38	23.4	11.7	1.0	185	165	305	3.3	536	580	.06	.28	.6	1
535	Creamy fudge from mix and water. 1 cup	245	15	830	7	16	5.1	6.7	3.1	183	96	218	2.7	238	Trace	.05	.20	.7	Trace
536	White— 1 cup	319	11	1,200	2	21	12.7	5.1	.5	260	48	38	Trace	57	860	Trace	.06	Trace	Trace
	Candy:																		
537	Caramels, plain or chocolate— 1 oz	28	8	115	1	3	1.6	1.1	.1	22	42	35	.4	54	Trace	.01	.05	.1	Trace
	Chocolate:																		
538	Milk, plain— 1 oz	28	1	145	2	9	5.5	3.0	.3	16	65	65	.3	109	80	.02	.10	.1	Trace
539	Semisweet, small pieces (60 per oz). 1 cup or 6-oz pkg	170	1	860	7	61	36.2	19.8	1.7	97	51	255	4.4	553	30	.02	.14	.9	0
540	Chocolate-coated peanuts— 1 oz	28	1	160	5	12	4.0	4.7	2.1	11	33	84	.4	143	Trace	.10	.05	2.1	Trace
541	Fondant, uncoated (mints, candy corn, other). 1 oz	28	8	105	Trace	1	.1	.3	.1	25	4	2	.3	1	0	Trace	Trace	Trace	0
542	Fudge, chocolate, plain— 1 oz	28	8	115	1	3	1.3	1.4	.6	21	22	24	.3	42	Trace	.01	.03	.1	Trace
543	Gum drops— 1 oz	28	12	100	Trace	Trace	—	—	—	25	2	Trace	.1	1	0	0	0	0	0
544	Hard— 1 oz	28	1	110	0	Trace	—	—	—	28	6	2	.5	1	0	0	0	0	0
545	Marshmallows— 1 oz	28	17	90	1	Trace	—	—	—	23	5	2	.5	2	0	0	Trace	0	0
	Chocolate-flavored beverage powders (about 4 heaping tsp per oz):																		
546	With nonfat dry milk— 1 oz	28	2	100	5	1	.5	.3	Trace	20	167	155	.5	227	10	.04	.21	.2	1
547	Without milk— 1 oz	28	1	100	1	1	.4	.2	Trace	25	9	48	.6	142	0	.01	.03	.1	0
548	Honey, strained or extracted— 1 tbsp	21	17	65	Trace	0	0	0	0	17	1	1	.1	11	0	Trace	.01	Trace	Trace
549	Jams and preserves— 1 tbsp	20	29	55	Trace	Trace	—	—	—	14	4	2	.2	18	Trace	Trace	.01	Trace	Trace
550	1 packet	14	29	40	Trace	Trace	—	—	—	10	3	1	.1	12	Trace	Trace	.01	Trace	Trace
551	Jellies— 1 tbsp	18	29	50	Trace	Trace	—	—	—	13	4	1	.3	14	Trace	Trace	.01	Trace	Trace
552	1 packet	14	29	40	Trace	Trace	—	—	—	10	3	1	.2	11	Trace	Trace	Trace	Trace	1
	Sirups:																		
	Chocolate-flavored sirup or topping:																		
553	Thin type— 1 fl oz or 2 tbsp	38	32	90	1	1	.5	.3	Trace	24	6	35	.6	106	Trace	.01	.03	.2	0
554	Fudge type— 1 fl oz or 2 tbsp	38	25	125	2	5	3.1	1.6	.1	20	48	60	.5	107	60	.02	.08	.2	Trace
	Molasses, cane:																		
555	Light (first extraction)— 1 tbsp	20	24	50	—	—	—	—	—	13	33	9	.9	183	—	.01	.01	Trace	—
556	Blackstrap (third extraction)— 1 tbsp	20	24	45	—	—	—	—	—	11	137	17	3.2	585	—	.02	.04	.4	—
557	Sorghum— 1 tbsp	21	23	55	—	—	—	—	—	14	35	5	2.6	—	—	—	.02	Trace	—
558	Table blends, chiefly corn, light and dark. 1 tbsp	21	24	60	0	0	0	0	0	15	9	3	.8	1	0	0	0	0	0
	Sugars:																		
559	Brown, pressed down— 1 cup	220	2	820	0	0	0	0	0	212	187	42	7.5	757	0	.02	.07	.4	0
	White:																		
560	Granulated— 1 cup	200	1	770	0	0	0	0	0	199	0	0	.2	6	0	0	0	0	0
561	1 tbsp	12	1	45	0	0	0	0	0	12	0	0	Trace	Trace	0	0	0	0	0
562	1 packet	6	1	23	0	0	0	0	0	6	0	0	Trace	Trace	0	0	0	0	0
563	Powdered, sifted, spooned into cup. 1 cup	100	1	385	0	0	0	0	0	100	0	0	.1	3	0	0	0	0	0

VEGETABLE AND VEGETABLE PRODUCTS

(A)	(B)	(C)	(D)	(E)	(F)	(G)	(H)	(I)	(J)	(K)	(L)	(M)	(N)	(O)	(P)	(Q)	(R)	(S)
	Asparagus, green:																	
	Cooked, drained:																	
	Cuts and tips, 1 1/2- to 2-in lengths:																	
564	From raw--- 1 cup	94	30	3	Trace	---	---	---	5	30	73	0.9	265	1,310	0.23	0.26	2.0	38
565	From frozen--- 1 cup	93	40	6	Trace	---	---	---	6	40	115	2.2	396	1,530	.25	.23	1.8	41
	Spears, 1/2-in diam. at base:																	
566	From raw--- 4 spears	94	10	1	Trace	---	---	---	2	13	30	.4	110	540	.10	.11	.8	16
567	From frozen--- 4 spears	92	15	2	Trace	---	---	---	2	13	40	.7	143	470	.10	.08	.7	16
568	Canned, spears, 1/2-in diam, at base. 4 spears	93	15	2	Trace	---	---	---	3	15	42	1.5	133	640	.05	.08	.6	12
	Beans:																	
	Lima, immature seeds, frozen, cooked, drained:																	
569	Thick-seeded types (Fordhooks) 1 cup	74	170	10	Trace	---	---	---	32	34	153	2.9	724	390	.12	.09	1.7	29
570	Thin-seeded types (baby limas) 1 cup	69	210	13	Trace	---	---	---	40	63	227	4.7	709	400	.16	.09	2.2	22
	Snap:																	
	Green:																	
	Cooked, drained:																	
571	From raw (cuts and French style). 1 cup	92	30	2	Trace	---	---	---	7	63	46	.8	189	680	.09	.11	.6	15
	From frozen:																	
572	Cuts--- 1 cup	92	35	2	Trace	---	---	---	8	54	43	.9	205	780	.09	.12	.5	7
573	French style--- 1 cup	92	35	2	Trace	---	---	---	8	49	39	1.2	177	690	.08	.10	.4	9
574	Canned, drained solids (cuts). 1 cup	92	30	2	Trace	---	---	---	7	61	34	2.0	128	630	.04	.07	.4	5
	Yellow or wax:																	
	Cooked, drained:																	
575	From raw (cuts and French style). 1 cup	93	30	2	Trace	---	---	---	6	63	46	.8	189	290	.09	.11	.6	16
	From frozen (cuts):																	
576	From frozen (cuts)--- 1 cup	92	35	2	Trace	---	---	---	8	47	42	.9	221	140	.09	.11	.5	8
577	Canned, drained solids (cuts). 1 cup	92	30	2	Trace	---	---	---	7	61	34	2.0	128	140	.04	.07	.4	7
	Beans, mature. See Beans, dry (items 509-515) and Blackeye peas, dry (item 516).																	
	Bean sprouts (mung):																	
578	Raw--- 1 cup	89	35	4	Trace	---	---	---	7	20	67	1.4	234	20	.14	.14	.8	20
579	Cooked, drained--- 1 cup	91	35	4	Trace	---	---	---	7	21	60	1.1	195	30	.11	.13	.9	8
	Beets:																	
	Cooked, drained, peeled:																	
580	Whole beets, 2-in diam.--- 2 beets	89	30	1	Trace	---	---	---	7	14	23	.5	208	20	.03	.04	.3	6
581	Diced or sliced--- 1 cup	91	55	2	Trace	---	---	---	12	24	39	.9	354	30	.05	.07	.5	10
	Canned, drained solids:																	
582	Whole beets, small--- 1 cup	89	60	2	Trace	---	---	---	14	30	29	1.1	267	30	.02	.05	.2	5
583	Diced or sliced--- 1 cup	89	65	2	Trace	---	---	---	15	32	31	1.2	284	30	.02	.05	.2	5
584	Beet greens, leaves and stems, cooked, drained. 1 cup	94	25	2	Trace	---	---	---	5	144	36	2.8	481	7,400	.10	.22	.4	22
	Blackeye peas, immature seeds, cooked and drained:																	
585	From raw--- 1 cup	72	180	13	1	---	---	---	30	40	241	3.5	625	580	.50	.18	2.3	28
586	From frozen--- 1 cup	66	220	15	1	---	---	---	40	43	286	4.8	573	290	.68	.19	2.4	15
	Broccoli, cooked, drained:																	
	From raw:																	
587	Stalk, medium size--- 1 stalk	91	45	6	1	---	---	---	8	158	112	1.4	481	4,500	.16	.36	1.4	162
588	Stalks cut into 1/2-in pieces- 1 cup	91	40	5	Trace	---	---	---	7	136	96	1.2	414	3,880	.14	.31	1.2	140
	From frozen:																	
589	Stalk, 4 1/2 to 5 in long--- 1 stalk	91	10	1	Trace	---	---	---	1	12	17	.2	66	570	.02	.03	.2	22
590	Chopped--- 1 cup	92	50	5	1	---	---	---	9	100	104	1.3	392	4,810	.11	.22	.9	105
	Brussels sprouts, cooked, drained:																	
591	From raw, 7-8 sprouts (1 1/4- to 1 1/2-in diam.). 1 cup	88	55	7	1	---	---	---	10	50	112	1.7	423	810	.12	.22	1.2	135
592	From frozen--- 1 cup	89	50	5	Trace	---	---	---	10	33	95	1.2	457	880	.12	.16	.9	126

(Dashes (—) denote lack of reliable data for a constituent believed to be present in measurable amount)

Item No. (A)	Foods, approximate measures, units, and weight (edible part unless footnotes indicate otherwise) (B)	Grams	Water (C) Per cent	Food energy (D) Cal- ories	Pro- tein (E) Grams	Fat (F) Grams	Fatty Acids Satu- rated (total) (G) Grams	Unsaturated Oleic (H) Grams	Lino- leic (I) Grams	Carbo- hydrate (J) Grams	Calcium (K) Milli- grams	Phos- phorus (L) Milli- grams	Iron (M) Milli- grams	Potas- sium (N) Milli- grams	Vitamin A value (O) Inter- national units	Thiamin (P) Milli- grams	Ribo- flavin (Q) Milli- grams	Niacin (R) Milli- grams	Ascorbic acid (S) Milli- grams
	VEGETABLE AND VEGETABLE PRODUCTS—Con.																		
	Cabbage:																		
	Common varieties:																		
	Raw:																		
593	Coarsely shredded or sliced- 1 cup-	70	92	15	1	Trace	—	—	—	4	34	20	0.3	163	90	0.04	0.04	0.2	33
594	Finely shredded or chopped- 1 cup-	90	92	20	1	Trace	—	—	—	5	44	26	.4	210	120	.05	.05	.3	42
595	Cooked, drained- 1 cup-	145	94	30	2	Trace	—	—	—	6	64	29	.4	236	190	.06	.06	.4	48
596	Red, raw, coarsely shredded or sliced. 1 cup-	70	90	20	1	Trace	—	—	—	5	29	25	.6	188	30	.06	.04	.3	43
597	Savoy, raw, coarsely shredded or sliced. 1 cup-	70	92	15	2	Trace	—	—	—	3	47	38	.6	188	140	.04	.06	.2	39
598	Cabbage, celery (also called pe-tsai or wongbok), raw, 1-in pieces. 1 cup-	75	95	10	1	Trace	—	—	—	2	32	30	.5	190	110	.04	.03	.5	19
599	Cabbage, white mustard (also called bokchoy or pakchoy), cooked, drained. 1 cup-	170	95	25	2	Trace	—	—	—	4	252	56	1.0	364	5,270	.07	.14	1.2	26
	Carrots:																		
	Raw, without crowns and tips, scraped:																		
600	Whole, 7 1/2 by 1 1/8 in, or strips, 2 1/2 to 3 in long. 1 carrot or 18 strips-	72	88	30	1	Trace	—	—	—	7	27	26	.5	246	7,930	.04	.04	.4	6
601	Grated- 1 cup-	110	88	45	1	Trace	—	—	—	11	41	40	.8	375	12,100	.07	.06	.7	9
602	Cooked (crosswise cuts), drained. 1 cup-	155	91	50	1	Trace	—	—	—	11	51	48	.9	344	16,280	.08	.08	.8	9
	Canned:																		
603	Sliced, drained solids- 1 cup-	155	91	45	1	Trace	—	—	—	10	47	34	1.1	186	23,250	.03	.05	.6	3
604	Strained or junior (baby food) 1 oz (1 3/4 to 2 tbsp)-	28	92	10	Trace	Trace	—	—	—	2	7	6	.1	51	3,690	.01	.01	.1	1
	Cauliflower:																		
605	Raw, chopped- 1 cup-	115	91	31	3	Trace	—	—	—	6	29	64	1.3	339	70	.13	.12	.8	90
	Cooked, drained:																		
606	From raw (flower buds)- 1 cup-	125	93	30	3	Trace	—	—	—	5	26	53	.9	258	80	.11	.10	.8	69
607	From frozen (flowerets)- 1 cup-	180	94	30	3	Trace	—	—	—	6	31	68	.9	373	50	.07	.09	.7	74
	Celery, Pascal type, raw:																		
608	Stalk, large outer, 8 by 1 1/2 in, at root end. 1 stalk-	40	94	5	Trace	Trace	—	—	—	2	16	11	.1	136	110	.01	.01	.1	4
609	Pieces, diced- 1 cup-	120	94	20	1	Trace	—	—	—	5	47	34	.4	409	320	.04	.04	.4	11
	Collards, cooked, drained:																		
610	From raw (leaves without stems)- 1 cup-	190	90	65	7	1	—	—	—	10	357	99	1.5	498	14,820	.21	.38	2.3	144
611	From frozen (chopped)- 1 cup-	170	90	50	5	1	—	—	—	10	299	87	1.7	401	11,560	.10	.24	1.0	56
	Corn, sweet:																		
	Cooked, drained:																		
612	From raw, ear 5 by 1 3/4 in- 1 ear[61]-	140	74	70	2	1	—	—	—	16	2	69	.5	151	[62]310	.09	.08	1.1	7
	From frozen:																		
613	Ear, 5 in long- 1 ear[61]-	229	73	120	4	1	—	—	—	27	4	121	1.0	291	[62]440	.18	.10	2.1	9
614	Kernels- 1 cup-	165	77	130	5	1	—	—	—	31	5	120	1.3	304	[62]580	.15	.10	2.5	8
	Canned:																		
615	Cream style- 1 cup-	256	76	210	5	2	—	—	—	51	8	143	1.5	248	[62]840	.08	.13	2.6	13
	Whole kernel:																		
616	Vacuum pack- 1 cup-	210	76	175	5	1	—	—	—	43	6	153	1.1	204	[62]740	.06	.13	2.3	11
617	Wet pack, drained solids- 1 cup-	165	76	140	4	1	—	—	—	33	8	81	.8	160	[62]580	.05	.08	1.5	7
	Cowpeas. See Blackeye peas. (Items 585-586).																		
	Cucumber slices, 1/8 in thick (large, 2 1/8-in diam.; small, 1 3/4-in diam.):																		
618	With peel- 6 large or 8 small slices	28	95	5	Trace	Trace	—	—	—	1	7	8	.3	45	70	.01	.01	.1	3

(A)	(B)	Measure	Grams	(C)	(D)	(E)	(F)	(G)	(H)	(I)	(J)	(K)	(L)	(M)	(N)	(O)	(P)	(Q)	(R)	(S)
619	Without peel	6 1/2 large or 9 small pieces	28	96	5	Trace	Trace	—	—	—	1	5	5	0.1	45	Trace	0.01	0.01	0.1	3
620	Dandelion greens, cooked, drained	1 cup	105	90	35	2	1	—	—	—	7	147	44	1.9	244	12,290	.14	.17	—	19
621	Endive, curly (including escarole)— raw, small pieces	1 cup	50	93	10	1	Trace	—	—	—	2	41	27	.9	147	1,650	.04	.07	.3	5
622	Kale, cooked, drained: From raw (leaves without stems and midribs)	1 cup	110	88	45	5	1	—	—	—	7	206	64	1.8	243	9,130	.11	.20	1.8	102
623	From frozen (leaf style)	1 cup	130	91	40	4	1	—	—	—	7	157	62	1.3	251	10,660	.08	.20	.9	49
	Lettuce, raw: Butterhead, as Boston types:																			
624	Head, 5-in diam	1 head[63]	220	95	25	2	Trace	—	—	—	4	57	42	3.3	430	1,580	.10	.10	.5	13
625	Leaves	1 outer or 2 inner or 3 heart leaves	15	95	Trace	Trace	Trace	—	—	—	Trace	5	4	.3	40	150	.01	.01	Trace	1
	Crisphead, as Iceberg:																			
626	Head, 6-in diam	1 head[64]	567	96	70	5	1	—	—	—	16	108	118	2.7	943	1,780	.32	.32	1.6	32
627	Wedge, 1/4 of head	1 wedge	135	96	20	1	Trace	—	—	—	4	27	30	.7	236	450	.08	.08	.4	8
628	Pieces, chopped or shredded	1 cup	55	96	5	Trace	Trace	—	—	—	2	11	12	.3	96	180	.03	.03	.2	3
629	Looseleaf (bunching varieties including romaine or cos), chopped or shredded pieces	1 cup	55	94	10	1	Trace	—	—	—	2	37	14	.8	145	1,050	.03	.04	.2	10
630	Mushrooms, raw, sliced or chopped	1 cup	70	90	20	2	Trace	—	—	—	3	4	81	.6	290	Trace	.07	.32	2.9	2
631	Mustard greens, without stems and midribs, cooked, drained	1 cup	140	93	30	3	1	—	—	—	6	193	45	2.5	308	8,120	.11	.20	.8	67
632	Okra pods, 3 by 5/8 in, cooked	10 pods	106	91	30	2	Trace	—	—	—	6	98	43	.5	184	520	.14	.19	1.0	21
	Onions: Mature: Raw:																			
633	Chopped	1 cup	170	89	65	3	Trace	—	—	—	15	46	61	.9	267	[65]Trace	.05	.07	.3	17
634	Sliced	1 cup	115	89	45	2	Trace	—	—	—	10	31	41	.6	181	[65]Trace	.03	.05	.2	12
635	Cooked (whole or sliced), drained	1 cup	210	92	60	3	Trace	—	—	—	14	50	61	.8	231	[65]Trace	.06	.06	.4	15
636	Young green, bulb (3/8 in diam.) and white portion of top	6 onions	30	88	15	Trace	Trace	—	—	—	3	12	12	.2	69	Trace	.02	.01	.1	8
637	Parsley, raw, chopped	1 tbsp	4	85	Trace	Trace	Trace	—	—	—	Trace	7	2	.2	25	300	Trace	.01	Trace	6
638	Parsnips, cooked (diced or 2-in lengths)	1 cup	155	82	100	2	Trace	—	—	—	23	70	96	.9	587	50	.11	.12	.2	16
	Peas, green: Canned:																			
639	Whole, drained solids	1 cup	170	77	150	8	1	—	—	—	29	44	129	3.2	163	1,170	.15	.10	1.4	14
640	Strained (baby food)	1 oz (1 3/4 to 2 tbsp)	28	86	15	1	Trace	—	—	—	3	3	18	.3	28	140	.02	.03	.3	3
641	Frozen, cooked, drained	1 cup	160	82	110	8	Trace	—	—	—	19	30	138	3.0	216	960	.43	.14	2.7	21
642	Peppers, hot, red, without seeds, dried (ground chili powder, added seasonings)	1 tsp	2	9	5	Trace	Trace	—	—	—	1	5	4	.3	20	1,300	Trace	.02	.2	Trace
	Peppers, sweet (about 5 per lb, whole), stem and seeds removed:																			
643	Raw	1 pod	74	93	15	1	Trace	—	—	—	4	7	16	.5	157	310	.06	.06	.4	94
644	Cooked, boiled, drained	1 pod	73	95	15	1	Trace	—	—	—	3	7	12	.4	109	310	.05	.05	.4	70
	Potatoes, cooked:																			
645	Baked, peeled after baking (about 2 per lb, raw)	1 potato	156	75	145	4	Trace	—	—	—	33	14	101	1.1	782	Trace	.15	.07	2.7	31
	Boiled (about 3 per lb, raw):																			
646	Peeled after boiling	1 potato	137	80	105	3	Trace	—	—	—	23	10	72	.8	556	Trace	.12	.05	2.0	22
647	Peeled before boiling	1 potato	135	83	90	3	Trace	—	—	—	20	8	57	.7	385	Trace	.12	.05	1.6	22
	French-fried, strip, 2 to 3 1/2 in long:																			
648	Prepared from raw	10 strips	50	45	135	2	7	1.7	1.2	3.3	18	8	56	.7	427	Trace	.07	.04	1.6	11
649	Frozen, oven heated	10 strips	50	53	110	2	4	1.1	.8	2.1	17	5	43	.9	326	Trace	.07	.01	1.3	11
650	Hashed brown, prepared from frozen	1 cup	155	56	345	3	18	4.6	3.2	9.0	45	28	78	1.9	439	Trace	.11	.03	1.6	12
	Mashed, prepared from— Raw:																			
651	Milk added—	1 cup	210	83	135	4	2	.7	.4	Trace	27	50	103	.8	548	40	.17	.11	2.1	21

[61] Weight includes cob. Without cob, weight is 77 g for item 612, 126 g for item 613.
[62] Based on yellow varieties. For white varieties, value is trace.
[63] Weight includes refuse of outer leaves and core. Without these parts, weight is 163 g.
[64] Weight includes core. Without core, weight is 539 g.
[65] Value based on white-fleshed varieties. For yellow-fleshed varieties, value in International Units (i.u.) is 70 for item 633, 50 for item 634, and 80 for item 635.

(Dashes (—) denote lack of reliable data for a constituent believed to be present in measurable amount)

Item No. (A)	Foods, approximate measures, units, and weight (edible part unless footnotes indicate otherwise) (B)		Grams	Water (C) Per-cent	Food energy (D) Cal-ories	Pro-tein (E) Grams	Fat (F) Grams	Fatty Acids Satu-rated (total) (G) Grams	Unsaturated Oleic (H) Grams	Lino-leic (I) Grams	Carbo-hydrate (J) Grams	Calcium (K) Milli-grams	Phos-phorus (L) Milli-grams	Iron (M) Milli-grams	Potas-sium (N) Milli-grams	Vitamin A value (O) Inter-national units	Thiamin (P) Milli-grams	Ribo-flavin (Q) Milli-grams	Niacin (R) Milli-grams	Ascorbic acid (S) Milli-grams
	VEGETABLE AND VEGETABLE PRODUCTS—Con.																			
	Potatoes, cooked—Continued																			
	Mashed, prepared from—Continued																			
	Raw—Continued																			
652	Milk and butter added	1 cup	210	80	195	4	9	5.6	2.3	0.2	26	50	101	0.8	525	360	0.17	0.11	2.1	19
653	Dehydrated flakes (without milk), water, milk, butter, and salt added.	1 cup	210	79	195	4	7	3.6	2.1	.2	30	65	99	.6	601	270	.08	.08	1.9	11
654	Potato chips, 1 3/4 by 2 1/2 in oval cross section.	10 chips	20	2	115	1	8	2.1	1.4	4.0	10	8	28	.4	226	Trace	.04	.01	1.0	3
655	Potato salad, made with cooked salad dressing.	1 cup	250	76	250	7	7	2.0	2.7	1.3	41	80	160	1.5	798	350	.20	.18	2.8	28
656	Pumpkin, canned	1 cup	245	90	80	2	1	—	—	—	19	61	64	1.0	588	15,680	.07	.12	1.5	12
657	Radishes, raw (prepackaged) stem ends, rootlets cut off.	4 radishes	18	95	5	Trace	Trace	—	—	—	1	5	6	.2	58	Trace	.01	.01	.1	5
658	Sauerkraut, canned, solids and liquid.	1 cup	235	93	40	2	Trace	—	—	—	9	85	42	1.2	329	120	.07	.09	.5	33
	Southern peas. See Blackeye peas (items 585-586).																			
	Spinach:																			
659	Raw, chopped	1 cup	55	91	15	2	Trace	—	—	—	2	51	28	1.7	259	4,460	.06	.11	.3	28
	Cooked, drained:																			
660	From raw	1 cup	180	92	40	5	1	—	—	—	6	167	68	4.0	583	14,580	.13	.25	.9	50
	From frozen:																			
661	Chopped	1 cup	205	92	45	6	1	—	—	—	8	232	90	4.3	683	16,200	.14	.31	.8	39
662	Leaf	1 cup	190	92	45	6	1	—	—	—	7	200	84	4.8	688	15,390	.15	.27	1.0	53
663	Canned, drained solids	1 cup	205	91	50	6	1	—	—	—	7	242	53	5.3	513	16,400	.04	.25	.6	29
	Squash, cooked:																			
664	Summer (all varieties), diced, drained	1 cup	210	96	30	2	Trace	—	—	—	7	53	53	.8	296	820	.11	.17	1.7	21
665	Winter (all varieties), baked, mashed.	1 cup	205	81	130	4	1	—	—	—	32	57	98	1.6	945	8,610	.10	.27	1.4	27
	Sweetpotatoes:																			
	Cooked (raw, 5 by 2 in; about 2 1/2 per lb):																			
666	Baked in skin, peeled	1 potato	114	64	160	2	1	—	—	—	37	46	66	1.0	342	9,230	.10	.08	.8	25
667	Boiled in skin, peeled	1 potato	151	71	170	3	1	—	—	—	40	48	71	1.1	367	11,940	.14	.09	.9	26
668	Candied, 2 1/2 by 2-in piece	1 piece	105	60	175	1	3	2.0	.8	.1	36	39	45	.9	200	6,620	.06	.04	.4	11
	Canned:																			
669	Solid pack (mashed)	1 cup	255	72	275	5	1	—	—	—	63	64	105	2.0	510	19,890	.13	.10	1.5	36
670	Vacuum pack, piece 2 3/4 by 1 in.	1 piece	40	72	45	1	Trace	—	—	—	10	10	16	.3	80	3,120	.02	.02	.2	6
	Tomatoes:																			
671	Raw, 2 3/5-in diam. (3 per 12 oz pkg.).	1 tomato[6]	135	94	25	1	Trace	—	—	—	6	16	33	.6	300	1,110	.07	.05	.9	[6][7]28
672	Canned, solids and liquid	1 cup	241	94	50	2	Trace	—	—	—	10	[6]14	46	1.2	523	2,170	.12	.07	1.7	41
673	Tomato catsup	1 cup	273	69	290	5	1	—	—	—	69	60	137	2.2	991	3,820	.25	.19	4.4	41
674	Tomato catsup	1 tbsp	15	69	15	Trace	Trace	—	—	—	4	3	8	.1	54	210	.01	.01	.2	2
	Tomato juice, canned:																			
675	Cup	1 cup	243	94	45	2	Trace	—	—	—	10	17	44	2.2	552	1,940	.12	.07	1.9	39
676	Glass (6 fl oz)	1 glass	182	94	35	2	Trace	—	—	—	8	13	33	1.6	413	1,460	.09	.05	1.5	29
677	Turnips, cooked, diced	1 cup	155	94	35	1	Trace	—	—	—	8	54	37	.6	291	Trace	.06	.08	.5	34
	Turnip greens, cooked:																			
678	From raw (leaves and stems)	1 cup	145	94	30	3	Trace	—	—	—	5	252	49	1.5	—	8,270	.15	.33	.7	68
679	From frozen (chopped)	1 cup	165	93	40	4	Trace	—	—	—	6	195	64	2.6	246	11,390	.08	.15	.7	31
680	Vegetables, mixed, frozen, cooked	1 cup	182	83	115	6	1	—	—	—	24	46	115	2.4	348	9,010	.22	.13	2.0	15

MISCELLANEOUS ITEMS

(A)	(B)	(g)	(C)	(D)	(E)	(F)	(G)	(H)	(I)	(J)	(K)	(L)	(M)	(N)	(O)	(P)	(Q)	(R)	(S)
	Baking powders for home use:																		
	Sodium aluminum sulfate:																			
681	With monocalcium phosphate monohydrate — 1 tsp	3.0	2	5	Trace	Trace	0	0	0	1	58	87	—	5	0	0	0	0	0
682	With monocalcium phosphate monohydrate, calcium sulfate — 1 tsp	2.9	1	5	Trace	Trace	0	0	0	1	183	45	—	—	0	0	0	0	0
683	Straight phosphate — 1 tsp	3.8	2	5	Trace	Trace	0	0	0	1	239	359	—	6	0	0	0	0	0
684	Low sodium — 1 tsp	4.3	2	5	Trace	Trace	0	0	0	2	207	314	—	471	0	0	.03	0	0
685	Barbecue sauce — 1 cup	250	81	230	4	17	2.2	4.3	10.0	20	53	50	2.0	435	900	.03	.03	.8	13
	Beverages, alcoholic:																			
686	Beer — 12 fl oz	360	92	150	1	0	0	0	0	14	18	108	Trace	90	—	.01	.11	2.2	—
	Gin, rum, vodka, whisky:																			
687	80-proof — 1 1/2-fl oz jigger	42	67	95	—	—	—	—	0	Trace	—	—	—	1	—	—	—	—	—
688	86-proof — 1 1/2-fl oz jigger	42	64	105	—	—	—	—	0	Trace	—	—	—	1	—	—	—	—	—
689	90-proof — 1 1/2-fl oz jigger	42	62	110	—	—	—	—	0	Trace	—	—	—	1	—	—	—	—	—
	Wines:																			
690	Dessert — 3 1/2-fl oz glass	103	77	140	Trace	0	0	0	0	8	8	—	—	77	—	.01	.02	.2	—
691	Table — 3 1/2-fl oz glass	102	86	85	Trace	0	0	0	0	4	9	10	.4	94	—	Trace	.01	.1	—
	Beverages, carbonated, sweetened, nonalcoholic:																			
692	Carbonated water — 12 fl oz	366	92	115	0	0	0	0	0	29	—	—	—	—	0	0	0	0	0
693	Cola type — 12 fl oz	369	90	145	0	0	0	0	0	37	—	—	—	—	0	0	0	0	0
694	Fruit-flavored sodas and Tom Collins mixer — 12 fl oz	372	88	170	0	0	0	0	0	45	—	—	—	—	0	0	0	0	0
695	Ginger ale — 12 fl oz	366	92	115	0	0	0	0	0	29	—	—	—	0	0	0	0	0	0
696	Root beer — 12 fl oz	370	90	150	0	0	0	0	0	39	—	—	—	0	0	0	0	0	0
	Chili powder. See Peppers, hot, red (item 642).																			
	Chocolate:																				
697	Bitter or baking, chocolate — 1 oz	28	2	145	3	15	8.9	4.9	.4	8	22	109	1.9	235	20	.01	.07	.4	0
	Semisweet, see Candy, chocolate (item 539).																			
698	Gelatin, dry — 1 7-g envelope	7	13	25	6	Trace	0	—	0	0	—	—	—	—	—	—	—	—	—
699	Gelatin dessert prepared with gelatin dessert powder and water — 1 cup	240	84	140	4	0	0	—	0	34	—	—	—	—	—	—	—	—	—
700	Mustard, prepared, yellow — 1 tsp or individual serving pouch or cup.	5	80	5	Trace	Trace	—	—	—	Trace	4	4	.1	7	—	—	—	—	—
	Olives, pickled, canned:																			
701	Green — 4 medium or 3 extra large or 2 giant.[69]	16	78	15	Trace	2	.2	1.2	.1	Trace	8	2	.2	7	40	Trace	Trace	—	—
702	Ripe, Mission — 3 small or 2 large.[69]	10	73	15	Trace	2	.2	1.2	.1	Trace	9	1	.1	2	10	Trace	Trace	—	—
	Pickles, cucumber:																			
703	Dill, medium, whole, 3 3/4 in long, 1 1/4-in diam — 1 pickle	65	93	5	Trace	Trace	—	—	—	1	17	14	.7	130	70	Trace	.01	Trace	4
704	Fresh-pack, slices 1 1/2-in diam, 1/4 in thick — 2 slices	15	79	10	Trace	Trace	—	—	—	3	5	4	.3	—	20	Trace	Trace	Trace	1
705	Sweet, gherkin, small, whole, about 2 1/2 in long, 3/4-in diam — 1 pickle	15	61	20	Trace	Trace	—	—	—	5	2	2	.2	—	10	Trace	Trace	Trace	1
706	Relish, finely chopped, sweet — 1 tbsp	15	63	20	Trace	Trace	—	—	—	5	3	2	.1	—	—	Trace	Trace	—	—
	Popcorn. See items 476-478.																			
707	Popsicle, 3-fl oz size — 1 popsicle	95	80	70	0	0	0	0	0	18	0	—	Trace	—	0	0	0	0	0

[66] Weight includes cores and stem ends. Without these parts, weight is 123 g.
[67] Based on year-round average. For tomatoes marketed from November through May, value is about 12 mg; from June through October, 32 mg.
[68] Applies to product without calcium salts added. Value for products with calcium salts added may be as much as 63 mg for whole tomatoes, 241 mg for cut forms.
[69] Weight includes pits. Without pits, weight is 13 g for item 701, 9 g for item 702.

(Dashes (—) denote lack of reliable data for a constituent believed to be present in measurable amount)

							Fatty Acids												
								Unsaturated											
Item No.	Foods, approximate measures, units, and weight (edible part unless footnotes indicate otherwise)		Water	Food energy	Protein	Fat	Saturated (total)	Oleic	Linoleic	Carbohydrate	Calcium	Phosphorus	Iron	Potassium	Vitamin A value	Thiamin	Riboflavin	Niacin	Ascorbic acid
(A)	(B)	Grams	(C) Percent	(D) Calories	(E) Grams	(F) Grams	(G) Grams	(H) Grams	(I) Grams	(J) Grams	(K) Milligrams	(L) Milligrams	(M) Milligrams	(N) Milligrams	(O) International units	(P) Milligrams	(Q) Milligrams	(R) Milligrams	(S) Milligrams
	MISCELLANEOUS ITEMS—Con.																		
	Soups:																		
	Canned, condensed:																		
	Prepared with equal volume of milk:																		
708	Cream of chicken------- 1 cup-------	245	85	180	7	10	4.2	3.6	1.3	15	172	152	0.5	260	610	0.05	0.27	0.7	2
709	Cream of mushroom------ 1 cup-------	245	83	215	7	14	5.4	2.9	4.6	16	191	169	.5	279	250	.05	.34	.7	1
710	Tomato------- 1 cup-------	250	84	175	7	7	3.4	1.7	1.0	23	168	155	.8	418	1,200	.10	.25	1.3	15
	Prepared with equal volume of water:																		
711	Bean with pork------- 1 cup-------	250	84	170	8	6	1.2	1.8	2.4	22	63	128	2.3	395	650	.13	.08	1.0	3
712	Beef broth, bouillon, consomme------- 1 cup-------	240	96	30	5	0	0	0	0	3	Trace	31	.5	130	Trace	Trace	.02	1.2	—
713	Beef noodle------- 1 cup-------	240	93	65	4	3	.6	.7	.8	7	7	48	1.0	77	50	.05	.07	1.0	Trace
714	Clam chowder, Manhattan type (with tomatoes, without milk). 1 cup-------	245	92	80	2	3	.5	.4	1.3	12	34	47	1.0	184	880	.02	.02	1.0	—
715	Cream of chicken------- 1 cup-------	240	92	95	3	6	1.6	2.3	1.1	8	24	34	.5	79	410	.02	.05	.5	Trace
716	Cream of mushroom------ 1 cup-------	240	90	135	2	10	2.6	1.7	4.5	10	41	50	.5	98	70	.02	.12	.7	Trace
717	Minestrone------- 1 cup-------	245	90	105	5	3	.7	.9	1.3	14	37	59	1.0	314	2,350	.07	.05	1.0	—
718	Split pea------- 1 cup-------	245	85	145	9	3	1.1	1.2	.4	21	29	149	1.5	270	440	.25	.15	1.5	1
719	Tomato------- 1 cup-------	245	91	90	2	3	.5	.5	1.0	16	15	34	.7	230	1,000	.05	.05	1.2	12
720	Vegetable beef------- 1 cup-------	245	92	80	5	2	—	—	—	10	12	49	.7	162	2,700	.05	.05	1.0	—
721	Vegetarian------- 1 cup-------	245	92	80	2	2	—	—	—	13	20	39	1.0	172	2,940	.05	.05	1.0	—
	Dehydrated:																		
722	Bouillon cube, 1/2 in------- 1 cube-------	4	4	5	1	Trace				Trace	—	—	—	4	—	—	—	—	—
	Mixes:																		
	Unprepared:																		
723	Onion------- 1 1/2-oz pkg-------	43	3	150	6	5	1.1	2.3	1.0	23	42	49	.6	238	30	.05	.03	.3	6
	Prepared with water:																		
724	Chicken noodle------- 1 cup-------	240	95	55	2	1	—	—	—	8	7	19	.2	19	50	.07	.05	Trace	Trace
725	Onion------- 1 cup-------	240	96	35	1	1	—	—	—	6	10	12	.2	58	Trace	Trace	Trace	Trace	2
726	Tomato vegetable with noodles. 1 cup-------	240	93	65	1	1	—	—	—	12	7	19	.2	29	480	.05	.02	.5	5
727	Vinegar, cider------- 1 tbsp-------	15	94	Trace	Trace	0	0	0	0	1	1	1	.1	15	—	—	—	—	—
728	White sauce, medium, with enriched flour. 1 cup-------	250	73	405	10	31	19.3	7.8	.8	22	288	233	.5	348	1,150	.12	.43	.7	2
	Yeast:																		
729	Baker's, dry, active------- 1 pkg-------	7	5	20	3	Trace				3	3 [70]	90	1.1	140	Trace	.16	.38	2.6	Trace
730	Brewer's, dry------- 1 tbsp-------	8	5	25	3	Trace				3	17 [70]	140	1.4	152	Trace	1.25	.34	3.0	Trace

[70] Value may vary from 6 to 60 mg.

APPENDIX B

TRICEPS SKINFOLD
THICKNESS

TRICEPS SKINFOLD THICKNESS: YOUTH, 1–17 YEARS, UNITED STATES: 1971–1974

Race and Age in Years	Number in Sample	Estimated Population in Thousands	Mean	Standard Deviation	Percentile								
					5th	10th	15th	25th	50th	75th	85th	90th	95th

Triceps Skinfold in Millimeters

MALES

WHITE

Race and Age	Number	Population	Mean	SD	5th	10th	15th	25th	50th	75th	85th	90th	95th
1	211	1,402	10.7	3.0	7.0	7.0	7.5	8.0	10.0	12.0	14.0	15.0	16.5
2	217	1,461	9.9	2.6	6.0	6.5	7.0	8.0	10.0	12.0	12.5	13.0	14.7
3	226	1,536	9.9	2.6	6.5	7.0	7.0	8.0	10.0	11.0	12.5	13.5	14.5
4	229	1,547	9.6	2.4	6.0	7.0	7.0	8.0	10.0	11.0	12.0	12.5	14.0
5	207	1,319	9.8	3.2	6.0	6.5	7.0	7.5	9.0	11.0	12.5	13.5	15.0
6	126	1,343	8.9	3.1	5.5	5.6	6.0	7.0	9.0	10.0	12.0	12.5	14.0
7	125	1,718	9.1	3.5	5.0	6.0	6.0	7.0	8.0	10.5	12.0	13.5	17.0
8	116	1,644	9.1	3.3	5.0	5.5	6.0	7.0	8.5	10.5	12.0	13.0	16.0
9	117	1,636	11.1	4.8	5.5	6.5	6.5	7.5	10.0	14.0	17.0	17.0	19.0
10	148	1,909	11.1	4.2	5.5	6.0	7.0	8.0	10.0	14.0	15.5	17.0	19.5
11	132	1,823	12.5	6.5	6.0	6.0	7.0	8.0	10.0	15.0	19.0	20.5	24.5
12	152	1,970	12.4	6.1	6.0	6.0	7.0	8.5	11.0	14.0	18.0	21.0	27.0
13	129	1,697	11.7	6.7	5.0	5.0	6.0	7.0	10.0	14.0	19.0	22.0	25.5
14	134	1,730	10.9	6.4	4.0	5.0	6.0	7.0	9.0	13.0	18.0	20.0	24.0
15	124	1,728	10.2	6.1	4.0	5.0	6.0	6.0	8.0	12.0	15.0	19.0	24.0
16	128	1,752	10.1	5.2	4.0	5.0	5.0	6.5	9.0	12.5	15.0	17.0	22.0
17	139	1,831	9.3	5.4	4.5	5.0	5.5	6.0	7.5	11.0	13.0	15.0	19.0

BLACK

Race and Age	Number	Population	Mean	SD	5th	10th	15th	25th	50th	75th	85th	90th	95th
1	72	280	9.4	3.4	4.5	6.0	7.0	8.0	8.0	11.0	12.0	13.0	15.0
2	77	267	10.1	3.2	4.5	6.0	6.5	8.0	10.0	12.0	14.0	15.0	15.0
3	72	212	9.1	2.6	6.0	6.5	6.5	7.0	9.0	10.5	12.0	12.0	13.0
4	74	260	8.0	2.6	5.0	5.0	5.0	6.5	7.0	9.0	10.0	10.5	15.0
5	64	226	7.7	3.4	4.5	5.0	5.0	5.0	7.0	9.0	10.0	12.0	15.5
6	52	321	7.1	1.8	4.0	4.0	5.0	6.0	7.0	8.0	9.0	9.0	9.0
7	38	253	7.5	3.2	4.0	4.0	4.0	5.0	6.5	9.0	11.5	13.0	15.0
8	33	203	7.8	3.4	4.0	5.0	5.0	6.0	6.5	10.0	11.0	11.0	12.5
9	52	383	8.2	3.9	3.5	4.0	4.5	6.0	7.0	8.0	12.0	13.0	18.0
10	33	251	9.1	5.3	5.0	5.0	6.0	6.0	7.5	10.0	13.0	15.0	20.0
11	43	313	8.0	5.0	4.0	4.0	5.0	5.0	6.0	8.5	11.0	12.0	15.0
12	47	316	9.4	7.0	4.0	4.0	4.5	6.0	7.5	10.7	11.0	15.0	24.0
13	45	281	8.2	4.4	4.0	5.0	5.0	5.0	7.0	8.5	11.0	19.0	19.0
14	39	282	6.6	2.6	3.5	3.5	3.5	5.0	6.5	7.0	8.0	9.0	12.0
15	43	310	8.9	6.1	4.0	4.5	5.0	5.0	6.5	9.0	10.0	21.0	21.0
16	41	267	7.2	4.8	4.0	4.0	4.0	5.0	6.0	7.5	8.0	11.0	15.0
17	35	235	8.7	5.8	3.5	3.5	5.0	5.0	7.0	10.5	12.0	12.0	23.2

FEMALES

WHITE

Race and Age	Number	Population	Mean	SD	5th	10th	15th	25th	50th	75th	85th	90th	95th
1	189	1,328	10.2	2.8	6.0	7.0	7.0	8.0	10.0	12.0	13.0	13.5	15.5
2	203	1,434	10.6	2.6	7.0	7.5	8.0	9.0	10.0	12.0	13.5	14.0	15.0
3	211	1,438	11.1	2.6	7.0	8.0	8.5	9.0	11.0	13.0	13.5	14.0	15.0
4	204	1,339	10.8	2.6	7.5	8.0	8.0	9.0	10.5	12.0	13.0	14.5	16.0
5	224	1,416	10.7	3.7	6.0	7.0	8.0	8.5	10.0	13.0	15.0	15.0	17.5
6	125	1,445	10.6	3.3	6.5	7.0	7.5	8.0	10.5	12.0	13.0	14.0	16.0
7	122	1,507	10.9	4.2	4.0	6.0	7.0	8.0	11.0	12.0	15.0	15.5	17.5
8	117	1,507	12.4	4.7	7.0	8.0	8.0	9.0	11.5	15.0	16.5	18.0	22.0
9	129	1,751	13.6	4.6	7.5	8.0	9.0	10.0	13.0	16.0	18.0	20.0	22.0
10	148	1,855	13.4	4.8	7.5	8.0	8.5	10.0	12.5	15.5	19.0	20.0	23.0
11	122	1,569	14.9	6.1	8.0	8.5	9.0	10.0	13.0	17.5	23.0	24.5	28.5
12	128	1,506	15.2	5.6	8.0	9.0	10.0	11.0	14.0	18.5	20.0	23.0	26.0
13	153	1,886	16.2	6.8	7.0	8.0	10.0	11.5	15.0	20.0	24.0	25.0	28.5
14	132	1,731	17.8	7.3	9.0	9.5	10.5	13.0	16.7	21.0	24.0	28.5	33.0
15	125	1,752	17.7	6.7	9.0	10.5	11.0	13.0	17.0	21.0	24.0	25.0	28.5
16	141	1,933	18.2	6.6	10.0	10.5	12.5	14.0	17.0	21.0	24.0	26.0	32.1
17	117	1,549	19.8	8.0	10.0	12.0	12.5	13.5	19.0	24.0	26.5	29.5	35.0

From the National Center for Health Statistics, Department of Health and Human Services. Health and Nutrition Examination Survey I, 1971–1974.

TRICEPS SKINFOLD THICKNESS: YOUTH, 1–17 YEARS,
UNITED STATES: 1971–1974 (*Continued*)

Race and Age in Years	Number in Sample	Estimated Population in Thousands	Mean	Standard Deviation	Percentile								
					5th	10th	15th	25th	50th	75th	85th	90th	95th

Triceps Skinfold in Millimeters

FEMALES

BLACK

Race and Age in Years	Number in Sample	Estimated Population in Thousands	Mean	Standard Deviation	5th	10th	15th	25th	50th	75th	85th	90th	95th
1	73	257	10.0	3.0	5.5	5.5	7.0	8.0	10.0	12.0	13.0	14.0	15.0
2	66	261	10.0	2.3	7.0	8.0	8.0	8.0	10.0	11.0	12.0	14.0	15.5
3	78	245	9.7	2.9	6.0	7.0	7.0	8.0	10.0	11.0	12.0	13.0	14.0
4	73	246	8.8	2.7	5.0	6.0	7.0	7.0	8.0	10.5	12.0	13.0	14.0
5	88	265	9.4	3.9	5.0	5.0	6.5	7.0	8.0	10.0	12.0	13.5	17.0
6	50	336	9.0	3.1	5.5	6.0	6.0	8.0	8.0	10.0	11.5	12.0	13.0
7	46	241	10.1	4.0	5.0	6.0	7.0	7.5	9.0	11.0	17.5	18.0	18.0
8	35	293	11.5	5.1	5.0	6.5	7.0	8.0	10.0	13.5	18.0	18.0	23.0
9	41	247	10.2	5.1	5.5	6.0	6.0	6.5	8.0	12.0	18.0	18.0	20.0
10	48	303	11.7	5.6	6.5	6.5	7.0	7.5	10.0	16.0	18.0	19.0	24.0
11	42	315	12.7	6.4	4.0	5.0	6.5	7.5	10.0	18.0	22.0	23.0	23.0
12	47	284	13.6	7.6	5.5	6.0	6.0	7.5	12.0	17.0	22.0	25.0	30.0
13	44	287	16.1	7.0	7.0	8.5	10.0	11.0	14.0	18.0	24.0	24.0	33.5
14	50	265	15.9	6.7	8.0	8.0	9.0	10.5	14.0	20.5	24.0	24.5	24.5
15	46	411	14.0	7.6	6.5	6.5	8.0	10.0	12.5	16.0	16.5	20.0	32.8
16	33	203	18.9	8.0	8.0	8.0	10.0	12.0	19.0	24.0	24.5	33.0	33.1
17	39	239	16.9	6.6	7.5	9.0	11.0	12.0	14.5	20.0	24.0	28.0	31.0

APPENDIX C

RECIPES

BEVERAGES

STRAWBERRY COOLER

INGREDIENTS

1 pint fresh strawberries
¼ cup honey (optional)
2 cups vanilla ice milk
1 qt milk, skim or low fat

METHOD

1. Blend berries and honey until smooth.
2. Add the ice milk and 1 cup of the milk; blend again. Add remaining milk and blend 20 seconds.

Courtesy of Susan Leifer, R.D.

CITRUS COOLER

INGREDIENTS

¼ cup frozen orange juice
1 fresh peach (sliced) or
   1 canned peach
1 cup yogurt, low fat
1 Tblsp lemon juice
1 Tblsp honey (optional)
3 ice cubes

METHOD

1. Combine ingredients and blend about 30 seconds.

Courtesy of Susan Leifer, R.D.

PINEAPPLE SMOOTHIE

INGREDIENTS

1 cup pineapple juice
½ cup milk, skim or low fat
½ cup diced pineapple
1 banana

METHOD

1. Combine ingredients and blend about 30 seconds.

Courtesy of Susan Leifer, R.D.

ORANGE FLIP

INGREDIENTS

1 cup orange juice
¼ cup milk, skim or low fat
1 Tblsp sugar (optional)
¼ tsp vanilla
5 ice cubes

METHOD

1. Process all ingredients in a blender.
2. Garnish with orange slices and serve.

Courtesy of Susan Leifer, R.D.

PINEAPPLE-ORANGE SHAKE

INGREDIENTS

2 cups plain yogurt, low fat
1 cup skim or low-fat milk
1 cup pineapple chunks
juice from 1 orange

METHOD

1. Blend at top speed until smooth.

Courtesy of Susan Leifer, R.D.

BREAKFAST BOOSTER

INGREDIENTS

1 banana
1 cup milk, skim or low fat
1 cup apple juice
1 Tblsp honey (optional)
dash of nutmeg
dash of cinnamon

METHOD

1. Blend until smooth.

Courtesy of Susan Leifer, R.D.

BLUEBERRY SHAKE

INGREDIENTS

1 cup blueberries (or other
   available berries)
½ cup milk, skim or low fat
½ cup yogurt, low fat
1 tsp honey (optional)
dash of cinnamon

METHOD

1. Blend until smooth.
2. Garnish with lemon slice, if desired.

Courtesy of Susan Leifer, R.D.

CINNAMON CRANAPPLE CIDER

INGREDIENTS

1 qt cranberry juice
½ gallon apple cider
3 sticks of cinnamon

METHOD

1. Mix juice and cider in large pot or dutch
    oven, add cinnamon sticks, and simmer
    for 10 minutes.

BREADS

CARROT NUT BREAD

INGREDIENTS

2 egg whites
3 Tblsp vegetable oil
½ cup white sugar
½ cup brown sugar

½ cup water
½ cup non-fat dry milk
1 tsp vanilla
1½ cup flour (½ whole wheat)
1½ tsp baking soda
½ tsp baking powder
½ tsp salt (optional)

1 tsp cinnamon
1 cup grated carrots
¼ cup wheat germ
½ cup chopped nuts (optional)

METHOD

1. Beat egg whites in medium mixing bowl. Beat in oil, sugars, water, dry milk, and vanilla.
2. In another bowl, stir together flour, soda, baking powder, salt, and cinnamon. Stir dry ingredients into sugar mixture.
3. Stir in carrots, wheat germ, and nuts.
4. Pour into greased 8½ × 4½ × 2½-inch bread pan. Bake at 325° F for 55-65 minutes.

From the Test Kitchen of the Kansas Wheat Commission.

BANANA BREAD

INGREDIENTS

2 cups flour (1 cup whole wheat and 1 cup all-purpose)
1 tsp baking soda
1 tsp salt (optional)
3-4 over-ripe bananas, mashed
3 Tblsp sour milk (3 Tblsp skim milk and 1 tsp lemon juice)
2 eggs
½ cup sugar
½ cup margarine
½ cup chopped walnuts

METHOD

1. Cream sugar and margarine; add mashed bananas, slightly beaten eggs, and sour milk. Blend well.
2. In another bowl, combine dry ingredients. Mix with above ingredients.
3. Add nuts.

4. Oil two mini-loaf pans. Pour batter into each pan.
5. Bake 55 minutes at 325° F.

Courtesy of Carol Tuckwell.

BANANA-BRAN MUFFINS

INGREDIENTS

1¼ cups flour (½ whole wheat)
1 Tblsp baking powder
¼ tsp salt (optional)
2 Tblsp sugar
2 cups bran flakes cereal
1¼ cups milk, skim or low fat
2 egg whites
3 Tblsp vegetable oil
1 mashed banana
1 cup raisins

METHOD

1. Stir together flour, baking powder, salt, and sugar. Set aside.
2. In another bowl, mix bran flakes and milk. Let stand until softened.
3. Add egg whites, oil, banana, and raisins to milk mixture. Then add to dry ingredients, mixing well.
4. Divide batter into 12 greased muffin cups. Bake at 400° F for 25 minutes.

Courtesy of Susan Leifer, R.D.

OATMEAL APPLE MUFFINS

Portion: 1 muffin
Yield: 12 muffins
Nutrients/Portion: 102 Calories.

INGREDIENTS

¾ cup rolled oats, quick cooking
¾ cup + 2 Tblsp 2% milk

1 egg
2 Tblsp oil
2 Tblsp molasses
¾ cup grated apple
1¼ cup flour
1 Tblsp baking powder
½ tsp cinnamon
½ tsp salt

METHOD

1. Preheat oven to 400° F. Grease 12 muffin tins.
2. Soak oats in milk for 15 minutes.
3. Add egg, oil, molasses, and apple and mix well.
4. Sift flour, baking powder, cinnamon, and salt, and add to oat mixture. Stir until just combined.
5. Fill muffin tins ½ to ¾ full. Bake 20 minutes.

Courtesy of the Division of Nutritional Sciences, Cornell Cooperative Extension.

CRUNCHY RHUBARB MUFFINS

INGREDIENTS

¾ cup brown sugar
½ cup vegetable oil
1 egg
½ cup buttermilk
½ tsp salt
1 tsp vanilla
1½ cups flour
½ cup chopped nuts
1 tsp baking soda
1 cup finely chopped rhubarb
Topping:
   ¼ cup brown sugar
   ½ tsp cinnamon
   ¼ cup chopped nuts

METHOD

1. Combine sugar, oil, egg, buttermilk, and vanilla; mix well.
2. Sift flour, salt, and baking soda into oil mixture. Add rhubarb and nuts.
3. Pour into greased muffin tins.
4. Combine topping ingredients and sprinkle on top of batter.
5. Bake 30 minutes at 325° F.

Courtesy of Leona Busse.

REFRIGERATOR MUFFINS

INGREDIENTS

2 cups bran flakes
2 cups boiling water
2 cups sugar
1 cup margarine
4 eggs
1 qt buttermilk
5 cups flour (½ whole wheat, ½ all purpose)
5 tsp baking soda
1 Tblsp salt
2 cups bran buds

METHOD

1. Mix together the bran flakes and boiling water, then cool.
2. Mix remaining ingredients in large mixing bowl. Add cooled bran flakes and stir.
3. Pour into greased muffin tin. Bake 12 minutes at 400° F. Batter can be kept for 3-4 weeks in refrigerator.

Courtesy of Linda Petersen, R.D.

CINNAMON APPLESAUCE MUFFINS

Portion: 1 muffin
Yield: 12 muffins

Nutrients/Portion: 155 Calories; 1.8 gm dietary fiber, 3 gm protein, 5 gm fat, 26 gm carbohydrate, 215 mg sodium.

INGREDIENTS

1¼ cups all-purpose flour
1 Tblsp baking powder
¼ tsp salt
½ tsp ground cinnamon
¼ cup sugar
2½ cups Kellogg's Raisin Bran cereal
¼ cup milk
1 cup applesauce
1 egg
¼ cup vegetable oil

METHOD

1. Stir together flour, baking powder, salt, cinnamon, and sugar. Set aside.
2. In large mixing bowl, combine Kellogg's Raisin Bran cereal, milk, and applesauce. Let stand about 5 minutes or until cereal is softened. Add egg and oil. Beat well.
3. Add flour mixture, stirring only until combined. Portion batter evenly into 12 greased 2½-inch muffin-pan cups.
4. Bake at 400° F about 20 minutes or until lightly browned. Serve warm or cooled.

Courtesy of the Kellogg Company.

BRAN BATTER ROLLS

Portion: 1 roll
Yield: 16 rolls
Nutrients/Portion: 125 Calories; for All-Bran cereal, 2.4 gm dietary fiber, 4 gm protein, 3 gm fat, 23 gm carbohydrate, 305 mg sodium; for Bran Buds cereal, 2.2 gm dietary fiber, 4 gm protein, 3 gm fat, 23 gm carbohydrate, 280 mg sodium

INGREDIENTS

1 cup Kellogg's All-Bran or Bran Buds cereal
2½ to 3 cups all-purpose flour
2 Tblsp sugar
1½ tsp salt
1 package active dry yeast
1 cup milk
½ cup water
2 Tblsp margarine or butter
1 egg, slightly beaten
Poppy seed (optional)
Sesame seed (optional)

METHOD

1. In large bowl of electric mixer, stir together Kellogg's All-Bran cereal, 1 cup flour, sugar, salt and yeast. Set aside.
2. In small saucepan, heat milk, water and margarine until warm (115° to 120° F). Add to cereal mixture. Reserve 1 tablespoon of egg. Add remaining egg to cereal mixture. Beat 30 seconds at low speed of electric mixer, scraping bowl constantly. Beat 3 minutes at high speed.
3. By hand, stir in enough remaining flour to make a stiff batter. Cover loosely. Let rise in warm place until double in volume. Stir down batter. Portion batter evenly into 16 greased 2½-inch muffin-pan cups. Brush tops of rolls with reserved egg. Sprinkle with poppy or sesame seed, if desired.
4. Bake at 400° F for 18 to 20 minutes or until golden brown. Serve warm.
5. For lighter texture rolls, after portioning dough into muffin-pan cups, let rise in warm place until almost double in volume. Do not cover. Bake at 400° F about 15 minutes or until golden brown.

Courtesy of the Kellogg Company.

BREAKFAST IDEAS

CRUNCHY YOGURT

½ cup low-fat yogurt
¼ cup granola or trail mix

ENERGY BOOSTER

1 whole-wheat english muffin or
  whole-wheat toast
1 Tblsp peanut butter
Top with banana slices or raisins

CEREAL TREAT

1 oz natural grain cereal
½ cup low-fat plain yogurt
¼ cup favorite fresh fruit

MÛSLI (Swiss Oatmeal)

Yield: 4 servings

INGREDIENTS

1 cup rolled oats
1 cup boiling water
2 Tblsp honey
2 cups chopped fresh or dried fruits
  (apples, berries, grapes, peaches,
  raisins, apricots)
½-1 cup plain low-fat yogurt or skim milk

METHOD

1. Add oatmeal to water and soak overnight.
2. Before serving combine the oat-water mixture with honey, fruit, and yogurt or milk.

Courtesy of the American Institute for Cancer Research.

BUTTERMILK TOASTER PANCAKES

Portion: 1 pancake
Yield: 12 4-inch pancakes

INGREDIENTS

3 eggs
1 Tblsp brown sugar, packed
1 cup flour, unsifted
1 Tblsp baking powder
½ tsp salt
⅔ cup buttermilk
2 Tblsp oil

METHOD

1. Preheat griddle.
2. Beat eggs with brown sugar until very light, about 2 minutes.
3. Mix dry ingredients. Stir gently into beaten eggs.
4. Add buttermilk and oil. Stir only until mixed. Batter will be lumpy.
5. For each pancake, pour ¼ cup batter onto hot griddle.
6. Cook until surface is covered with bubbles, turn, and cook other side until light brown.
7. Cool on rack.
8. Place pancakes in an airtight container with waxpaper between layers. Or wrap singly in foil.
9. Label and store in freezer.

To reheat in toaster:

10. Remove from freezer and unwrap pancakes to be reheated.
11. Set toaster on medium-low setting.
12. Toast pancakes, twice if necessary, to heat through.

Courtesy of the United States Department of Agriculture.

OAT PANCAKES

Portion: 3 pancakes
Yield: 12 pancakes
Nutrients/Portion: 236 Calories; 2 gm dietary fiber, 8 gm protein, 8 gm fat, 33 gm carbohydrate, 361 mg sodium, 147 mg calcium, 1 mg cholesterol

INGREDIENTS

1 cup all-purpose flour
½ cup Quaker Oats (quick or old fashioned, uncooked)
1 Tblsp baking powder
½ tsp salt (optional)
1 cup skim milk
¼ cup egg substitute or 1 egg, beaten
2 Tblsp vegetable oil

METHOD

1. Heat griddle over medium-high heat (or preheat electric griddle or skillet to 375° F). Oil lightly.
2. Combine dry ingredients. Add milk, egg substitute and oil; stir just until dry ingredients are moistened.
3. For each pancake, pour about ¼ cup batter on hot griddle. Turn when tops are covered with bubbles and edges look cooked. Turn only once.

Courtesy of the Quaker Oats Company.

DESSERTS

CRUNCHY APPLE CRISP

Portion: 1 serving
Yield: 4 servings
Nutrients/Portion: 201 Calories; 2 gm dietary fiber, 3 gm protein, 9 gm fat, 27 gm carbohydrate, 29 mg sodium, 19 mg calcium

INGREDIENTS

4 cups peeled sliced apples
¼ cup water or apple juice
4 tsp brown sugar substitute or firmly packed brown sugar
2 tsp lemon juice
¾ tsp cinnamon
½ cup Quaker Oats (quick or old fashioned, uncooked)
2 Tblsp chopped walnuts
1 Tblsp brown sugar substitute or firmly packed brown sugar
1 Tblsp soft vegetable oil margarine

METHOD

1. Combine apples, water, brown sugar substitute, lemon juice, and cinnamon; toss lightly to coat apples.
2. Layer mixture on bottom of 8-inch square glass baking dish.
3. Heat oven to 375° F. Combine oats, nuts, and brown sugar substitute. Add margarine; mix well.
4. Sprinkle over apples. Bake about 30 minutes or until apples are tender and topping is lightly browned.

Serve warm or chilled.

Courtesy of the Quaker Oats Company.

WHOLE-WHEAT CREPES WITH STRAWBERRIES

The crepe:

1 cup flour
  (½ cup whole wheat,
  ½ cup all-purpose)
1 cup skim or low-fat milk
1 egg
1 Tblsp oil
¼ tsp salt (optional)

Filling:
1 qt strawberries, hulled
  and sliced
sugar or sugar substitute,
  as desired

Topping:
1 cup vanilla low-fat yogurt
½ cup toasted, sliced almonds

*Other fresh or frozen sliced fruit or berries
 may be used in place of fresh strawberries.

METHOD

1. Beat all ingredients in blender until smooth.
2. Heat a few drops of oil in a 6-inch crepe or omelette pan. Pour just enough batter to coat bottom of pan. When crepe appears to solidify, lift edges gently and flip.
3. Crepes can be made in advance and refrigerated. To reheat, place crepes on a plate over a pan of simmering water. Cover with foil loosely.
4. Layer prepared strawberries with sugar or sugar substitute (or use unsweetened berries). Chill for several hours.
5. To serve, place berries in center of warm crepe, wrap, and place seam side down on plate. Top with a dollop of vanilla yogurt and sliced almonds.

Courtesy of Susan Leifer, R.D.

DIPS/SPREADS/DRESSINGS

SPINACH DIP

INGREDIENTS

1 package dry vegetable soup mix
1 package frozen chopped spinach
  (drain well)
8 oz low-fat mayonnaise-type
  salad dressing
8 oz low-fat plain yogurt or
  low-fat sour cream
drained, chopped water chestnuts
  (optional)

METHOD

1. Blend all ingredients. Let chill a few hours for flavors to blend.
2. Put in hollowed-out round rye or wheat bread loaf. Use bread pieces for dipping.

Courtesy of Susan Leifer, R.D.

MOCK SOUR CREAM

INGREDIENTS

½ cup uncreamed (dry) cottage cheese
¼ cup milk
1 Tblsp vegetable oil
1 tsp lemon juice

METHOD

1. Blend until smooth.

Courtesy of Susan Leifer, R.D.

VEGETABLE DIP

Yield: 1 cup

INGREDIENTS

1 cup low fat cottage cheese
2 Tblsp skim milk
1 Tblsp green pepper, finely chopped
1 Tblsp onion, finely chopped
1 Tblsp radish, finely chopped
⅛ tsp garlic or onion powder

METHOD

1. Mix cottage cheese and milk in blender until smooth.
2. Stir in remaining ingredients.
3. Chill several hours before serving. Serve with crisp, raw vegetables (carrots, cucumbers, celery, cauliflower, broccoli, green peppers).

Courtesy of Susan Leifer, R.D.

DILL DIP

INGREDIENTS

1 cup low-fat sour cream
¾ cup low-calorie mayonnaise-type salad dressing
1 Tblsp onion flakes
1 Tblsp parsley flakes
1 Tblsp dill weed

METHOD

1. Combine all ingredients.
2. Chill several hours before serving.

Courtesy of Susan Leifer, R.D.

YOGURT-DILL DRESSING

Portion: 1 Tblsp
Yield: 1 cup
Nutrients/Portion: 10 calories, 0.2 gm total fat (0.1 gm saturated fat), 1 mg cholesterol

INGREDIENTS

8 oz plain low-fat yogurt
2 tsp onion, very finely chopped
1 tsp lemon juice
½ tsp dill weed, crushed
¼ tsp dry mustard
⅛ tsp garlic powder

METHOD

1. Mix all ingredients thoroughly.
2. Chill until served.
3. Serve over tossed green salad.

Reprinted from Food 2 *by the American Dietetic Association.*

MAIN DISHES

BEEF

MOCK BEEF STROGANOFF

Portion: 1 serving
Yield: 4 servings (½ cup stroganoff and ⅓ cup noodles)
Nutrients/Portion: 220 Calories; 4.9 gm total fat (2.0 gm saturated fat), 70 mg cholesterol

INGREDIENTS

¾ lb beef round steak, boneless
¼ lb fresh mushrooms
½ cup onion, sliced
½ cup beef broth, condensed
½ cup water
1 Tblsp catsup
⅛ tsp pepper
2 Tblsp flour
1 cup buttermilk
1⅓ cups (about 1¾ cups uncooked)
   noodles, cooked, unsalted

METHOD

1. Trim all fat from steak. Slice steak across the grain into thin strips, about ⅛ inch wide and 3 inches long. (It is easier to slice meat thinly if it is partially frozen.)
2. Wash and slice mushrooms.
3. Cook beef strips, mushrooms, and onion in nonstick frypan until beef is lightly browned.
4. Add broth, water, catsup, and pepper. Cover and simmer until beef is tender, about 45 minutes.
5. Mix flour with about ¼ cup of the buttermilk until smooth; add remaining buttermilk. Stir into beef mixture. Cook, stirring constantly, until thickened.
6. Serve over noodles.

Reprinted from Food 2 *by The American Dietetic Association.*

STIR-FRY BEEF WITH VEGETABLES

Portion: 1 serving
Yield: 4 servings (about ¾ cup)
Nutrients/Portion: 210 Calories with sherry, 190 Calories with broth; 8.5 gm total fat (2.6 gm saturated fat), 55 mg cholesterol with sherry, 57 mg cholesterol with broth

INGREDIENTS

¾ lb beef round steak, boneless
4 tsp oil
⅓ cup carrots, ⅛ inch diagonal slices
⅓ cup onion, sliced
⅓ cup celery, ⅛ inch diagonal slices
2 cups fresh mung bean sprouts
½ Tblsp cornstarch
½ tsp ground ginger
⅛ tsp garlic powder
1 Tblsp soy sauce
¼ cup sherry (optional)

METHOD

1. Trim all fat from steak. Slice steak across the grain into thin strips, about ⅛ inch wide and 3 inches long. (It is easier to slice meat thinly if it is partially frozen.)

2. Heat 2 tsp of the oil in frypan. Add beef strips and stir-fry over moderately high heat, turning pieces constantly, until beef is no longer red, about 2-3 minutes.
3. Remove beef from frypan.
4. Heat remaining 2 tsp of oil in frypan. Add carrots; stir-fry 1 minute.
5. Add onion, celery, and bean sprouts; continue to stir-fry until vegetables are tender crisp, about 3-4 minutes.
6. Mix cornstarch, ginger, and garlic powder with soy sauce and sherry until smooth. Add slowly to vegetables, stirring constantly. Continue cooking until bubbly.
7. Stir in beef.
8. Reduce heat and cook, covered, 1 minute.

Reprinted from Food 2 *by The American Dietetic Association.*

SAUCY STUFFED PEPPERS

Portion: 1 stuffed pepper half
Yield: 12 servings
Nutrients/Portion: 155 Calories; 3 gm dietary fiber, 16 gm protein, 3 gm fat, 129 mg sodium, 32 mg calcium, 34 mg cholesterol

INGREDIENTS

6 medium green peppers
1¼ cups water
2 cups tomato juice
One 6-oz can tomato paste
1 tsp oregano leaves, crushed
½ tsp garlic powder
½ tsp basil leaves, crushed
1 lb lean ground beef
1½ cups Quaker Oats (quick or old fashioned, uncooked)
1 medium tomato, chopped
¼ cup chopped carrot
¼ cup chopped onion

METHOD

1. Heat oven to 350° F.
2. Cut peppers in half lengthwise; remove membrane and seeds; set aside.
3. Combine water, 1 cup tomato juice, tomato paste, ½ tsp oregano, ¼ tsp garlic, and basil. Simmer 10 to 15 minutes.
4. Combine beef, oats, remaining 1 cup tomato juice, ½ tsp oregano, and ¼ tsp garlic with tomato, carrot, and onion; mix well.
5. Fill each green pepper half with about ⅓ cup meat mixture. Place in 13x9-inch glass baking dish. Pour sauce evenly over peppers.
6. Bake 45 to 50 minutes.

Courtesy of the Quaker Oats Company.

BEEF TACOS

Portion: 2 tacos
Yield: 6 servings
Nutrients/Portion: 270 Calories (without taco sauce)

INGREDIENTS

12 taco shells, fully cooked
1 lb ground beef
¼ cup onion, chopped
8 oz can tomato sauce
2 tsp chili powder
1 cup tomato, chopped
1 cup lettuce, shredded
½ cup (2 oz) natural sharp cheddar cheese, shredded
taco sauce (as desired)

METHOD

1. Heat taco shells as directed on package.

2. Brown ground beef and onion in a frypan. Drain off excess fat.
3. Stir in tomato sauce and chili powder. Bring to a boil.
4. Reduce heat. Cook 10-15 minutes uncovered, stirring occasionally, until mixture is dry and crumbly.

5. Fill heated taco shells with approximately 2 Tblsp meat mixture.
6. Mix tomato, lettuce, and cheese. Spoon about 2 Tblsp over beef in taco shells.
7. Drizzle with taco sauce, as desired.

Courtesy of the United States Department of Agriculture.

POULTRY

GRILLED, MARINATED CHICKEN

INGREDIENTS

4-6 chicken breast halves, skin removed
1 8 oz bottle low-calorie Italian dressing

METHOD

1. Arrange chicken breasts meat-side down in 9x13 baking dish.
2. Pour bottle of dressing over chicken. Let marinate in refrigerator for at least 2 hours.
3. Prepare outdoor grill and cook until done, or place chicken on broiling pan and broil under preheated broiler.

Courtesy of Susan Leifer, R.D.

CHICKEN BURRITOS

Yield: 8 servings

INGREDIENTS

2 whole large chicken breasts, skinned and boned
2 Tblsp salad oil
1 small onion, chopped
1½ tsp chili powder
1 10 oz can pinto beans, drained
1 4 oz can chopped green chilies, drained
½ cup mild or hot salsa or taco sauce
8 8 inch flour tortillas
1 small tomato, chopped
low-fat sour cream and guacamole, to taste

METHOD

1. Cut chicken breasts into ½ inch chunks. In 10 inch skillet over high heat, cook chicken in oil until pieces turn white, stirring constantly. Remove chicken to plate.
2. Cook onion in remaining oil over medium heat until tender. Stir in chili powder. Cook 1 minute, stirring constantly. Stir in chicken, beans, chilies, salsa, and sugar; heat through.
3. Meanwhile, steam tortillas as label directs, until soft and hot.
4. Top each tortilla with about ½ cup of chicken mixture in lengthwise strip down center. Fold left and right side of tortilla over mixture; tuck one under the other.
5. To serve, top each burrito with 1 Tblsp sour cream and 1 Tblsp guacamole; sprinkle chopped tomato over the burrito.

Courtesy of Susan Leifer, R.D.

CHICKEN AND BROCCOLI CASSEROLE

INGREDIENTS

2 10 oz pkg. frozen, chopped broccoli
2 Tblsp vegetable oil
1 lb raw chicken breasts, skinned, boned, and cut into ½ inch pieces.
1 Tblsp flour
¾ cup canned chicken broth
¼ cup dry white wine (optional)
salt and pepper to taste
½ cup canned mushroom pieces

METHOD

1. Preheat oven to 350° F.
2. Place broccoli in 1 qt casserole dish.
3. Heat oil in frying pan and sauté chicken strips on both sides. Place on top of broccoli in casserole.
4. Stir flour into remaining oil in fry pan. Gradually add chicken broth and wine, stirring until thickened; season to taste. Pour sauce over chicken and broccoli in dish. Scatter mushrooms on top.
5. Bake for 45 minutes.

Courtesy of Susan Leifer, R.D.

BRAN PARMESAN CHICKEN

Portion: 1 serving
Yield: 4 servings
Nutrients/Portion: 395 Calories; 2.3 gm dietary fiber, 36 gm protein, 19 gm fat, 19 gm carbohydrate, 415 mg sodium

INGREDIENTS

1½ cups Kellogg's Bran Flakes cereal
1 egg
¼ cup milk
¼ cup all-purpose flour
⅛ tsp salt
dash pepper
⅛ tsp ground sage
3 Tblsp grated parmesan cheese
4 chicken pieces, washed and patted dry (1 to 1½ lb)
1 Tblsp margarine or butter, melted

METHOD

1. Crush Kellogg's Bran Flakes cereal to measure ¾ cup. Set aside.
2. In small mixing bowl, beat egg and milk slightly. Add flour, salt, pepper, sage, and cheese, stirring until smooth. Dip chicken pieces in egg mixture. Coat with cereal. Place in single layer, skin side up, in greased or foil-lined shallow baking pan. Drizzle with margarine.
3. Bake at 350° F about 45 minutes or until tender. Do not cover pan or turn chicken while baking.

Courtesy of the Kellogg Company.

CHICKEN AND ZUCCHINI

Portion: 1 serving
Yield: 4 servings (about ⅔ cup)
Nutrients/Portion: 125 Calories; 3.7 gm total fat (0.4 gm saturated fat), 51 mg cholesterol

INGREDIENTS

3 chicken breast halves, boneless, skinless
2 tsp oil
1 clove garlic, cut in fourths
1 Tblsp soy sauce
⅓ cup celery, thinly sliced
2 oz can mushroom slices, drained
1 cup zucchini squash, cut in thin strips
2 tsp cornstarch
3 Tblsp water

METHOD

1. Slice chicken into thin strips, about ⅛ inch wide. (It is easier to slice chicken thinly if it is partially frozen.)
2. Heat oil in non stick frypan. Add chicken and garlic.
3. Cook, stirring constantly, until chicken turns white, about 5 minutes. Remove garlic pieces.
4. Stir in soy sauce.
5. Add celery, mushrooms, and squash.
6. Cook, covered, until vegetables are tender crisp, about 4 minutes.
7. Mix cornstarch with water until smooth. Add slowly to chicken mixture, stirring constantly.
8. Continue cooking until ingredients are coated with a thin glaze, about 1 minute.

Reprinted from Food 2 *by The American Dietetic Association.*

BARBECUE BAKED CHICKEN

Yield: 4-5 servings

INGREDIENTS

1 can (6 oz) tomato paste
1 cup water
¼ cup vinegar
2 Tblsp sugar
1 Tblsp chili powder
1 tsp dry mustard
½ tsp paprika
¼ tsp cayenne pepper
¼ tsp garlic powder
1 frying chicken, skin removed, cut up

METHOD

1. Prepare barbeque sauce by combining all ingredients except chicken in medium-size saucepan, stirring to blend. Simmer 5 minutes, stirring occasionally.
2. Arrange chicken in shallow baking pan or on a broiler pan; brush with sauce.
3. Bake at 350° F for 60-70 minutes, or until tender, turning occasionally and brushing with sauce.

Courtesy of the R.T. French Co.

FISH

CRISPY FISH

Yield: 4 servings

INGREDIENTS

2 small plain bagels
½ tsp paprika
½ tsp salt (optional)
¼ tsp pepper

½ tsp onion powder
1-1½ pounds fish fillets (cod, sole, haddock)
¾ cup buttermilk, or skim
1 lemon, cut in wedges

METHOD

1. Preheat oven to 425° F. Spray cookie sheet with cooking spray.

2. Put bagel and seasonings in blender and process until fine. Dip fish in milk and coat with crumbs.
3. Arrange on pan. Bake for 25-30 minutes. Serve with lemon.

Courtesy of Susan Leifer, R.D.

FISH CREOLE

INGREDIENTS

1 lb sole or haddock, defrosted
1 8 oz can tomato sauce
1 2 oz can sliced mushrooms, drained
½ green pepper, diced
1 stalk celery, sliced
3 Tblsp water
1½ Tblsp minced onion

METHOD

1. Rinse fish and pat dry. Arrange in baking dish.
2. Combine tomato sauce, mushrooms, green pepper, celery, water, and onion. Pour evenly over fish.
3. Bake 350° F until fish flakes easily.
4. To microwave, cover with plastic wrap, venting at one corner, and microwave at high for 8-10 minutes. Rotate dish at 4 minutes.
5. Let stand 5 minutes before serving to blend flavors.

Courtesy of Susan Leifer, R.D.

LEMON BAKED FISH

Portion: 2 oz
Yield: 6 servings

INGREDIENTS

1 lb flounder or haddock fillets, fresh or frozen
1 Tblsp butter or margarine, melted
4 tsp lemon juice
1 tsp lemon rind, grated
⅛ tsp salt
dash pepper
⅛ tsp rosemary

METHOD

1. Thaw frozen fish. Preheat oven to 350° F.
2. Divide fish into 6 servings. Place in single layer in a baking pan.
3. Mix fat, lemon juice, lemon rind, salt, pepper, and rosemary. Pour over fish.
4. Bake for 25 minutes or until fish flakes easily when tested with a fork.

Courtesy of the United States Department of Agriculture.

PORK

PORK TOFU AND VEGETABLES

Yield: 4 servings

INGREDIENTS

1 package (10½ oz) Kikkoman Tofu, drained, or ½ block (16 oz size) fresh tofu
½ lb bok choy or romaine lettuce, washed
2 Tblsp cornstarch, divided
4 Tblsp soy sauce, divided
¼ lb boneless lean pork
2 tsp minced fresh ginger root
1 clove garlic, minced
½ tsp sugar
2 Tblsp vegetable oil, divided
1 medium onion, chunked
10 cherry tomatoes, halved
¾ cup water

METHOD

1. Cut tofu into ½ inch cubes; drain well.
2. Cut bok choy into 1 inch squares.
3. Blend 1 Tblsp cornstarch, 3 Tblsp soy sauce, and ¾ cup water; set aside.
4. Cut pork into thin strips.
5. Combine remaining cornstarch and soy sauce with the ginger, garlic, and sugar; stir in pork.
6. Heat 1 Tblsp oil in wok or large skillet over high heat. Add pork and stir-fry 1 minute; remove.
7. Heat remaining oil in same wok. Add onion; stir-fry 2 minutes.
8. Add bok choy; stir-fry 1 minute.
9. Add tomatoes, pork, and soy sauce mixture. Cook and stir until sauce thickens.
10. Gently fold in tofu; heat through.

Courtesy of Kikkoman International, Inc.

CURRIED PORK

Portion: 1 serving
Yield: 4 servings (½ cup curry and ½ cup rice)
Nutrients/Portion: 250 Calories; 5.6 gm total fat (1.5 gm saturated fat), 32 mg cholesterol

INGREDIENTS

¼ cup onion, chopped
2 cups tart apple, unpared, chopped
1 Tblsp oil
2 tsp flour
½ tsp salt
⅛ tsp ground ginger
1 tsp curry powder
1 cup skim milk
1 cup pork, cooked, diced
2 cups brown rice, cooked, unsalted

METHOD

1. Cook onion and apple in oil until tender.
2. Stir in flour, salt, ginger, and curry powder.
3. Add milk slowly, stirring constantly; cook until thickened.
4. Add pork. Heat to serving temperature.
5. Serve over rice.

Reprinted from Food 2 *by The American Dietetic Association.*

TURKEY

THREE BEAN TURKEY BAKE

Yield: 6 servings

INGREDIENTS

1 Tblsp cooking oil
1 package (1¼ lb) fresh ground turkey
1 cup chopped onion
1 clove garlic, finely chopped
1 can (16 oz) pork and beans in tomato
   sauce
1 can (16 oz) kidney beans, drained
1 can (16 oz) cut green beans, drained
½ cup catsup
2 Tblsp brown sugar, packed
1 Tblsp prepared mustard

METHOD

1. Heat oven to 350° F. Heat oil in large
   skillet over medium-high heat until hot.
2. Crumble turkey into skillet.
3. Stir in onion and garlic. Cook until turkey
   is no longer pink; drain.
4. Mix turkey mixture and remaining ingredients in 2½ qt casserole. Add salt and
   pepper to taste.
5. Bake until hot and bubbly (about 30
   minutes).

Courtesy of the Turkey Store Cookbook, *Jerome Foods, Inc.*

HERBED TURKEY AND ZUCCHINI SKILLET DISH

Yield: 4 servings

INGREDIENTS

2 Tblsp fresh lemon juice
2 cloves garlic, finely chopped
½ tsp dried oregano leaves
½ tsp basil leaves
1 package (1¼ lb) fresh turkey breast slices
1 Tblsp butter or margarine
1 Tblsp cooking oil
8 oz fresh mushrooms, sliced
2 medium zucchini, thinly sliced
2 green onions, sliced

METHOD

1. Mix lemon juice, garlic, oregano, and
   basil; brush over both sides of turkey.
2. Heat butter and oil in large skillet over
   medium-high heat until butter is melted.
3. Cook turkey in butter mixture until no
   longer pink (about 2 minutes on each
   side). Remove to warm platter (keep
   warm).
4. Stir mushrooms, zucchini, and onions into
   skillet. Cook until zucchini is almost tender. Add salt and pepper to taste.
5. Arrange vegetables on platter with turkey.

Courtesy of the Turkey Store Cookbook, *Jerome Foods, Inc.*

CURRIED STUFFED GREEN PEPPERS

Yield: 6 servings

INGREDIENTS

1 cup cooked white rice
6 large green peppers
1 Tblsp butter or margarine
1 package (1¼ lb) fresh ground turkey
½ cup onion, chopped
⅓ cup celery, chopped
1 cup chicken broth
2 Tblsp flour
2 Tblsp parsley flakes

2 tsp curry powder
Paprika (optional)

METHOD

1. Heat oven to 350° F.
2. Cut thin slices from stem end of each pepper. Remove seeds and membranes; rinse.
3. Cook peppers in enough boiling water to cover for 3 minutes; drain.
4. Heat butter in large skillet over medium-high heat until melted.
5. Crumble turkey into skillet; stir in onion and celery. Cook until turkey is no longer pink; drain.
6. Mix chicken broth and flour; stir into turkey mixture. Cook, stirring constantly, until mixture thickens and boils.
7. Remove from heat. Stir in rice and remaining ingredients. Add salt and pepper to taste.
8. Stuff each pepper with turkey mixture. Stand each pepper upright in square baking dish, 8 × 8 × 2 inches. Cover tightly with aluminum foil and bake until hot (about 30 minutes).
9. Sprinkle with paprika if desired.

Courtesy of the Turkey Store Cookbook, *Jerome Foods, Inc.*

HOT TURKEY SANDWICHES

Yield: 4 sandwiches

INGREDIENTS

1 package (1¼ lb) fresh turkey breast slices
½ cup bottled Italian dressing
1 Tblsp cooking oil
8 3 × 2 inch slices Swiss cheese
2 large pieces pocket bread (pita bread), cut into halves
2 Tblsp mayonnaise or salad dressing
2 cups alfalfa or sprouts

1 medium avocado, peeled and sliced
1 large tomato, sliced

METHOD

1. Place turkey and Italian dressing in shallow glass dish. Let stand 15 minutes; drain.
2. Heat oil in large skillet over medium high heat until hot. Cook turkey in oil for 2 minutes; turn.
3. Top each turkey slice with cheese. Cook until turkey is no longer pink (about 2 minutes). Add salt and pepper to taste.
4. Open pocket bread halves, forming a pocket. Spread insides with mayonnaise or salad dressing.
5. Place 2 turkey slices in each half. Top turkey with sprouts, avocado, and tomato.

Courtesy of the Turkey Store Cookbook, *Jerome Foods, Inc.*

TURKEY ALMOND STIR FRY

Yield: 4 servings

INGREDIENTS

1 package (1¼ lb) fresh turkey breast tenderloins
2 Tblsp cooking oil
1 medium onion, thinly sliced
1 stalk celery, cut diagonally into thin slices
2 cups fresh mushrooms, sliced
1 package (6 oz) frozen Chinese pea pods
¾ cup chicken broth
1 Tblsp cornstarch
2 Tblsp soy sauce
¼ tsp ground ginger
⅓ cup slivered almonds, toasted
Rice (optional)

METHOD

1. Cut turkey into 1 inch cubes. Add salt and pepper to taste.

2. Heat oil in large skillet or wok over medium high heat until hot.
3. Add turkey; stir-fry until no longer pink (about 3 minutes).
4. Add onion and celery; stir fry 1 minute.
5. Add mushrooms; stir-fry 1 minute.
6. Add pea pods; stir-fry 1 minute.

7. Mix broth, cornstarch, soy sauce, and ginger.
8. Stir into turkey mixture. Heat to boiling, stirring constantly. Boil and stir 1 minute.
9. Top with almonds. Serve with rice if desired.

Courtesy of the Turkey Store Cookbook, *Jerome Foods, Inc.*

VEGETARIAN ENTREES

VEGETABLE QUICHE

Yield: 6 servings

INGREDIENTS

1 (9 inch) baked pie shell
¾ to 1 cup drained, cooked mixed vegetables
½ cup (2 oz) shredded cheddar cheese
6 eggs
1 cup half and half or milk
1 Tblsp instant minced onion
½ tsp salt
½ tsp oregano leaves, crushed

METHOD

1. Sprinkle vegetables and cheese into pie shell.
2. Beat together remaining ingredients until well blended. Pour over vegetables and cheese.
3. Bake in preheated 375° F. oven until knife inserted near center comes out clean, 30 to 40 minutes. Let stand 5 minutes before serving.

Courtesy of the American Egg Board.

LASAGNA

INGREDIENTS

Italian-style tomato sauce (see recipe below)
9 lasagna noodles, uncooked whole wheat or spinach
2 cups ricotta cheese or 2 cups cottage cheese with 2 eggs, blended smooth
½ lb raw spinach, washed and chopped or one 10 oz package spinach, frozen and thawed
1 lb mozzarella cheese, part skim, shredded
¼ cup parmesan or romano cheese, grated

METHOD

1. Assemble ingredients in a 9 × 13 inch pan in this order:
   (a) Thin layer of sauce on bottom.
   (b) Three noodles, side by side.
   (c) Half the filling and half the spinach.
   (d) One third of the remaining sauce.
   (e) Half the mozzarella cheese.
   (f) Another three noodles.
   (g) Remaining filling and spinach.
   (h) Another ⅓ of the sauce.
   (i) Remaining mozzarella cheese.

(j) Remaining three noodles.
(k) Remaining sauce.
(l) Top with parmesan or romano cheese.
2. Bake 45 minutes (uncover for the last 10) at 375° F. Let stand 10 minutes before cutting and serving.

Courtesy of Susan Leifer, R.D.

ITALIAN-STYLE TOMATO SAUCE

INGREDIENTS

1 Tblsp olive oil
1 cup onion, chopped
2 cloves garlic, minced
1 cup green pepper, chopped
2 tsp basil
1 tsp oregano
2 bay leaves
4 8 oz cans tomato sauce
1 6 oz can tomato paste
1 cup chopped tomatoes
½ tsp pepper
1 cup fresh mushrooms, chopped or 1 8 oz can mushroom pieces and stems

METHOD

1. Sauté oil, onion, garlic, green pepper, basil, oregano, and bay leaves until onions are clear and soft.
2. Then remove the bay leaves and add the tomato sauce and paste, chopped tomatoes, pepper, and mushrooms.
3. Turn heat down to low. Cover and simmer at least 45 minutes, stirring occasionally.

Courtesy of Susan Leifer, R.D.

CHEESE FONDUE

Portion: 1 serving
Yield: 6 servings (about ½ cup each) mixture, without bread

INGREDIENTS

1 cup cottage cheese, creamed
¼ cup milk
2 Tblsp butter or margarine
1½ Tblsp cornstarch
dash garlic powder
¼ tsp dry mustard
¾ cup milk
1 cup (4 oz) pasteurized process sharp cheddar cheese, shredded
½ cup (2 oz) pasteurized process Swiss cheese, shredded
1 lb loaf French bread, cut in cubes

METHOD

1. Mix cottage cheese with ¼ cup milk in a blender until smooth.
2. Melt fat in a saucepan.
3. Stir in cornstarch, garlic powder, and dry mustard; mix well.
4. Add ¾ cup milk. Cook over medium heat, stirring constantly until thickened (about 2-3 minutes).
5. Reduce heat. Stir in cottage cheese mixture.
6. Add remaining cheeses, stirring until cheeses are melted.
7. Serve with cubes of French bread for dipping into fondue mixture.
8. Fondue may be transferred to a preheated fondue pot or chafing dish if desired. Keep hot during serving by using an alcohol burner, canned heat, or candle burner.

Courtesy of the United States Department of Agriculture.

WHOLE-WHEAT PIZZA

INGREDIENTS

1½ tsp dry active yeast
½ cup lukewarm water
1 cup whole-wheat flour
½ cup white flour
1 Tblsp oil
Topping:
   1 Tblsp olive oil
   1 medium onion, chopped
   1 15 oz can tomato purée
   1 green pepper, diced
   ¼ lb fresh mushrooms, thinly sliced
   ½ tsp basil
   ½ tsp oregano
   ½ tsp pepper
   1 tsp brown sugar
   6 oz shredded cheese (½ cheddar, ½ part-
      skim mozzarella)

METHOD

1. Dissolve yeast in water. Stir in flours and oil.
2. Knead on floured board until smooth (about 3 minutes).
3. Place dough in clean buttered bowl and butter top. Cover and let rise until double.
4. Meanwhile, pour olive oil in saucepan. Add chopped onion and sauté over medium heat until soft and clear.
5. Add remaining ingredients (except cheese) and simmer 10 minutes.
6. After dough has risen, spread over well-oiled 12 to 14 inch pizza pan. Bake 8-10 minutes at 400° F.
7. Spread tomato mixture over crust; bake 5-10 minutes, until edges brown lightly.
8. Sprinkle cheese evenly on top of pizza and bake until cheese has melted.

Courtesy of the Wisconsin Nutrition Education and Training Program.

VEGETABLE TABOULI

Portion: 1 serving
Yield: 4 servings (1¼ to 1½ cups each)

INGREDIENTS

1⅓ cup dry bulgur (cracked wheat)
¼ to ½ cup chopped green pepper
1-2 cups cooked kidney beans or garbanzo
   beans (⅓ cup dry or 10 oz canned)
¼ cup finely chopped fresh mint
3-4 Tblsp sliced green onions
2-3 tsp salad oil
1 tsp dried dill
¼ cup wine vinegar (or more to taste)
½ cup finely chopped parsley

METHOD

1. Soak bulgur in 3 cups hot water for 1 hour.
2. Drain and squeeze out water.
3. Stir in peppers, beans, and other ingredients.
4. Chill for several hours. May be served as is or on lettuce leaves.

Reprinted with permission from the American Institute for Cancer Research.

FOUR BEAN CASSEROLE

INGREDIENTS

8 slices imitation bacon
½ cup brown sugar
½ tsp garlic powder
½ cup vinegar (cider)
1 tsp dry mustard
4 large onions, sliced
16 oz can of each: baked beans, lima beans,
   butter beans, kidney beans

METHOD

1. Fry bacon: remove from pan.

2. Fry onions in remaining grease. Add sugar, garlic, mustard, vinegar and cook covered for 20 minutes.
3. Add four cans of beans.
4. Crumble bacon and add to casserole.
5. Bake 1 hour at 350° F.

Courtesy of Scherle Barth, R.D.

RED BEANS AND RICE

Yield: 4-6 servings

INGREDIENTS

¾ cup chopped onion
½ cup chopped celery
2 cloves garlic
1 Tblsp margarine
1½ cups cooked kidney beans (½ cup dry or 16 oz can)
2 cups cooked brown rice
2 Tblsp chopped fresh parsley (1½ tsp dried)
⅛ tsp pepper

METHOD

1. Cook onion, celery, and garlic in margarine until tender.
2. Remove garlic and add remaining ingredients. Simmer together for 5 minutes to blend flavors.

Reprinted with permission from the American Institute for Cancer Research.

PASTA, RICE, AND STUFFING

WILD SUNFLOWER STUFFING

Portion: ¾ cup
Yield: 100 servings

INGREDIENTS

5½ cups (2 lbs 5 oz) wild rice, uncooked
1½ gallon water
4 tsp salt
1 50 oz. package stuffing mix
4 cups sunflower kernels, roasted

METHOD

1. Bring water to boil. Add rice and salt. Cover tightly and simmer 35-45 minutes or until liquid is absorbed.
2. Make stuffing according to package directions.
3. Combine rice and stuffing. Stir in sunflower kernels before serving.

Courtesy of the National Sunflower Association and North Dakota State Wheat Commission.

HERBED SPINACH PASTA

Portion: 1 serving
Yield: 5 servings
Nutrients/Portion: 160 Calories; 2.2 gm dietary fiber, 5 gm protein, 9 gm fat, 14 gm carbohydrate, 380 mg sodium

INGREDIENTS

¼ cup Kellogg's All-Bran cereal
¼ cup grated parmesan cheese
dash pepper
¼ tsp basil leaves
½ tsp oregano leaves
1 tsp snipped fresh parsley
½ package (5 oz, 3½ cups) spinach pasta ribbons
2 Tblsp margarine or butter, melted

METHOD

1. Crush Kellogg's All-Bran cereal to crumbs.

2. Stir in parmesan cheese, pepper, basil, oregano and parsley. Set aside.
3. Cook pasta ribbons according to package directions just until tender. Drain. Gently toss hot ribbons with margarine.
4. Add cereal mixture, tossing until well combined. Serve immediately.

Courtesy of the Kellogg Company.

SAVORY BRAN-RICE PILAF

Portion: 1 serving
Yield: 6 servings
Nutrients/Portion: 190 Calories; 5.2 gm dietary fiber, 4 gm protein, 9 gm fat, 30 gm carbohydrate, 615 mg sodium

INGREDIENTS

½ cup uncooked, long grain brown or white rice
1 chicken bouillon cube
¼ cup margarine or butter
¼ cup chopped onion
½ cup chopped celery
1 jar (2½ oz, ½ cup) sliced mushrooms, drained
¼ cup sliced water chestnuts
1 cup Kellogg's All-Bran cereal
¼ tsp ground sage
½ tsp basil leaves
⅛ tsp pepper
½ cup water

METHOD

1. Cook rice according to package directions, adding bouillon cube and omitting the salt and butter called for in package directions.
2. While rice is cooking, melt margarine in large frypan. Stir in onion, celery, mushrooms and water chestnuts.
3. Cook over medium heat, stirring occasionally, until celery is almost tender.
4. Gently stir in cooked rice, Kellogg's All-Bran cereal, sage, basil, pepper, and water. Cover and cook over very low heat about 15 minutes. Serve immediately.

Courtesy of the Kellogg Company.

SALADS

VEGETABLE PASTA SALAD

Yield: 8 to 10 servings

INGREDIENTS

½ (1 lb) package rotini macaroni (about 3 cups)
½ cup vegetable oil
⅓ cup lemon juice from concentrate
2 Tblsp grated parmesan cheese
2 Tblsp water
1 (0.75 oz) package garlic and herb salad dressing mix
1½ cups sliced zucchini
2 small tomatoes, seeded and diced
1 cup shredded carrots
1 cup sliced fresh mushrooms (about 4 oz)

METHOD

1. Cook rotini according to package directions; drain.
2. Meanwhile, in 1-pint jar with tight-fitting lid or cruet, combine oil, lemon juice, cheese, water, and salad dressing mix; shake well.
3. In large bowl, combine *hot* pasta, dressing, and remaining ingredients.
4. Chill several hours or overnight.

Courtesy of ReaLemon® lemon juice from concentrate.

TURKEY TACO SALAD

Yield: 6 servings

INGREDIENTS

1 Tblsp cooking oil
1 package (about 1¼ lb) fresh ground turkey
1 medium onion, chopped
1 package (1¼ oz) taco seasoning mix
½ tsp chili powder (optional)
1 cup water
8 cups lettuce, bite-size pieces
3 medium tomatoes, chopped
1 medium green pepper, chopped
1½ cups Monterey Jack or cheddar cheese, shredded
3 cups corn chips
sour cream (optional)
black olives (optional)

METHOD

1. Heat oil in skillet over medium high heat until hot.
2. Crumble turkey into skillet; stir in onion. Cook until turkey is no longer pink and onion is tender; drain.
3. Stir in seasoning mix, chili powder, and water. Heat to boiling; reduce heat. Simmer, stirring occasionally, 15 minutes. Add salt and pepper to taste.
4. Layer lettuce, tomatoes, and green pepper in salad bowls.
5. Spoon turkey mixture over top. Sprinkle with cheese. Garnish with corn chips, dairy sour cream, and sliced ripe olives if desired.

Courtesy of the Turkey Store Cookbook, *Jerome Foods, Inc.*

SUNFLOWER AND PASTA SALAD

Portion: 1½ cups
Yield: 4 servings

INGREDIENTS

1 (6½ oz) can water packed tuna, drained
1 cup celery, diced
1 Tblsp onion, diced
2 Tblsp lemon juice
2 Tblsp sauterne wine (optional)
⅔ cup salad dressing
1 cup green grapes, cut in half
1 cup mandarin oranges, drained
4 oz salad size pasta, dry
¾ cup sunflower kernels
black olives, sunflower kernels, or mandarin oranges for garnish

METHOD

1. In a bowl mix tuna, celery, onion, lemon juice, and wine. Marinate for several hours.
2. Add salad dressing and mix well.
3. Cook pasta according to package directions. Rinse with cold water.
4. Gently blend in pasta, grapes, oranges, and sunflower kernels. Add salt if sunflower kernels are not salted. Best when chilled.

Courtesy of the National Sunflower Association.

LENTIL SALAD

Portion: ¾ cup
Yield: 4 servings
Nutrients/Portion: 268 Calories

INGREDIENTS

1 qt water
1 tsp salt
1 cup dried lentils
1 small bay leaf
¼ cup minced onion
2 Tblsp minced parsley
2 cloves garlic, finely chopped
½ cup canned whole tomatoes, drained and chopped
¼ cup diced carrots
1 Tblsp red wine vinegar
½ tsp Worcestershire sauce
⅛ tsp Tabasco sauce
½ tsp pepper
3 Tblsp oil

METHOD

1. Salt water and bring to a boil in 2 qt saucepan. Add lentils and bay leaf. Reduce heat and simmer covered for 20 to 30 minutes or until lentils are tender but not mushy. Drain well and discard bay leaf.
2. Transfer lentils to a serving bowl and stir in onions, parsley, garlic, tomatoes, and carrots.
3. To make dressing, combine vinegar, Worcestershire sauce, Tabasco, pepper, and oil.
4. Pour dressing over lentil mixture, and toss gently but thoroughly.
5. Cover tightly with foil or plastic wrap and refrigerate for at least 30 minutes.

Courtesy of the Division of Nutritional Sciences, Cornell Cooperative Extension.

FRUITED CHICKEN SALAD

INGREDIENTS

2-3 cup diced or shredded cooked chicken (or turkey)
1 cup salad dressing (light or regular)
1 cup seedless grapes, halved

½ cup sliced almonds
green, leafy lettuce

METHOD

1. Mix chicken, salad dressing, grapes, and almonds in bowl.
2. Refrigerate mixture 1-2 hours.
3. Place each serving on a lettuce leaf.

Courtesy of Susan Leifer, R.D.

COTTAGE CHEESE WITH VEGETABLES

Portion: ¾ cup
Servings: 4
Nutrients/Portion: 95 Calories; 1.2 gm total fat (0.7 gm saturated fat), 5 mg cholesterol

INGREDIENTS

16 oz low-fat cottage cheese
½ cup carrots, shredded
1 tsp onion, very finely chopped or 1 small green onion, sliced
2 Tblsp green pepper, very finely chopped
2 Tblsp celery, chopped
½ cup cucumber, chopped
2 radishes, sliced
⅛ tsp pepper
salad greens (as desired)

METHOD

1. Mix all ingredients (except salad greens) together lightly.
2. Serve on crisp salad greens.

Reprinted from Food 2 *by The American Dietetic Association.*

CHEF'S SALAD

Portion: 2 cups
Yield: 4 servings

Nutrients/Portion: (salad dressing not included) With turkey: 125 Calories, 5.1 gm total fat (2.4 gm saturated fat), 41 mg cholesterol; with chicken, 115 Calories, 4.6 gm total fat (2.3 gm saturated fat), 37 mg cholesterol

INGREDIENTS

1 cup turkey or chicken, cooked, diced
1 qt lettuce, bite-size pieces, slightly packed
⅓ cup celery, sliced
3 Tblsp green pepper, diced
1 green onion, thinly sliced
1 large tomato, cut in wedges
¼ cup natural cheddar cheese, diced
low-calorie salad dressing as desired

METHOD

1. Toss all ingredients (except cheese and salad dressing) together lightly.
2. Sprinkle cheese over each serving.
3. Serve with favorite low-calorie salad dressing.

Reprinted from Food 2 *by The American Dietetic Association.*

SANDWICH FILLINGS

HUMMUS

INGREDIENTS

1 1 lb can garbanzos, drained
3 Tblsp juice from garbanzos
⅓ cup tahini (sesame paste)
2 cloves garlic, crushed
⅓ cup lemon juice
¼ tsp salt

METHOD

1. In blender, whirl all ingredients until smooth.
2. Serve with pita (or pocket) bread, crackers, or fresh vegetable sticks.

Courtesy of the Wisconsin Nutrition Education and Training Program.

BREADS 'N SPREADS

Put any of the following spreads between two slices of whole-wheat bread, and then create some tasty "fillers" of your own!

- Sliced cooked chicken, thinly sliced tomatoes, and shredded Gruyère cheese
- Spinach leaves, marinated cucumber slices, Swiss cheese, and thinly sliced tomatoes
- Sliced cooked turkey, cranberry sauce, and lettuce
- Cottage cheese and alfalfa sprouts
- Drained flaked tuna, finely chopped celery, chopped green onion, finely chopped radishes, and cottage cheese thinned with lemon juice
- Diced cooked chicken, diced apples, pineapple chunks, lettuce leaves, curry powder, and a half-and-half mixture of mayonnaise and plain yogurt
- Cooked lean ground beef, finely chopped boiled potato, and finely chopped pickled beets
- Peanut butter and banana slices

Courtesy of the Division of Nutritional Sciences, Cornell Cooperative Extension.

SNACKS

FRUITED YOGURT

INGREDIENTS

½ cup low-fat yogurt
1 tsp vanilla
½ cup unsweetened fruit
sugar substitute, to taste

METHOD

1. Mix all ingredients together, adding sugar substitute as desired.
2. This recipe can be frozen to be used as a frozen dessert or snack.

Courtesy of Susan Leifer, R.D.

FROZEN GRAPES

Wash and freeze seedless grapes (or try strawberries) for an easy snack idea.

Courtesy of Susan Leifer, R.D.

POPCORN

Sprinkle parmesan cheese, dill weed, red pepper, or any favorite spice on hot popcorn for a change from salt. Try tossing in a few unsalted roasted peanuts, sunflower seeds, or toasted pumpkin seeds.

Courtesy of Susan Leifer, R.D.

CALIFORNIA WALKING SALAD

INGREDIENTS

1 lb seedless grapes, pulled from stem
1 red apple, cored and cubed
½ cup raisins
¼ cup toasted slivered almonds
1 head iceburg lettuce, cored, drained, and chilled

METHOD

1. In bowl, mix grapes, apple, raisins, and almonds.
2. Carefully remove lettuce leaves from head, one at a time. Put ½ cup of fruit-nut mixture in each lettuce cup. Serve out of hand.

Courtesy of the California Table Grape Commission.

CEREAL PEANUT MIX

Yield: 8 cups

INGREDIENTS

4 cups Kellogg's Crispix cereal
2 cups pretzel rings or twists
1 cup peanuts
¼ cup butter or margarine
¼ cup peanut butter
1 cup raisins

METHOD

1. Combine Kellogg's Crispix cereal, pretzels, and peanuts in $13 \times 9 \times 2$ inch baking pan. Set aside.
2. In small saucepan, combine butter and peanut butter. Stir over low heat until melted and smooth.
3. Pour over cereal mixture, stirring to coat evenly.
4. Bake at 350° F for 8 minutes, stirring occasionally.
5. Remove from oven. Stir in raisins. Spread on absorbent paper to cool.

Courtesy of the Kellogg Company.

CAMP-OUT SNACK MIX

Yield: 5½ cups

INGREDIENTS

4 cups Kellogg's Crispix cereal
½ cup raisins
½ cup peanuts
¼ cup sunflower nuts or seeds
¼ cup diced dates or prunes

METHOD

1. Combine all ingredients. Store tightly covered or in individual plastic bags.

Courtesy of the Kellogg Company.

MIXED DRY CEREAL AND NUTS

Portion: ⅓ cup
Yield: 9 servings

INGREDIENTS

2 Tblsp margarine
1¼ cups unsalted roasted peanuts
2½ cups assorted unsweetened, ready-to-eat cereals
1 tsp paprika
¼ tsp onion powder
⅛ tsp garlic powder
1¼ tsp chili powder

METHOD

1. Preheat oven to 250° F.
2. Melt margarine in large baking pan in oven.
3. Remove pan from oven, stir in nuts and cereals, mix well.
4. Sprinkle with seasonings; stir well.
5. Bake uncovered in oven 20-30 minutes, or until light-colored cereals begin to brown. Stir every 10 minutes.
6. Serve warm or cooled.

7. Store cooled cereal snack in tightly closed containers.
8. If snack needs recrisping, reheat in 250° F oven for a few minutes.

Courtesy of the United States Department of Agriculture.

OATMEAL PEANUT BUTTER COOKIES

Portion: 1 cookie
Yield: 5 dozen cookies
Nutrients/Portion: 59 Calories

INGREDIENTS

¼ cup shortening
¾ cup brown sugar, packed
¼ cup water
2 eggs
1 cup peanut butter
1 tsp vanilla
1 cup grated carrot
1 cup flour
½ tsp baking soda
½ tsp salt
3 cups rolled oats, quick cooking

METHOD

1. Preheat oven to 375° F.
2. Cream shortening and sugar. Blend in water, eggs, peanut butter, vanilla, and carrot.
3. Sift flour, soda, and salt together and stir into other ingredients.
4. Stir in oats until completely moistened.
5. Roll dough into 1 inch diameter balls and place on greased baking sheet. Press balls flat with a fork.
6. Bake 10-12 minutes.

Courtesy of the Division of Nutritional Sciences, Cornell Cooperative Extension.

SOFT PRETZELS

Portion: 1 pretzel
Yield: 12 pretzels
Nutrients/Portion: 54 Calories

INGREDIENTS

4 or 4½ cups bread flour
1 package active dry yeast
1 tsp salt
1⅓ cups water (120°-130° F)
3 Tblsp oil
1 Tblsp honey
coarse salt, poppy seeds, or sesame seeds

METHOD

1. Stir together 2 cups of flour, yeast, and salt.
2. Add liquid ingredients and beat 3-4 minutes.
3. Add enough additional flour to make a soft, yet manageable, dough. Knead 8-10 minutes until smooth.
4. Divide dough into 12 equal portions and roll each section into a 15-inch rope.
5. Roll lightly in coarse salt or seeds and shape into a pretzel.
6. Place on greased baking sheet and bake in 425° F oven for 20 minutes.

Courtesy of the North Dakota State Wheat Commission.

STRAWBERRY-YOGURT POPSICLES

Portion: 1 popsicle
Yield: 12 popsicles

INGREDIENTS

2 cartons (10 oz each) frozen strawberries, thawed
1 Tblsp unflavored gelatin
16 oz yogurt, plain
12 3 oz paper cups
12 wooden sticks
aluminum foil

METHOD

1. Drain strawberries.
2. Place drained liquid in a saucepan and sprinkle with gelatin. Cook over low heat, stirring constantly, until gelatin dissolves.
3. Mix strawberries, yogurt, and gelatin mixture in a blender until smooth.
4. Place cups on a tray or in a baking pan. Fill with blended mixture and cover cups with a sheet of aluminum foil.
5. Insert a stick for each popsicle by making a slit in the foil over the center of each cup.
6. Freeze popsicles until firm.
7. Run warm water on outside of cup to loosen each popsicle from the cup.

Courtesy of the United States Department of Agriculture.

SUNNY WHEAT DROPS

Portion: 1 cookie

INGREDIENTS

¾ cup shortening
1 cup brown sugar
½ cup + 2 Tblsp granulated sugar
1 egg
¼ cup milk
1 tsp vanilla
1 cup flour, all-purpose
½ tsp salt
½ tsp baking soda
1 tsp cinnamon
3½ cups oats, rolled, uncooked
⅔ cup raisins, packed
½ cup sunflower kernels

METHOD

1. Beat together first six ingredients.
2. Combine dry ingredients and then add to creamed mixture. Stir well.

3. Drop tablespoons of dough onto cookie sheets.
4. Bake at 350° F for 10 minutes.

Courtesy of the North Dakota State Wheat Commission and National Sunflower Association.

SOUPS

CHILI

Yield: 4-6 servings

INGREDIENTS

1 lb lean ground beef (optional)
1 medium onion, chopped
1 medium green pepper, chopped
1 tsp vegetable oil
1 Tblsp flour
1 16 oz can tomatoes
1 15 oz can kidney beans, undrained
2-4 tsp chili powder
1 bay leaf

METHOD

1. Brown green pepper and onion in oil or with ground beef in large skillet. Stir to crumble beef. Pour off excess fat.
2. Add flour, blending well.
3. Add kidney beans, tomatoes, chili powder, and bay leaf. Simmer 10 minutes, stirring occasionally.
4. Remove bay leaf.

Courtesy of the R.T. French Co.

POTATO SOUP

Portion: 1 cup
Yield: 4 servings
Nutrients/Portion: 135 Calories, 3.0 gm total fat (0.7 gm saturated fat), 2 mg cholesterol

INGREDIENTS

2 cups potatoes, diced
¼ cup carrots, shredded
¼ cup celery, chopped
2 Tblsp onion, chopped
½ tsp dill weed
1 cup boiling water
½ tsp salt
2 cups skim milk
1 Tblsp margarine
1 Tblsp flour
1 Tblsp water
Paprika to garnish

METHOD

1. Add vegetables and dill weed to boiling salted water. Cover and boil gently until vegetables are tender (about 15 minutes).
2. Stir to break up potatoes.
3. Add milk and margarine. Heat to simmering.
4. Mix flour with 1 Tblsp water until smooth. Add slowly to vegetable mixture, stirring constantly; heat until mixture just starts to boil.
5. Sprinkle each serving with paprika.

Reprinted from Food 2 *by The American Dietetic Association.*

TURKEY MINESTRONE

Yield: 8-10 servings

INGREDIENTS

2 Tblsp butter or margarine
2 Tblsp cooking oil
1 package (1¼ lb) fresh ground turkey
½ cup onion, chopped
2 cloves garlic, finely chopped
5 cups beef broth
2 cups cabbage, chopped
1 cup carrots, diced
1 cup zucchini, diced
1 can (15½ oz) whole tomatoes, undrained
1 tsp dried basil leaves
1 package (10 oz) frozen green beans, thawed
¼ cup parsley, snipped

METHOD

1. Heat butter and oil in Dutch oven over medium high heat until butter is melted.
2. Crumble turkey into Dutch oven; stir in onion and garlic. Cook until turkey is no longer pink.
3. Stir in broth, cabbage, carrots, zucchini, tomatoes, and basil; cut up tomatoes.
4. Add salt and pepper to taste; reduce heat.
5. Simmer until vegetables are tender (about 15 minutes).
6. Stir in beans and parsley. Simmer until heated through.

Courtesy of the Turkey Store Cookbook, *Jerome Foods, Inc.*

VEGETABLE SOUP

Portion: ¾ cup
Yield: 6 servings

INGREDIENTS

1 Tblsp oil
2 Tblsp green pepper, finely chopped
¼ cup onion, finely chopped
½ cup celery, finely chopped
1 cup carrot, shredded
10¾ oz can tomato soup, condensed
1¼ cups water
12 oz can vegetable juice cocktail

METHOD

1. Heat oil. Add vegetables and cook until tender.
2. Mix soup, water, and vegetable juice cocktail in a saucepan. Bring to a boil.
3. Add vegetables. Cover and heat to serving temperature.
4. Serve in mugs.

Courtesy of the United States Department of Agriculture.

VEGETABLES

BROCCOLI STIR-FRY

Yield: 4 servings

INGREDIENTS

4 cups thinly sliced fresh broccoli
1 cup thinly sliced carrots
1 cup thinly sliced mushrooms
¼ cup sliced Bermuda or other mild onion
2 Tblsp oil (vegetable)
1 cup fresh bean sprouts
2 tsp cornstarch
water
2 tsp salt-free chicken bouillon granules
½ tsp minced garlic
¼ tsp ground ginger
⅛ tsp red pepper

METHOD

1. Stir-fry broccoli, carrots, mushrooms, and onion in hot oil in large skillet over medium high heat about 3 minutes.
2. Add bean sprouts.
3. Stir cornstarch into a little cold water in a 1 cup measure. Add enough water to make 1 cup.
4. Add to vegetable mixture, along with bouillon, garlic, ginger, and red pepper. Simmer 2-3 minutes, stirring occasionally, until liquid thickens and vegetables are crisp to tender.

Courtesy of the R.T. French Co.

MARINATED VEGETABLES

Yield: 4 servings

INGREDIENTS

⅓ cup vinegar
⅓ cup vegetable oil
⅓ cup water
2 tsp sugar
1 tsp pepper
½ tsp oregano
¼ tsp garlic powder
⅛ tsp thyme leaves
dash cayenne pepper
1 small zucchini, sliced
12 oz fresh mushrooms
1 cup cherry tomatoes

METHOD

1. Combine vinegar, oil, water, and sugar in a small saucepan. Add seasonings; simmer 3-5 minutes.
2. Combine zucchini, mushrooms, and tomatoes in glass bowl. Add hot marinade and toss lightly.
3. Chill several hours or overnight, stirring occasionally.

Courtesy of the R.T. French Co.

HERBED BROCCOLI

Portion: ½ cup
Yield: 4 servings
Nutrients/Portion: 20 Calories; 0.2 gm total fat

INGREDIENTS

¾ lb fresh broccoli spears
2 tsp onion, finely chopped
½ tsp marjoram leaves
½ tsp basil leaves
¾ cups boiling water
4 lemon wedges

METHOD

1. Wash and trim broccoli; split thick stems.
2. Add broccoli, onion, and herbs to boiling water.

3. Cover and boil gently until broccoli is tender, about 10 minutes. Drain.
4. Serve with lemon wedge garnish.
5. A 10-oz package frozen broccoli spears may be used in place of fresh broccoli; cook frozen broccoli about 6 minutes.

Reprinted from Food 2 *by The American Dietetic Association.*

SEASONED GREEN BEANS

Portion: ½ cup
Yield: 4 servings
Nutrients/Portion: 40 Calories; 1.1 gm total fat (0.2 gm saturated fat)

INGREDIENTS

¼ cup onion, chopped
¼ cup celery, chopped
1 tsp margarine
3 cups frozen cut green beans
⅛ tsp garlic powder
⅛ tsp salt
dash pepper
¼ cup water

METHOD

1. Cook onion and celery in margarine in nonstick frypan until onion is clear.
2. Add remaining ingredients.
3. Cover and boil gently until beans are tender, about 10 minutes.

Reprinted from Food 2 *by The American Dietetic Association.*

GLOSSARY

Adipose tissue—Body tissue composed of fat cells.

Aerobic—Performed in the presence of oxygen.

Aflatoxin—A cancer-causing substance naturally occurring in moldy grains and peanuts.

Agribusiness—The business of producing and distributing food.

Albumin—A protein in the blood.

Algae—Seaweed.

Amenorrhea—Absence of menstruation.

Amino acid—The nitrogen-containing components which form protein and are the end products of protein digestion.

Amphetamine—Prescription appetite suppressant.

Anaerobic—Performed in the absence of oxygen.

Anemia—A reduction in the number of red blood cells in hemoglobin, or in volume of packed red blood cells.

Anorectic—Having no appetite.

Anorexia nervosa—An eating disorder characterized by rigid dieting, excess exercise, and abnormal weight loss.

Antibiotics—Substances that destroy or stop growth of bacteria and other microorganisms.

Antibodies—Protein subtances developed by the body in response to the presence of a foreign substance.

Antimicrobial—Chemical added to prevent food spoilage.

Antioxidant—A substance that limits oxygen's breakdown of fat.

Aquaculture—The cultivation of fish in an enclosed tank.

Arithmetical ratio—Difference between a number and its predecessor is always the same.

Artificial flavor—A flavor that can be made in a laboratory to taste or smell like a real food.

Aspartame—A nutritive sweetener that is composed of two amino acids and provides four Calories per gram.

Assembly—Collection and transport of raw products from individual farmers to a central location.

Atherosclerosis—A disease in which the inner walls of blood vessels become coated with cholesterol-containing plaque which interferes with blood flow and oxygen supply.

Baking soda—A chemical, sodium bicarbonate, that releases carbon dioxide when heated.

Basal metabolic rate (BMR)—The rate at which the body uses energy for internal operations.

Basal metabolism—Energy required for the body's internal operations.

Benzopyrene—A carcinogen produced when cooking meat over a flame such as charcoal grilling.

Beri-beri—Disease caused by a deficiency of thiamin.

Bile—A fat emulsifier that is secreted by the liver, stored in the gallbladder, and released into the small intestine when fat leaves the stomach.

Blood glucose level—The amount of blood sugar in the body.

Body image—Mental image a person has of his or her own physical appearance.

Bran—The outer layer of a kernel of grain.

Brand name—A product labeled as produced and distributed by a major company.

Broker—A person employed in wholesaling who lines up buyers and sellers and arranges for shipment of products.

Brucellosis—A bacterial disease that can be transmitted through milk to humans.

Bulimia—An eating disorder characterized by recurrent episodes of binge eating and vomiting or abuse of laxatives or diuretics.

Caffeine—A stimulant present in coffee, tea, some soft drinks, and medications.

Calciferol—Chemical name for vitamin D.

Calcium—Major mineral in the body needed for bone and teeth development.

Calorie—The amount of heat energy needed to raise the temperature of one kilogram of water one degree centigrade.

Carbohydrate—A nutrient composed of carbon, hydrogen, and oxygen which provides energy to the body. Sugar, starch, and fiber are carbohydrates.

Carcinogen—A substance that causes cancer.

Carrier-mediated diffusion—A process where molecules are carried across a membrane with the help of another molecule.

Carrying capacity—A biological system's ability to support only a given number of living things.

Cell—The basic unit of structure of all animals and plants. Cells combine to form tissue.

Cellulose—The main dietary fiber which cannot be digested. Instead cellulose absorbs water in the colon and increases stool bulk.

Centralized food distribution—Shipping raw products to a central location for processing, manufacturing, and marketing throughout the country.

Chlorophyll—A green pigment present in leaves that traps the sun's energy.

Cholesterol—A fat-like substance, produced in the liver and found in foods of animal origin, needed for several body processes.

Chromium—Trace mineral required for body to store and use glucose.

Chronic disease—A disorder that develops over time and recurs.

Chyme—The mixture of food, water, and enzymes in the stomach.

Cirrhosis—Injury of liver tissue which may be caused by excess consumption of alcoholic beverages.

Clostridium botulinum—A spore-producing bacterium that is very resistant to heat. Requires temperatures above the boiling point of water to kill the bacterium.

Co-carcinogen—A substance that favors the development of the cancer after cancer is already present.

Colostrum—Yellowish fluid, rich in proteins which provide immunity, produced prior to breast milk.

Commodity purchase—The United States Department of Agriculture purchase of surplus perishable food items, resulting in a decreased market supply.

Community gardening—Individuals growing food on public land.

Complementary proteins—Foods with different essential amino acid composition that when combined achieve a higher protein value.

Conglomerate—A company that operates two or more industries.

Contaminants—Unanticipated additives which can enter the food supply by chance and are not desired in food.

Contraception—Prevention of pregnancy.

Cooperative—Member ownership and control of a business with products sold as close to wholesale cost as possible, or members are offered annual rebates.

Culture—A set of customs shared by a group of people.

Decentralized Food Distribution—Regional production and distribution.

Deficiency—Lack or shortage of a substance needed for health.

Dehydration—Abnormal loss of body fluids.

Demineralization—Loss of calcium and phosphorus from bone.

Dental plaque—A coating of bacteria and sugar on tooth enamel.

Diabetes mellitus—A metabolic disorder involving the control and use of energy nutrients, resulting in abnormal blood glucose regulation.

Diet—Collection of foods regularly consumed by an individual or group of people.

Dietary fiber—Non-digestible carbohydrate.

Digestion—Chemical and mechanical breakdown of food.

Disaccharide—Two single sugars bonded together to form sucrose, lactose, or maltose.

Distribution—Flow of products from producer to consumer.

Diuretic—A substance that causes the kidneys to increase the excretion of urine.

Diversify—Expand operations to include companies that produce other types of products.

Diverticulosis—The out-bulging (out-pocketing) of the colon associated with the lack of dietary fiber.

Edema—The accumulation of excess fluid in body tissues.

Elbow breadth—Measurement of elbow used to determine frame size.

Emulsify—To make fat soluble in water.

Emulsifier—Substance used to help oil or fat mix with water.

Endosperm—The inner portion of a kernel of grain which is composed primarily of starch.

Energy—The capacity to do work.

Energy balance—Energy intake equals energy expended.

Enriched—A refined product to which nutrients lost during processing are replaced to their original level.

Entree—Main dish at a meal.

Enzymes—Protein substances that speed up chemical reactions.

Epidemiology—Study of the incidence and distribution of disease.

Ergogenic aid—Any factor that enhances exercise performance.

Esophagus—Tube through which food passes en route from the mouth to the stomach.

Essential nutrient—A required substance which the body is unable to make, so it must be obtained from the diet.

Export subsidy—Offering of government credit to foreign purchasers of United States agricultural products to increase exports.

Express—Exert pressure and/or suction on breast to extract milk.

Famine—Extreme scarcity of food.

Farmer's market—Direct selling of produce to consumers by a group of farmers.

Fats—Non-water-soluble carbon-containing substances which provide a concentrated source of energy.

Fetal alcohol syndrome—Set of physical and mental defects in infants born to mothers who abused alcoholic beverages during pregnancy.

Fetus—The term given to a developing baby from the second month of pregnancy until birth.

Finite—Limited.

Flavor enhancer—A substance which has no flavor itself, but makes another flavor more noticeable.

Fluoride—Mineral that adds strength to bones and teeth.

Food chain—System involving the transfer of food energy from one organism to another. The sequence begins with green plants which are energy producers, then moves to plant eaters, and then to meat eaters.

Food pattern—Composite of foods typically eaten by an individual or group.

Food technologist—Scientist who studies the properties of food and the effect of processing on food safety and acceptability.

Fortified—A product to which nutrients are added at higher than natural levels or to foods not originally a source of the nutrient.

Frame size—Determination of body build or bone structure as small, medium, or large.

Futurist—A person who analyzes and predicts social change.

Gastric lipase—Enzyme involved in breaking down of short-chain triglycerides into component fatty acids and glycerol.

Generally Recognized As Safe (GRAS)—An additive thought of as safe for intentional addition to foods, but has not necessarily been tested.

Gene-splicing—Scientific method that allows genetic material from plants to be combined.

Generic—A product that does not identify a producer's name.

Genetic engineering—Altering the genetic make-up of plants and animals.

Geometrical ratio—The ratio between numbers is always the same such as 2, 4, 8, 16, 32, 64.

Germ—Portion of a whole grain kernel rich in vitamin E, thiamin, and riboflavin.

Glucose—A simple sugar that is the end product of starch digestion and provides the body with readily available energy. Plants produce this sugar through the process of photosynthesis.

Glycogen—Starch stored in the body which serves as a source of energy.

Goiter—Enlarged thyroid gland caused by lack of iodine.

Green revolution—The use of advanced scientific agricultural methods by nations previously lacking self-sufficiency in food production.

Health food—A vague term used to describe foods believed to have health-promoting qualities.

Heart attack—A disorder that occurs when oxygen supply to the heart muscle is inadequate causing tissue cells to die.

Heartburn—Burning chest pain and discomfort that may occur after eating high-fat or spicy foods.

Hemoglobin—An iron-containing protein in the blood that carries oxygen.

Hemorrhaging—Abnormal bleeding.

Herbicide—Agent that destroys or inhibits plant growth.

Heredity—Genetic characteristics passed from parents to children.

Hold method—Type of pasteurization where milk is heated to 145° F, held at this temperature for 30 minutes, then cooled to 45° F or lower.

Horizontal integration—Capturing a greater market share through expanding production or by purchasing a business that produces the same product.

Hormones—Chemical substances that are released into the blood to control body processes.

Hunger—Weakened condition resulting from lack of food.

Hydrogenation—Chemical process of adding hydrogen to an oil to make a more solid product or increase shelf-life.

Hydrolysis—Splitting apart of food particles by the addition of water.

Hydroponics—The growing of crops indoors in nutrient-rich water instead of soil.

Hypertension—High blood pressure measured as a systolic greater than 140 and a diastolic of 90.

Immunity—State of being resistant to illness through production of antibodies which protect against foreign proteins.

Import quota—Established ceilings on the amounts of an item that can be imported to limit foreign supply and protect domestic producers.

Industrial society—A society in which production and consumption of manufactured goods are the major economic activities.

Information society—A society in which the creation and distribution of information form the economic base.

Input—Resources used for production. In farming, inputs include labor, animal power, energy, machinery, and chemicals.

Insulin—A hormone released by the pancreas that enables cells to take up glucose in the blood for use as energy.

Intrastate—Occurring within a state.

Intrinsic factor—A protein produced in the stomach required for the absorption of vitamin B_{12}.

Ion—Electrically charged particle.

Iron-deficiency anemia—Lack of iron results in small, pale red blood cells which are unable to carry as much oxygen.

Jobbers—Persons representing two or more smaller companies that deal in different types of food products.

Joules—Term used to describe energy

value of food in the metric system; 1 Kilocalorie equals 4.2 Joules.

Ketosis—Presence of excess ketones in the blood as the result of fat breakdown.

Kilocalorie—A unit of measurement of the amount of heat produced when food is oxidized, or burned; 1000 Calories equals 1 Kilocalorie.

Kwashiorkor—Malnutrition that develops when Calories are adequate, but protein is deficient. Symptoms include dry, brittle, orangish hair and protruding stomach caused by fluid retention.

Lacto-ovo vegetarian—Diet pattern that includes milk, milk products, eggs, and plant foods.

Leached—Term used to describe the loss of water soluble vitamins from a food into water or the cooking medium.

Leavening agent—Natural or chemical agent that reacts in the presence of heat or water to release carbon dioxide.

Life-style—The way an individual lives.

Linoleic acid—A fatty acid that the body cannot produce by itself, making it essential to obtain in the diet.

Lipase—Pancreatic enzyme that splits fat into digestive end products of free fatty acids and glycerol.

Lymph system—Network of vessels involved in the collection of tissue fluids known as lymph; it also provides transport of fats from the intestinal tract to the thoracic duct.

Major minerals—Minerals found in fairly large amounts in the body.

Malnutrition—Poor nourishment result-ing from too many or too few Calories or nutrients.

Maltase—The enzyme needed to split maltose into two glucose molecules.

Manganese—A trace mineral essential for production of several enzymes related to energy and protein metabolism.

Marasmus—A type of malnutrition resulting from both calorie and protein deficiency, producing a skeleton-like appearance.

Markets—Voluntary exchanges between buyers and sellers.

Meat analogs—Foods made from plant proteins that are designed to simulate meat.

Megadose—A large amount generally defined as 10 times or more than the RDA level of vitamins and minerals.

Megaloblastic anemia—Production of enlarged red blood cells due to lack of folacin.

Metabolism—The process of building up and breaking down body tissue.

Methemoglobinemia—A condition that can develop in young infants who take in too much nitrate.

Microvilli—Microscopic projections on each villus that increase the surface area of the small intestine enhancing absorption.

Minerals—Inorganic (non-carbon-containing) compounds that are required in small amounts to regulate body reactions.

Molybdenum—A trace mineral needed for enzyme function.

Monosaccharide—Single sugar including glucose, fructose, and galactose.

Mottling—Tooth discoloration.

Myoglobin—A muscle protein responsible for transporting oxygen to cells.

Natural—Often means foods with minimal processing and without additives.

Natural flavors—Flavors that are extracted from whole foods.

Nausea—Upset stomach.

Neutralize—A process by which an acid is weakened.

Nicotine—Chemically active substance in tobacco.

Nicotinic acid—Chemical name for niacin.

Nitrate—A naturally occurring substance, added to cured meats, which in the presence of stomach acid is converted to nitrosamine.

Nitrogen fixation—The ability of bacteria on the roots of legumes to collect nitrogen from the air and transform it into nitrates, providing needed fertilizer for plant growth.

Nutrient deficiency—Inadequate amount of a nutrient in the body due to poor intake, malabsorption, excess excretion, or nutrient-drug interaction.

Nutrient density—A mathematical comparison of a food's nutrient content to Calorie content.

Nutrients—Chemical substances required for proper functioning of the body. The six major classes of nutrients are fat, water, carbohydrate, protein, vitamins, and minerals.

Nutrition—The science of food and its use in the body.

Nutritional status—An evaluation of nutritional health.

Obesity—A condition of excess body fat.

Oil—A fat which is a liquid at room temperature.

Organic—Technically means containing carbon, however used as a health food term to describe foods grown without chemicals.

Osmosis—Passive diffusion through a semipermeable membrane which equalizes concentrations of particles on each side.

Osteomalacia—A deficiency disorder in adults caused by lack of vitamin D.

Osteoporosis—A calcium deficiency disease that results in a decreased amount of bone mass in the body.

Output—Productivity as measured by the amount of food produced from available resources.

Oxalic acid—A calcium-binding substance found in spinach, chard, and chocolate.

Oxygen—A colorless, tasteless gas produced and released into the atmosphere by plants for humans and animals to breathe. The most common element on earth.

Pancreas—Abdominal organ which produces digestive enzymes and the hormone insulin.

Peer review—Review of a person's published research by a group of colleagues with similar training and experience.

Pellagra—A deficiency disease caused by lack of niacin.

Peristalsis—Involuntary muscle action which moves food particles through the digestive tract.

Pernicious anemia—Type of blood disorder that results from a lack of vitamin B_{12} and/or intrinsic factor.

Pesticides—Chemicals used to destroy pests such as insects and rodents.

Phenylpropanolamine—A non-prescription drug that suppresses the appetite.

Photosynthesis—A complex process of producing chemical energy—glucose—through the combination of solar energy with carbon dioxide in the cells of green plants.

Phytic acid—A mineral-binding substance found in whole grains.

Pinocytosis—A process in which membrane cells surround and swallow very large molecules for transport across membranes.

Placebo—Something that makes a person feel better because he or she expects to feel better, not due to any physical or biological effect on the body.

Polysaccharide—Many sugars linked together to form starch or fiber.

Portal blood stream—Blood vessels carrying nutrient from the digestive systems to the liver.

Preservation—Processes of preventing food spoilage in order to save foods for future use.

Price support programs—Laws which permit Congress to determine the price at which the United States Department of Agriculture will buy certain products in the market place, thus decreasing the supply and stabilizing price.

Processing—Altering of food by any physical, chemical, or biological means.

Production quota—An established ceiling on the amount of a product which can be produced.

Prosumer—An individual who performs many services and produces products for his or her own use.

Protein—Nutrient composed of nitrogen-containing substances called amino acids which are required for building body tissue.

Proteinuria—Excretion of protein in the urine.

Recommended Dietary Allowances (RDA)—Standards which represent levels of nutrients and energy intake believed to be adequate for the nutritional needs of practically all healthy Americans.

Reconstituted—Process of rehydrating dried foods.

Refined—A grain which has the bran layer and usually the germ removed.

Region—A geographic area of the country.

Regulated—Food additives that are tested and controlled.

Retailers—People who sell products to consumers.

Retinol equivalents—Units of measure used to describe vitamin A content.

Rickets—A disorder in children resulting from a lack of vitamin D.

Risk factor—Practices associated with an increased chance of disease.

Saccharin—An artificial non-caloric sweetener.

Saliva—A fluid secreted by glands into the mouth which aid in food digestion.

Salivary amylase—An enzyme which begins to split the starch molecule chemically in the mouth.

Satiety—A feeling of fullness.

Saturated fatty acid—The bonds of the carbon atoms of this fatty acid are full and unable to accept any more hydrogen atoms.

Scurvy—Deficiency disease caused by lack of vitamin C.

Selenium—A trace mineral that is part of an enzyme which protects cells from being destroyed by oxygen.

Set-point—A theory that the body has a predetermined normal fat level.

Shelf life—The length of time a food can be kept or the date before which food should be eaten.

Short time method—Type of pasteurizing where milk is heated to 161° F for 15 seconds, then quickly cooled to 50° F or lower.

Skin caliper—Instrument used to measure subcutaneous fat.

Sodium chloride—Chemical name for table salt.

Solid weight—Product weight after liquid is removed.

Specific Dynamic Effect (SDE)—Increased expenditure of energy needed to digest food.

Sports anemia—An increase in blood plasma volume without a similar increase in red blood cell mass believed to be normal response to exercise.

Sprouts—Seeds harvested a few days after sprouting.

Standards of fill—Requirements for the amount of a product in a container.

Standards of identity—States what ingredients, amounts, or proportions must be included in the product.

Standards of quality—Limit on the type of defects that are allowed in a product.

Staple—The main food item in a person's or population group's diet pattern.

Starch—A complex form of carbohydrate including such sources as wheat, rice, and corn.

Starvation—The state of dying from hunger.

Stroke—A disorder caused by inadequate flow of oxygen to brain tissue resulting in tissue death in affected area.

Subcutaneous fat—Layer of fat just beneath the skin.

Subscapular skin fold—A measure of body fat taken underneath the shoulder blades.

Subsidy—A grant of public money to a private enterprise that produces a needed item for the general public.

Sugar—The simplest form of a carbohydrate found naturally in milk, honey, fruit, and sugar cane.

Tariffs—Taxes imposed on imported goods to increase the price giving domestically produced products a price advantage.

Testimonials—The relating of personal experience or observation which may be persuasive but not necessarily factual.

Textured vegetable protein—Dried, processed soybean fibers.

Thoracic duct—Channel where lymph fluids and transported fat enter the portal blood stream.

Tocopherol—Chemical name for vitamin E.

Tofu—Calcium-precipitated soybean curd.

Tooth decay—Dental disease caused by bacterial breakdown of sugars in the mouth which form an acid that erodes tooth enamel.

Toxic—Harmful or poisonous.

Toxicants—Harmful or poisonous substances.

Trace minerals—Minerals found in the body in very small amounts.

Transportation systems—Routes of transport including roads, railways, and waterways.

Triceps skin fold—Measurement of subcutaneous fat taken on the back of the arm midway between the elbow and shoulder.

Triglyceride—The most common fat in the human diet which is composed of three fatty acids and a glycerol molecule.

Trypsin—An enzyme secreted into the small intestine to further break down protein.

Tryptophan—An essential amino acid that the body is able to convert to niacin.

Tuberculosis—An infectious disease caused by a bacterium with transmission by contact with an infected person or cow, or through drinking contaminated milk.

Undernutrition—A state of poor nutritional status characterized by inadequate energy or nutrients.

Unit pricing—The price of a product per ounce or pound.

Unsaturated fatty acid—Some chemical bonds of the carbon atoms of this fatty acid molecule are still unfilled, so they are able to accept additional hydrogen atoms.

Values—A collection of beliefs and feelings about what is good, worthy, and correct.

Vegan—Diet pattern consisting only of plant foods.

Vegetarian—Meatless diet pattern.

Vertical integration—Buying and controlling several steps in production and marketing of a product.

Villi—Folds and projections on the interior of the small intestine that increase the surface area for nutrient absorption.

Vitamins—Organic (carbon-containing) compounds required in very small amounts to regulate body reactions and ensure health.

Water—Nutrient required for diluting and transporting other nutrients and waste products, for maintaining body temperature, and for creating the coating for body joints.

Wellness—Achieving optimum health by prevention of disease through life-style changes.

Wholesalers—Those who sell or supply a product to a retailer.

Yeast—A one-celled plant which is a natural leavening agent.

INDEX

CREDITS

Figure 1.1. Florida Department of Commerce/Division of Tourism
Figure 1.3. World Bank Photo
Figure 1.4. Courtesy of Champion International Corporation
Figure 1.5. Florida Department of Commerce/Division of Tourism
Figure 1.6. Florida Department of Commerce/Division of Tourism
Figure 1.7. Photo courtesy of Gerber Products Company
Figure 1.8. USDA Photo
Figure 1.9. © 1986, Gordon K. Morioka. Location courtesy of Our Lady of Mercy, Cincinnati
Figure 2.1A. USDA Photo
Figure 2.1B. National Macaroni Institute
Figure 2.2. USDA Photo
Figure 2.4. The National Basketball Association
Figure 2.5. Girl Scouts of the U.S.A.
Figure 2.6. North Dakota Economic Development Commission
DEPARTMENT OF HOUSING AND URBAN DEVELOPMENT
Figure 3.2. Photo provided courtesy of Rohm and Haas Company
Figure 3.3. John Deere & Company
Figure 3.6. Courtesy of Nabisco Brands, Inc.
Figure 3.7. American Oil Chemist's Society
Figure 3.8. North Dakota Department of Tourism
Figure 3.9. UNRWA
Figure 4.1. Free China News and Information Bureau

Figure 4.2. PHOTO BY W. R. GRACE & COMPANY
Figure 4.3. © Betty McKenney
Figure 4.7A. Alcoa
Figure 4.8. H. Armstrong Roberts
Figure 4.9. Courtesy of International Paper Company
Figure 4.10. USDA Photo
Figure 5.1. USDA Photo
Figure 5.2. USDA Photo
Figure 5.3. USDA Photo
Figure 5.4. USDA Photo
Figure 5.5. Deere & Company
Figure 5.9. Culinary Institute of America
Figure 5.10. NCR Corporation
Figure 5.12. © 1980 WILL McINTYRE, PHOTO RESEARCHERS
Figure 6.1. Warner-Lambert Company
Figure 6.2. Courtesy Verbatim Corporation
Figure 6.3. Merck & Co., Inc.
Figure 6.5. Petit Format/Nestle/Science Source/Photo Researchers, Inc.
Figure 6.6. H. Armstrong Roberts, Inc.
Figure 7.1. Peter Vandermark/Stock Boston
Figure 7.3. Merced County Chamber of Commerce
Figure 7.4. Picture of Weight Watcher's® meeting provided by Weight Watchers International. Weight Watchers® is a registered trademark of Weight Watchers International, Incorporated
Figure 8.1. H. Armstrong Roberts, Inc.
Figure 8.2. Girl Scouts of the U.S.A.
Figure 8.3. Kathryn Dudek/PHOTO NEWS
Figure 8.7. Kathryn Dudek/PHOTO NEWS

Figure 9.1. World Bank Photo by Witlin
Figure 9.2. Dean Foods
Figure 9.3. © 1986, Gordon Morioka.
Location courtesy of Our Lady of Mercy,
Cincinnati
Figure 9.6. H. Armstrong Roberts, Inc.
Figure 10.1. USDA Photo
Figure 10.2. California Raisin Advisory Board
Figure 10.3. Grant Heilman Photography
Figure 10.5. National Archives Trust
Figure 10.6. USDA Photo
Figure 10.9. Used with permission, Gerber
Products Company
Figure 11.1. New York Convention & Visitors
Bureau
Figure 11.2. USDA Photo
Figure 11.3. USDA Photo
Figure 11.5. General Foods Corporation/
USDA Photo
Figure 11.8. USDA Photo
Figure 11.9. SPERRY NEW HOLLAND
Figure 12.1. Berg & Associates/Photo by
Margaret C. Berg

Figure 12.2. R. P. Kingston/The Picture Cube
Figure 12.3. Stock, Boston/E. Schowengerdt
Figure 12.4. USDA Photo
Figure 13.4. USDA Photo
Figure 13.6. Michael Plack/Berg & Associates
Figure 13.8. Arnold Kaplan/Berg &
Associates
Figure 13.9. The Prudential Insurance
Company of America
Figure 14.1. OXFAM AMERICA
Figure 14.2. Photo courtesy of Abbott
Laboratories
Figure 14.3. World Bank Photo by Ed
Huffman
Figure 14.4. World Bank Photo by Hadar
Figure 14.5. NASA
Figure 14.6A. USDA Photo/Llewellyn
Figure 14.6B. Tourism British Columbia,
Canada
Figure 14.7. USDA Photo